Modern Psychotherapeutic Practice

Innovations In Technique

Science and Behavior Books brings to those interested in the behavioral sciences important and timely books produced economically in durable vinyl covers. We solicit opinions and ideas from our readers.

This is an Original Edition in vinyl covers

Modern Psychotherapeutic Practice

Innovations In Technique

Edited by

Arthur Burton

Professor of Psychology, Sacramento State College

SCIENCE AND BEHAVIOR BOOKS, INC.

577 College Avenue, Palo Alto, California 94306

Modern Psychotherapeutic Practice
A. Burton

CONTRIBUTORS

-Gaetano Benedetti, M. D. , is Professor of Mental
Hygiene and Psychotherapy at the University of Basel,
Basel, Switzerland.

-Arthur Burton, Ph. D. , is Professor of Psychology at
Sacramento State College, Sacramento, California, and
in private practice.

-Viktor E. Frankl, M. D. , Ph. D. , is Professor of
Neurology and Psychiatry at the University of Vienna,
and Chief of the Department of Neurology at the
Poliklinik Hospital.

-Don D. Jackson, M. D. , is Director of the Mental
Research Institute of Palo Alto, California, on the
Editorial Board of Family Process, and Associate
Clinical Professor of Psychiatry at Stanford University.

-Harold Kelman, M. D. , D. Md. Sc. , is Dean of the
American Institute for Psychoanalysis, and Editor of
the American Journal of Psychoanalysis.

-Jane Pearce, M. D. , Ph. D. , is Assistant Director of
Research at the William Alanson White Institute of
Psychiatry, Psychoanalysis, and Psychology, and a
practicing psychoanalyst.

-Florence Powdermaker, M. D. , Ph. D. , formerly
Director of Residency Training Program for the
Veterans Administration, and Consultant to the
Supreme Committee of Allied Powers in Japan, is
in the private practice of psychiatry.

-C. Peter Rosenbaum, M. D. , is Assistant Professor
of Psychiatry, Stanford University School of Medicine,
and Chief of the Adult Psychiatric Clinic.

-William U. Snyder, Ph. D. , is Chairman of the
Department of Psychology and Director of Clinical
Training at Ohio University.

-Helm Stierlin, M. D. , Ph. D. , is Senior Supervising
Analyst at Sanatorium Bellevue, Kreuzlingen,
Switzerland.

-Frederick C. Thorne, M.D., Ph.D., is editor and
publisher of the Journal of Clinical Psychology, and
in private practice.

-John Warkentin, M.D., Ph.D., is with the Atlanta
Psychiatric Clinic and is a former President of the
American Academy of Psychotherapists.

-Carl A. Whitaker, M.D., is the founder of the
Atlanta Psychiatric Clinic and formerly President of
the American Academy of Psychotherapists.

-Cornelia B. Wilbur, M.D., is Assistant in Psychiatry
in the College of Physicians and Surgeons at Columbia
University and in the private practice of psychoanalysis.

-Otto Allen Will, Jr., M.D., is Director of Psychotherapy, Chestnut Lodge, Rockville, Maryland,
Visiting Professor of Psychiatry, University of
Chicago, and Training and Supervising Analyst in
the Washington Psychoanalytic Institute.

-Irvin Yalom, M.D., is Assistant Professor of
Psychiatry at Stanford University School of Medicine.

CONTENTS

PSYCHOPHYSICAL REACTIONS

HOMOSEXUAL REACTIONS

EXISTENCE REACTIONS

PREFACE

Collections of case studies have now become so common that one may ask the need for the present one.[1] If we confine ourselves to those case studies which deal with psychodiagnostic formulations primarily, or those which represent merely global descriptions of patient-situations in phenomenology or genesis, then no justification exists for still another such work. However, psychotherapy often assumes artistic forms which we must try to set into a scientific framework, and this requires exposure, replication, and generalization, as well as any possible relief for the patient. In my opinion, every psychotherapist should be forced to publish at least one treatment history a year, for in the cool light of his own appraisal, or that of his colleagues, his theories and techniques become subject to revaluation and reorganization not possible in any other way. It is, therefore, no great surprise to discover that the most qualified psychoanalysts and psychoanalytic psychotherapists eagerly accept invitations to join symposia such as this.

This volume, however, has still another justification. It is not representative of the current practice of psychoanalytic psychotherapy! It represents rather a paradigm of approaches which dares to improvise both in theory and methodology in a way not usually open to psychoanalytic psychotherapists. It seeks newer (and more adequate) conceptions of both patients and their psychotherapists; it daringly searches for ways of abbreviating treatment--without loss of efficiency; it extends conventional dyadic models to polyadic ones in various ramifications and settings; it points up the pervasive influence of dread and alienation in our culture, as well as anxiety and guilt, and seeks for an interpretation of man not only against a setting of psychopathology, but against the broader human condition. This is not therefore a book for the conventional psychoanalytic psychotherapist, and while I am fairly positive that some of it may not stand the test of time, the presentation of these viewpoints will most certainly provoke psychotherapists everywhere to greater self-understanding, psychotherapeutic creativity, and possibly to new treatment methodologies.

I have asked each contributor to this symposium to share his thinking processes about his patient with us by a formal questionnaire in an Addendum.[2] The contrasting variety of substance and styles in the replies is itself a study in American and Continental psychiatry but they, at any rate, serve to give us a deeper insight into the treatment process taking place.

---

1. Unfortunately this is not yet true for the publication of case studies in psychiatric and psychological journals.
2. There are three exceptions here because of the unconventionality or novelty of the material provided.

All names, places, dates, and other identification material have been disguised so that no patient needs to feel that he has found himself in these pages.

It is fitting to acknowledge my debt to Dr. Don D. Jackson, who while contributing to this work, has also served to help create and guide its destiny.

Arthur Burton

July 1, 1964

SCHIZOPHRENIC REACTIONS

THE BEGINNING OF PSYCHOTHERAPEUTIC EXPERIENCE

by Otto Allen Will

PROLOGOMENON

For twenty years I have devoted a portion of my time as a pyschiatrist to therapeutic endeavors with schizophrenic people. Often my efforts have been unsuccessful, and despite the opportunities in each case for learning, I have frequently found myself more puzzled than enlightened by my observations. I soon realized that I possessed no deep or unique insights into human behavior--which was, perhaps, insight in itself. Knowledge--what there is of it for me--came slowly, and I found that personal characteristics of my own might keep me from recognizing or owning the significances of events, and at times turned me from having anything to do with the events themselves. With the increase of experience, certain of my therapeutic goals and theories of disorder required modification, as did various more or less dearly held concepts of myself and others. Having need and respect for certainty and determinacy, I was more at ease when I could place matters in at least seemingly predictable cause and effect sequences, and felt distaste--if not careless contempt--for the vague and imprecise. I continue to seek clarity and simplicity in dealing with patterns of events, but have come to be more accepting and respectful of the uncertain and undeterminate aspects of human living.

As a psychotherapist I do not treat large numbers of patients, and must avoid generalizing too much from too little. Nonetheless, there is no need to devalue the individual and his particular experience because he does not therefrom speak for Everyman in all circumstances. Although I do not have any unusual gifts for the comprehending of obscure communicative processes, the difficulties that I found (and find) in making sense with my patients may in themselves be usefully informative. The data of psychotherapy is gathered by observation, this act being complicated by the past experiences, prejudices, expectations, and other characteristics of the participants, as well as by the necessary inclusion of themselves in the field of study. Although the profession of psychotherapy offers pleasures and rewards in addition to that of earning a living, it is, for the most part, hard work. One is required to question that which he does, and to learn from experience as best he can. The questioning can be unpleasant, challenging both our actions and our personal (often private) concepts of ourselves. Thus our successes and our failures may be felt as unusually personal; they often seem to be intimate extensions

of ourselves. Nevertheless, both are subjects for investigation--
not for exultation or lamentation. Despite times of discouragement and
self-doubt-- and even times of exuberance and unchecked enthusiasm--
my interests in the schizophrenic mode of living, and in ways leading
to its useful modification, have continued.

My purpose in this presentation is to discuss some aspects of
my early interests in this work, indicating that human behavior, however disordered, may often be simply comprehensible, and, what may
be equally important, one does not need to be all-understanding to be
of some help to another. What I report is not in the ordinary sense a
therapeutic "success"; the patient did not prosper as I hoped he would,
but I was, notwithstanding, enlightened. Sometimes--not being blinded
by what one thinks of as success--one may be able to learn humbly from
the structure of one's disappointment.

Shortly I shall describe something of my first experience in
intensive psychotherapy with a schizophrenic person. How I came to
meet him, to spend time with him, and in part through him to become
increasingly involved in problems of schizophrenia and psychotherapy,
are matters relevant to this presentation. In briefly surveying the
course of my early contacts with schizophrenic people I shall speak
personally. To do so is in keeping with my view that understanding
of the therapeutic process is furthered by information concerning the
therapist as well as the patient.

BACKGROUND OF EXPERIENCE

As a college student, while enrolled in a course in "abnormal"
psychology, I occasionally attended "demonstrations" of odd human
behavior at a local public institution for the insane. Crowded with
other students in a small lecture hall, I watched patients exhibit their
"pathology, " and heard accounts of such psychiatric marvels as cerea
flexibilitas, command negativism, and delusions or "false beliefs. "
In the lobby adjacent to the meeting place was a glass-fronted cabinet
in which was displayed a collection of "foreign bodies"--cutlery,
rocks, and so on--which patients had swallowed or otherwise insert-
ed into their bodies, and which had been removed therefrom by medically directed efforts before or after the deaths of the recipients.
Despite the industry and concern of the obviously busy physicians
who were attempting to teach me something, I was more embarrassed and puzzled than informed. I didn't know what ailed these patients; the performances, the accompanying words, and the things in
the cabinet did not enlighten me. The patients themselves seemed

like--were treated like--strange objects somehow divested of their
humanity. There was a vast and dreadful gulf between me and the
place where the patient stood or sat by his examiner. Across this
gulf voices came only faintly, and little of what was said was understood or even comprehensible. I saw no way to bridge this space and
had no strong desire to do so, as return from the far side seemed unlikely and remaining there akin to death. I felt a loneliness and shame,
and hoped that I should never have the ill fortune to succumb to the
disease dementia praecox, or in any way become a psychiatric patient.
Matters other than the psychiatric held my interests for some time,
but the remembrance of the hospital and its mocking inmates remained
with me. I could not dismiss these people as simply sick or as
less than human; they were too clearly sharp and violent caricatures
of humanity. Their at first seeming difference from me and my associates only intensified their likeness to us all, and at this I felt horrified and enthralled.

Some time later I visited a large "mental hospital" where "disturbed" patients were kept in isolation and were frequently purged for
for the purpose of removing from their bodies sundry bacteria that
might--according to some--release toxins which by absorption could
lead to madness. On such visits I saw various "results" of other
forms of treatment, their popularity of a few years before now on the
wane. Some had been treated with intrathecal horse serum; others
had suffered removal of teeth, tonsils, or portions of the intestine--
all in the search of elusive foci of infection.

Dementia praecox was looked upon no more hopefully in the
university than in the state hospital. As a student and intern I interviewed the patient, "took" a history, "kept" records, "observed" behavior, and "made" a diagnosis. Beyond that I could do little. I felt
frustrated in my wish to be a physician of action, ready--if not always
able--to remove the disease from the person; both the disease and
the person were lost (for me) in dementia praecox. Once the diagnosis was made, my difficulties were usually resolved by the patient's
early removal to a mental hospital. To many, dementia praecox was
the "living death, " and the sufferers were not for long objects of interest for those more concerned with treatable disorders.

In those days I was not familiar with much of the work of
others in the field, having read little beyond descriptive accounts,
and I did not have the perspicacity to grasp a concept of the person
behind the mask of behavior. Personal prejudices frequently obscured
for me that which was to be seen in the clinic or in the writings of

more experienced and insightful observers. I tended to be repelled by the odd and the unconventional, that being a time for me of wanting to be acceptable and successful on the terms of my associates. I had no wish to share the estrangement of my patients in any way. With the completion of history and diagnosis, I often felt lost; the patient and I were then alone, in awkward silence and mutual apprehension, with nothing to guide us, and nothing to do save guarding against exposure of ourselves.

Then came the news of insulin, and we soon were engaged in the variant activities of that form of treatment. Now we--the staff-- were less uncertain, our roles being familiar to us. We felt that we were doing something in the medical tradition, applying a medicine with a specialized technique in an effort to relieve a patient of a disease and help him regain his health. There being work for all to do-- nurses, doctors, and patients--group morale improved. Some patients improved, some did not, and some relapsed; danger was sharply emphasized by the prolonged or irreversible coma. Although there was hope and something to do, we reluctantly came to acknowledge that we had no "answer." Not knowing the nature of the disease to be treated, we could not speak assuredly of medicine, treatment, and cure. Dementia praecox had no clear beginning, no observable pathological features, no comprehensible distribution; there was only its course--traditionally said to be toward "degeneration."

The next therapeutic agent in my experience was metrazol. I well remember the lonely hospital rooms in the early morning hours, the frightened patient lying on the mat on the floor, the injection with its rapidly induced convulsion, and the feeling that one was engaged blindly in a traumatic procedure that promised little. I had no enthusiasm for this kind of treatment, was angry at my part in it, and was troubled at having nothing better to offer. Increasingly I turned my attention to the study of pediatrics and internal medicine.

Three years later, returning from overseas duty in wartime, I was assigned to the military section of a large civilian psychiatric hospital. The wards were crowded, the staff was small with a high rate of turnover, and the number of admissions of psychotic patients was high. At the time of my arrival, I sat for a period on a bench in a compound surrounded by hospital buildings, from the barred windows of which patients waved their arms, shouting for help or damning those whose charge it was to keep them locked in; others simply stared. Entering the buildings, one ran a gauntlet of noise-- a mixture of demand, despair, plea, and hate. I frequently had the impulse to leave, and probably would have done so had I not been attached there by orders, as were the patients. Although I had little psychiatric experience, there was a need for my services, and because of the shortage of personnel I frequently worked as internist as well as psychiatrist. I soon realized there were practical matters to be dealt with; patients required conventional medical and surgical care, proper food, good housing, clothing, opportunity for exercise and recreation, protection from destructive behavior, and the assurance of minimal respectful treatment by those who cared for them. These needs were not met automatically and perfectly; I had to pay personal attention to such matters--and they were in part my responsibility. In other words, I could not sit in my psychiatric office and let the rest of the hospital world go by. There were others to run that world, but it was evident that they required my help as I required theirs. Then there was the staff. Not highly paid, working hard, in many instances inadequately trained, often discouraged by the "lack of results" and doubts regarding the therapeutic significance of their own roles, and frustrated by being unable to meet the majority of the demands placed on them, they needed reassurance as to their own worth. In brief, a primary job of a psychiatrist in a hospital is to promote the morale and effectiveness of his staff--the therapeutic agent through which much of his work must be done.

In my years at this hospital I talked with many patients, the majority of whom were diagnosed as schizophrenic--a term replacing the given name dementia praecox. A majority of these improved rapidly ("spontaneously," some said, suggesting to me the concept of spontaneous generation in the days before Pasteur) and within two or three months left for their homes--some to "relapse" within the next few years. Others remained, being inexorably pushed by the mass of newcomers to wards where the chronically ill tended to settle down to lives of near social immobility. Electroshock was the popular form of treatment, and some favored lobotomy as the choice "when all else had failed." By then it was apparent that often "all else"--that is, nursing care and the attention of a therapist--had little prospect of anything but failure in the circumstances (the milieu) of their operation. As a physician in the traditional sense, I felt ineffective. The patient usually insisted that he was not ill, but mistreated, and did not seek or value my services; I was unsure about the nature of his disorder and did not know what to do about his complaints; one mode of treatment followed another, and my confidence in any of them declined. Despite all this, however, I found it difficult to accept a change in my conception of myself as a physician, of psychiatric disorder as a disease within a person, and of therapy as a method of restoring a previously existent state of good health. Circumstances led me to alter my views. Belatedly, I discovered that there were others who saw matters differently than I, and with difficulty--having so long held other opinions-- I heard a little of what there was to learn: I knew that I did not "understand" much of my patients' behavior, and they generally had little confidence in being understood. Why was there not more understanding? I discovered that I myself did not feel understood, that despite my training and experience I was repelled by some behavior, that I feared others might be repelled by me, and that the gulf between me and others--noted long past-- could be crossed (if at all) only through personal effort, accompanied by apprehension, doubt, and exposure of the self. Comprehension could come as I learned to observe sympathetically without insisting on immediate change in the field of observation. That is, if I wished to learn something about schizophrenic (or other human) behavior, I should study it respectfully and not try so quickly to change it to something else presumably more worthy and perhaps more suitable to my own needs. But observation could not be carried on without some degree of participation, and with this last often came discomfort. In brief, I was attracted to the task of becoming a psychotherapist-- a participant observer.

The above is, of course, an old story, perhaps not worth the retelling. In some ways, however, this story is always new, the history of psychiatry existing in the present as well as in the past. Despite our advances, the mythology, the superstition, the hardened beliefs, and the practices of the past exist with us today. Sliding back in climbing a hill of sand we may make progress, but in our advance we can see with us and ahead of us the evidence of where we stood before.

What follows now is an expression--in condensed form--of my current views of the therapeutic situation. Later in this presentation I shall discuss certain of the clinical experiences influential in the modification of my thinking about psychiatry, the psychiatric patient, and the psychotherapist.

THERAPY AND PSYCHIATRIC DISORDER

My concern at this juncture is the functional relationship that exists between those phenomena to which we refer as psychiatric illness and psychotherapy. Although I shall speak particularly of my association with a young man diagnosed as schizophrenic, my observations regarding therapy are generally relevant to the treatment of patients in other diagnostic categories. The behavior to which we refer as disordered, neurotic, crazy, or psychotic is, despite the variant and seemingly bizarre modes of its expression, in its essence simply human. The experiences of those most gravely deranged "mentally" differ only in degree from what each of us has known to some extent at various periods in his development. That which may appear as unfamiliar or mad may seem so only because much of our childhood and our dreams has been largely lost to us--recurring brilliantly or dimly on those occasions wherein we transiently relinquish the role of rational adult and are able once again--with delight or trepidation--to recall, in fragmentary fashion, something of that which we have been.

Those collections of processes to which we refer as "mental diseases" have been thought of as evidence of malfunction within a person, expressive of congenital, hereditary, or "organic" defect-- a state of sickness marked by functional and structural changes, to be treated by a physician applying a curative agent through the use of a technical procedure. This point of view has been demonstrably useful, but has limitations in its implication of dichotomies of health and sickness, body and mind, organic and mental, doctor and patient, leading to an often artificial separation of subject and object.

Psychiatric disorders may be looked upon as destructive, inadequate, inappropriate, or unduly complicated forms of human behavior, exhibited in an interpersonal field, and arising from experiences in previously existing social fields. The sickness with which we as therapists are called upon to deal is expressed in recurrent patterns of behavior, which have developed largely in response to cultural and other environmental influences, are useful but inadequate in the attainment of satisfactions and security, have not only defensive but communicative and relational functions, are not readily altered (having been formed in the development of the organism and become--as we put it--a "part" of the personality), and are seen to be characteristic of the patient in his living with others. In brief, without minimizing the biological basis of all behavior or attempting to ascribe first causes, our behavior reflects previous interpersonal experience, the current situation, and our anticipations of the future. A function of the psychiatrist--one which he can be expected to perform with a certain immediacy and accuracy--is to observe the significant interpersonal operations of his patient in the therapeutic (and directly or indirectly in other) situations, intervening on occasion in such fashion that increased comprehension and favorable (that is, movement from the more to the less complex) alteration of such operations may be advanced. From one point of view, psychiatry may be looked upon as the study of the modes of integration of man with his fellows, with a particular interest in those factors related to origin, perpetuation, and modification of that which is personally and socially inefficient and destructive.

The psychotherapeutic process is a special instance of an interpersonal relationship, in which, within certain limitations, the disordered behavior of the patient may be displayed, further comprehended, and (hopefully) modified constructively through the interaction of the participants. To a considerable extent, the development of those complicated forms of living which we speak of as neuroses and psychoses has its beginnings in the infant's and child's difficulties in gaining satisfactions, security, comprehension, and identity in the anxiety-laden, complex biological, cultural, and interpersonal requirements of the human world. In such disturbances early attitudes, misapprehensions, and behavioral deviations have not been corrected adequately by subsequent experience, with the result that learning has been deficient, important living situations have been avoided, misunderstood, or perceptually distorted, and there has been formed a restrictively biased, and unfortunately durable, view of human beings and their significance to one another. Through their appearance in the therapeutic field, beneficial and destructive experiences may be identified, a clearer distinction being made between the past and the present, and what has been evaluated as evil and good.

In summary, I am suggesting that psychiatric disorder and the psychotherapeutic procedure may be looked upon as social processes, arising from, and demonstrable in, interpersonal fields. In the therapeutic situation both patient and therapist are participant as well as observer, there being expected of the latter a degree of benign concern, detachment, experience, and skill that will enable him to further the understanding and self-realization of the other. Although long-existent and destructive patterns of living may be repeated in the course of therapy, the integration of these with the behavior of the therapist must in many ways differ from past integrations if the patient is to derive profit from the experience; that is, the new transactions, resembling the old in part, differ from the past in their greater clarity and simplicity, their recognizable benign quality, and their tolerance of personal growth.

In my further remarks about psychiatric treatment I shall attempt to avoid excessive generalization by referring to my work some years past with a young man diagnosed as schizophrenic. As I describe my relationship with John in greatly abbreviated form it may become more clear how some of us develop an interest in psychotherapy, and how certain forms of action came to be thought of as principles--not so much fundamental "truths" as essential or characteristic ingredients of the therapeutic operation, to be modified as increase of knowledge may require.

FIRST MEETING

Years ago, while on the staff of the military division of a large psychiatric hospital, I was called to consult about the "physical" illness of one of the gravely disturbed patients. Before visiting this man I looked at his brief hospital record and learned that he was a military officer of twenty-two who had left college to join the service and had made a good record while in training. After a few months at a small, isolated overseas station he had approached his senior officer declaring that the Holy Spirit had spoken to him in a manner so impressive that he could no longer serve as a combatant. He had come to feel that all war was evil, and he wished to convert others to his views. In the circumstances of war, those who held or expressed such ideas were not likely to be popular or highly esteemed; they made their associates uncomfortable. As the officer disregarded his duties, becoming increasingly confused, hallucinated, and preoccupied, he was transferred to the mainland, where, in a series of military hospitals, he was found to be psychotic, and was treated with electroshock without marked or lasting improvement. He was transferred to the hospital at which I was stationed about five months after the episode abroad, and had been on the ward for "regressed" patients in our hospital for two months prior to my first seeing him.

I clearly remember my meeting with John. I unlocked the door to a large ward occupied by sixty male patients. Some sat or lay on the floor, seeming to pay little or no attention to me as I walked by. Others paced up and down the hall or stood looking out of the iron-grilled windows onto the ground three floors below. A few cursed at me, and others stopped me, asking the commonplace, repetitious, and unanswerable questions: "Why am I here? When do I get out? Can't you listen to me? Doesn't anyone understand?"

I found John in the midst of a small group of those who were kept under constant special surveillance because of their suicidal and mutilative behavior. He lay on his back in bed, constantly twisting from side to side in efforts to free himself from the sheets which

were used to bind his arms, trunk, and legs to the bedframe. He was
thin, and his face was contorted, at times as if in fear, and again as
if elated by hearing something not audible to me. He bit at the restraints over his shoulders, spat at those who came near, and kept
up a constant mumbling that occasionally rose to a hoarse shout.
Much of what he uttered was too low to hear, or was (to me) an incomprehensible jumble of fragmentary phrases, interspersed with comments startling in their clarity and intensity of feeling. "The Spirit
has spoken to me," he cried out. "The destruction must end. Let
me die ... Let me go free to die ... Man must be born again."

In a conventional sense, John paid little attention to my presence; but he pulled away from me, feebly spat at me, and reduced
his outcry to a dull moaning as I carried out a physical examination
while his movements were in part restricted by attendants. He had
been incontinent of urine and feces for some time, and despite nursing
care had developed several decubitus ulcerations. As he would not
eat, he had been fed by nasal tube twice daily, and now had an acute
pharyngeal infection. He was feverish, he had a paroxysmal tachy-
cardia, and the presence of hematuria suggested a bacteremia. My
efforts to talk with this man were not successful, and I learned from
the medical and nursing staff that his disturbance had continued unabated since his admission, despite the use of barbiturate sedation
and hydrotherapy. Said one nurse, speaking for the group: "You can't
take your eyes off him. We have to tie him down, or he'll get out of
that bed and kill himself. He won't let you do anything for him; he
just turns away from you. I think he is determined to die--and maybe
he will in spite of all of us."

I also felt the desperate, urgent quality of this situation and
arranged for the man's transfer to the medical and surgical section
of the hospital. This was a time of great crowding in the institution;
the wards were filled far beyond their intended capacity, and it was
not easy to maintain adequate staffing with aides, nurses, and physicians. Contact between patients and personnel was usually irregular
and transient, and there was little opportunity for the development of
enduring, dependable, constructive relationships. Some patients,
improving rapidly after removal from situations of stress (and with or
without electroconvulsive therapy) left after a few months for their
homes. Those who did not show early favorable change drifted into the
category of "chronic," and were sent to other areas of the hospital
where professional staff was decreased, activities outside the units
lessened, and the morale of all concerned was consistent with the
ever-present, poorly hidden, rarely openly discussed acceptance of
hopelessness.

As I look back on this first meeting with the young officer I think of a number of observations that are relevant to concepts of psychiatric care. In outline form the observations are as follows:

1. The patient's condition was that of a medical emergency, not only in terms of his obvious physical ailments, but in terms of his state of near panic and his failure to improve in response to the treatment which he had received. Panic demands resolution, being a condition of disorganization intolerable to the human. Early psychiatric attention is required, as the resolution of such states may be suicide, self-mutilation, or the unhappy, and often lasting, retreat into the hebephrenic preoccupation or the paranoid reconstruction.

2. I was struck by the completeness of the organism's response. The patient seemed caught up in a holocaust of emotion, which he comprehended poorly if at all, and from which he could extricate himself only by his own destruction. In his struggles the totality of himself seemed to be involved. His large muscles were in almost constant motion, the discharge of feces and urine was uncontrolled, his hands and feet were cyanotic even after the removal of restraints, often he was wet with sweat, infections of the skin and mucous membranes had developed, and he attempted, sometimes successfully, to regurgitate the tube feedings. Whatever the causes of the disturbance, the reaction was not emotional, or mental, or organic, but was one involving the entire organism.

3. In the presence of this patient I was strongly moved by his distress. Although I felt a great urgency to do something to be of help to him, I did not know what to do, not comprehending the basic problem and being unable, therefore, to deal with logical sequences of cause and effect. Not knowing what to do about the psychiatric problem, I did what I could to treat its physical manifestations.

4. A degree of the patient's intense anxiety was communicated to me to my own considerable discomfort. As we could not talk meaningfully with each other, I felt isolated from this man. He seemed unapproachable, and I felt some awareness of his separateness from all of us and the need to cross somehow the widening space between us.

5. Unable to communicate verbally with the patient, and lost in my efforts to grasp the nature of his difficulty, I turned with relief to the more tangible tools of my profession--stethoscope, sphygmomanometer, and so on. They proved useful,

not only in the information provided by their operation, but as a means of maintaining contact with the man--as well as acceptable professional distance. In my preoccupation with the needed physical examination I could avoid too intense an involvement with his distress and my accompanying feelings of inadequacy.

6. I observed that although I wished to be of service to this man, I was also repelled by him. The odor of urine and feces was strong, saliva drooled from his mouth, he attempted to bite and hit me, and I could make little sense of what he said. I found that I wanted to get out of this situation in which all of my professional knowledge seemed of such little value. I wanted the patient to keep still, to go away, to disappear somehow without blame being attached to anyone; that is, I dreaded taking responsibility for one so ill and so incomprehensible to me. I disliked him for having affronted me with his strange, vast, and seemingly unending misery. Although I was ashamed of having such sentiments, I could not deny them. I was impressed by the mutuality of the tendency to withdraw--the patient from us, and the staff from him. Should such withdrawal be accomplished, death would appear to be the inevitable outcome.

7. A principle of therapy would seem to be the necessity for maintaining contact with the patient--for simply being with him. Simple as this concept might seem, I was discovering that it was not always easy to continue in operation.

THE TAKING OF ACTION

The next portion of this account can be told briefly. The young man continued to be grossly disturbed in the medical section of the hospital, fought care, refused medication, and could not be heavily sedated because of respiratory difficulties. With considerable hesitancy because of the risks involved, he was given a single electroconvulsive treatment. The results were favorable beyond our expectations. Within a few hours after the treatment the patient was alert, spoke coherently, accepted the necessary medical care without opposition, and no longer required restraints. He ate well, his physical condition improved rapidly, and within two days he was able to walk about his room.

The reaction of the staff to all of this was noteworthy. Delight followed astonishment, and there was a great sense of relief--the burden of dealing with the incomprehensible anxiety, with the violent destructiveness, and with the threat of death being for the time removed. John was now seen to be a tall, slender, moderately handsome, shy but amiable young man, who said that he did not know what had happened to him. Much attention was now given to him, and this he accepted in a reserved but obviously pleased manner.

By the third day after the treatment John was again more withdrawn. He looked puzzled and spoke of the Holy Spirit as saying that all men had sinned and must be punished. With medication and nursing care the evidences of bodily disease rapidly subsided, and he was given a total of six electroshocks within a period of two weeks. He quickly became less withdrawn, his physical condition was good, he dressed neatly in his uniform, and although he maintained a considerable reserve and spoke little, his behavior was not thought to be abnormal. He was polite to me, but not revealing, and he showed no interest in continuing any association with me. When I questioned him about his recent experiences, his earlier military service, and his family, he was stiffly evasive, gave little information, and sought to terminate the interview.

At this time my duties took me elsewhere, and I left with a feeling of satisfaction at this resolution of a difficult situation. During the following year I occasionally thought of John, having been greatly impressed by the gravity of his condition, by the bodily and other forms of its expression, by the intensity of his emotion, and by the changes produced by the electroshock--changes welcomed but not understood. Certain of the observations and questions then formulated as the consequence of my experience with this patient were as follows:

1. I realized that I knew very little of the nature of the man's disturbance. Why was he incontinent and unable to eat? Why did he seek to mutilate and kill himself? What interfered with his ability to communicate with others, and what was the meaning of his isolation?
2. The strange behavior might reflect one or more of the following:
   a. A disorder of the person somehow unrelated to previous interpersonal experience.
   b. Symbolic expressions of past events in the man's life, aspects of which had been tainted with anxiety, had been observed without adequate comprehension of their significance, or had been kept out of awareness through dissociation or repression, appearing now as frightening representations seemingly unrelated to the known self.

    c. Reactions to events in the current situation which could not be formulated, understood, or dealt with directly.

    d. Efforts to communicate matters of personal importance distorted by the feeling that the need to communicate was both urgent and dangerous.

    e. Obscure and complex attempts to establish and maintain needed relationships without running the risks involved in any relationship.

    f. A feeling of guilt, despair, and hopelessness requiring the ending of life with, perhaps, an idea of obtaining thereby some sort of rebirth or salvation.

3. We who cared for the patient were uncertain of his identity. Was he a military officer, a person somehow in contact with a deity, a case of something called schizophrenia, a hopeless patient, or simply a man? In refusing or being unable to accept the conventional role of patient, he denied roles familiar and important to us-- as aides, nurses, physicians, or whatever. He did not accept me as a psychiatrist, a doctor, a medical officer, an interested human, or as one whose "innate" benign qualities might be of interest or value to him. In other words, he did not play any familiar role reciprocal to mine; the feedback to my behavior with him was inappropriate from my point of view. In such a situation one's own sense of identity is recurrently shaken, in which case one may attempt to force the patient to adopt a more clearly defined role (perhaps one not suited to the patient), or may in order to "find oneself" again abandon the work. Striking in the care of this man was the periodic feeling of identity diffusion or loss experienced by personnel in contact with him. When the source of this personal uncertainty was not recognized, staff members tended to reestablish the sense of self by various forms of assertiveness or by withdrawal from the situation.

4. Considering the patient's difficulties in communication, his apparent fearfulness of others, his confusion, and his uncertain, variable perception of himself, was the hospital situation suited to his needs? The following observations about the ward on which the patient lived are relevant to this question.

a. The ward was crowded, and no privacy was possible on it. There was a shortage of personnel, contacts with patients were often hurried and impersonal, and there was a daily movement of patients and staff members as they were transferred from one ward to another. The atmosphere was one of anxiety and uncertainty in which it was difficult to maintain a sense of identity. Confusion was promoted by the lack of stability in the structure of the physical surroundings and the staffing pattern (that is, there was little sense of durability in the relationship to person or object), and there were few things in the environment (such as personal belongings from home and familiar faces) to emphasize one's identity. In such an atmosphere withdrawal may too easily be used in the attempt to deal with poorly comprehended difficulties.

b. The patient was "difficult," being abusive, anxious, dirty, hostile, negativistic, and frustrating to those who tried to take care of him. As he was also a serious suicidal risk, staff members felt constantly threatened by the possibility that he would injure or kill himself, and thus indirectly hurt them. It was easy to feel anger, contempt, and disgust as well as pity for this man. In an effort to overlook the recognition of such sentiments (felt to be professionally and personally improper) there was a marked tendency to avoid any unnecessary contact with him, explaining the distance by saying that one was busy, that the patient didn't "want" help, that he was "better off alone," or that he was "hopeless" and beyond relief.

c. There was an apparent mutuality in the reactions of patient and staff members. All concerned engaged in avoidance maneuvers and harbored feelings of despair and a growing conviction that the relationships between patient and personnel were "meaningless" or "useless." These attitudes, however, were usually not clearly in awareness, or were denied, being transmitted effectively and with ever lessening chances of correction by covert means.

d. The appearance of the signs of serious physical disorder led to the mobilization of concern for the patient. There was a feeling that perhaps not much could be done for something called schizophrenia, but that one could do something useful about bacterial infection. As an accompaniment of "organic" disease, the patient's identity became more clear; he was no longer "just a schizophrenic," he was a man with an infection. He was moved from the confusion of the larger ward to the quiet and privacy of a single room, where he had a more personalized contact with fewer people. Staff members, seeing John as a man in great need of conventional medical care, were less uncertain regarding their own identities; whereas a few days before they had often not known what to do or what was expected of them, they now felt more secure in their traditional roles of doctor and nurse with well-defined tasks to carry out. As the patient improved with shock, his appearance and behavior altered, and the stereotypes of "chronic" and "hopeless" were put aside for the moment. Seeing him as different, the staff acted differently toward him, and briefly he responded more appropriately to the conventions of the culture.

e. The destructive behavior of the patient had altered, but its comprehension had not been furthered. Had the motivations which it may have reflected been done away with somehow, or repressed, or dissociated once again? Had some defect of structure or function been corrected? With such questions it was clear that John was a stranger to us; in all our contacts with him he remained unknown. We could describe his symptoms and discuss his illness, but we could not talk about him--the man; we felt uncomfortably that we were in our essentials unknown to him--worse yet, of no importance to him. If John denied himself as a human, he also denied us, and in such a defeat of relatedness we could all feel guilty and troubled. It was from this situation of uncertain identity and the denial of self and others that we wished to withdraw.

5. A principle of therapy is related to the problem of identity.
    Anticipating the great uncertainty about personal identity
    that will be experienced by both patient and staff members,
    it is advisable to structure the treatment situation so
    that repeated, clear-cut confirmation of the self can be
    found by those operating in it. For example, a few personal
    possessions may remind the patient who he is; he is
    not a "schizophrenic," but a man, with a name, a history
    to be respected, and a future that need not be just a
    reflection of the unhappy present or a continuance of the
    worst of the past. Those who work therapeutically with
    psychotic people must have--or develop-- a considerable
    tolerance for uncertainty and the unpredictable. They
    should be able to work with determination--and a sense
    of pleasure as well as acceptance--in a world not clearly
    determined.

THE INTERVENING YEAR

A year passed, and I was again called upon to consult about
John. In the meantime he had been in the care of others, and I had
heard of him only intermittently. Once again he was in the medical
section of the hospital, having been sent there after becoming acutely
disturbed, breaking away from attendants, and casting himself head-
long into a wall. He had suffered a cerebral concussion, there was
blood in his spinal fluid, and once again he lay in restraints, twisting
about, refusing food or personal care, incontinent of urine and feces,
and calling out that all men were evil, that he had sinned and must
die.

I reviewed the hospital records, discovering that during the
year the patient had improved only to relapse. He had received a
total of thirty-five electroconvulsive treatments in several courses,
improving transiently but soon worsening again. He had gained
weight with sub- and light-coma insulin treatments, but had not
changed otherwise. With intravenous barbiturates he had become more
alert and had spoken, but this treatment was discontinued after his
development of severe respiratory difficulty. He had been on several
wards, cared for by many people, and was once again alone in a room,
struggling against restraints, and frightening in his seeming abandonment to destruction. When I visited him briefly, he gave no sign of
recognizing me, and I left. I felt that I was nothing to this man and
that, even should I wish to do so, I could not enter into his world of

loneliness and devastation, or in any way enable him to leave it.

In reviewing the situation at that time the following observations assumed importance for me:

1. John had now been in hospitals nearly two years, and seemed no better than when we had first met him. As the length of hospitalization increased, the chances (in terms of statistics) of his improving significantly decreased markedly. Nevertheless, it was evident that he continued to struggle; whatever the fight was, he had not abandoned it.

2. During his stay in the hospital John had not formed a relationship with anyone. His parents had visited him, but he either refused to see them or distressed and embarrassed them by his hostile and bizarre behavior. They occasionally wrote letters that he did not read, but they no longer visited him; and he evidenced no interest in them or in others. His isolation had increased.

3. John's identity was less clear than it had been a year before. He was moved from ward to ward, had no room of his own, and had no personal possessions to tie him with his past. His residence, its furnishings, his food, and his clothing were provided by the hospital administrators. For fear that he might injure himself he had been deprived of all objects that could be used self-destructively; there was nothing whereby he could be identified as the child of his parents; as the former inhabitant of his home town, as a military officer, as a college student, as a sane man . He was becoming lost in the mass, had become part of the "case load" of a series of hastening physicians who knew him not, and was a living reproach to those who had tried to help him and felt that they had failed.

4. It seemed likely that in a situation such as this despair would increase.

MY INTEREST IN THE PATIENT

Having been called on to see this man again, I did so, but had no useful recommendation to make regarding his further care. I had little confidence in the available treatment procedures and little understanding of what the man's needs might be. I thought that he did need relationship with others, an increase in his ability to express his thoughts, and a lessening of his intense anxiety. But these were statements of generalities, little more than a feebly pious expression of the obvious. I realized that a psychotherapist might be of use, but there was no one other than myself available, and I had never been favorably impressed by my ability to inspire confidence in a severely anxious person. Under ordinary circumstances I should have let the matter drop there.

However, my own living had changed. I had undergone a surgical procedure a few months before, and for the time being was unable to maintain my customary rush of activities. As certain of my own goals had to be at least temporarily abandoned, I laid aside some of my immediate responsibilities and found time to sit and look about me. The sudden and unexpected halt in my busy life shook my confidence in myself and in what had seemed to be a certain predictability in my living. Doubts came into my awareness, and I felt isolated from those who were not pushed aside as I felt myself to be. The decrease in action invited introspection.

Puzzling about John, I realized that I had seen many like him (that is, with his diagnosis) from a distance, but had not come to know any one of them well. I knew, as it were, the disorder, but not the disordered person. Not knowing what to do about John, I decided that it was enough to do what I could. So often one wants to do something other than what one can, the possible being mundane in comparison to the desirable. For example, the fact that what one can do with a patient may not guarantee his cure or even improvement is not justification for renouncing all efforts.

I read again the hospital records which revealed little of the man. He was an only child, described as having been the delight of his parents. He grew up in a small town, attended public schools, was moderately capable as a student, had some friends, played baseball, hunted and fished, and was described as quiet, unassuming, and "good." His mother was a pious but somewhat cheerless woman who kept house and was devoted to a branch of the Protestant church. She patiently bore what she felt to be the inadequacies and indignities of her husband's behavior, thinking of him as being crass and irreligious, and resenting his occasional drinking sprees and outbursts of anger, for which he was soon guilty and apologetic. Despite the father's outward display of aggressiveness, he seemed to be subservient to his wife, feeling "responsible" for her unhappiness and somehow to blame for her complaints of poor physical health.

John completed his high school course and went to college to study physics, leaving in his third year to enter officer-training in time of war. The history is not remarkable for evidence of clear-cut antecedents of psychiatric disorder, but it is noteworthy that in his adolescence John had shown little interest in women, occasionally spoke out against what he considered to be the irresponsible and wicked actions of his contemporaries, and spent increasing amounts of time with a few men (some much older than he) who were devoted to the study of the Bible. Although he had some friends, he had no one with whom he could talk about personal matters, and his sexual interests were largely ignored or sublimated--or, at least, not publicly displayed. He was well thought of in his community, particularly by his elders, but he was living more to himself, and I came to be of the opinion that no one, including his parents, knew him well. Of his military service prior to his declaration of the invasion by the Holy Spirit there was very little.

Having read the history, I came to the patient. By this time he had acquired a reputation as a patient--he was "difficult" and the prognosis was "poor." It was not easy for me to escape from the prejudices roused in me by that reputation. I tended to see the reputation rather than the person with whom it had become associated.

John was alone in a small room in the surgical section of the hospital. He lay in his bed in sheet restraints, turning his head away from me as I sat beside him in a chair. At times he pulled violently against the restricting cloth, muttering as he did so, but saying nothing that I could understand. His whispers or shouts were followed by periods of silence, sometimes lasting ten or fifteen minutes. Occasionally, when I spoke, he turned his head to spit at me, but otherwise he made no comprehensible reply to my remarks. I told him that I was concerned with finding out something about what ailed him, as it seemed to me that he was getting little satisfaction from his current way of living. I said that I would visit him daily for an hour or so at a time and would attempt to comprehend as best I could what went on. To all of this he seemingly paid no attention. For the next three months I visited him daily, and thereafter three to five times each week for a total of two and one-half years. As should now be evident, this is not a detailed account of psychotherapy, nor is it a report of successful treatment nor of correct technical procedures. In what follows, I have selected episodes from this period of treatment as illustrative of those concepts that may be thought of as principles.

ATTEMPT AT PSYCHOTHERAPY

As I sat in the room with John I soon found that I had little to say. He did not respond intelligibly to my remarks, and I often became preoccupied with my own thoughts. No longer so pushed to hurry--to get somewhere--I had time to listen, and as I waited in the silences I began to hear the sounds of the hospital as I had never heard them before. I became more aware of the ward social structure, of the more or less covert hierarchies of power among patients and personnel, and of the heavy timelessness of those who live alone while living with others. The world of the patient, while not mine, came a little closer to me.

Also, as I waited, my own feelings came more clearly into my awareness. My desire to help and understand often faded away, leaving puzzlement, or more commonly, annoyance, boredom, and a sense of frustration and impotence. Whereas I had at first made many suggestions to John and openly speculated about the possible causes of his behavior, I eventually ran out of ideas. Occasionally I would realize that during the course of an hour I had presented perhaps a dozen different theories about his difficulties, with attendant suggestions about how he might better live his life. If John heard me, he must have learned that I was not sure of my ground. Not being sure is not disastrous; pretending to be sure, or being sure when one has no right to be, are attitudes likely to be destructive to the development of confidence in another.

Frequently I felt discouraged and foolish, and wondered how I could justify what I was doing. At times I expressed my feelings of puzzlement or despair or rage, but John seemed to pay no more attention to these personal declarations than to anything else I said. Often I lost myself in daydreams, thinking of the past and future and evading the entanglement of the present, and then would feel guilty at having been so detached from my role as observer. Again, there seemed to be nothing in my mind, and I guessed that perhaps my thoughts were no more repetitive and stereotyped than those of my patient, whose fantasies (judging from his behavior) seemed to be terrible, but were not necessarily varied and rich.

I realized that some of the patient's activities repelled me or simply made me anxious. I then asked myself what I wanted this man to do. The answer seemed simple: I wanted him to eat, to stop his attempts to hurt himself; I wanted him to recognize me, to talk in a conventional and logical fashion, paying proper attention to sequences of cause and effect; I wanted him to discuss his past, to talk about his relationship with me, and to connect the past with the present so that his behavior might be seen to make sense and insight thus be advanced.

In all of these wants, legitimate as they might seem to be, I was declaring that the man in his present state was unacceptable to me. I came to be of the opinion that "desirable" change could come only as the "undesirable" could be accepted. One way to change behavior is to learn something about it--its forms, patterns, motivations, goals; if one is too intent on change, however, he may learn little about the behavior and may derogate the person whose behavior is of necessity a revelation of himself. It became apparent that despite my expressed wish to know my patient well, I often retreated before his exposure of himself to me, and he in turn retired from my withdrawal.

An example is the disgust that I felt at John's incontinence. A nurse always cleaned the patient before my visit, and thus I was "spared" this unpleasant contact with him, the assumption being that I,

as the physician, would deal with my patient through words alone.
Such an attitude made little sense in view of the fact that my patient
was, for the most part, mute, and much of our communication was
nonverbal. Finally realizing this, I assisted, when the need arose,
in the bathing of the patient, finding that, while he did not speak of
this activity, he did not resist it. I also discovered that as I took a
more active part in the patient's care, in his cleansing and feeding,
I felt more at ease with him and less repelled by his unconventional
expressions.

Each day I spent time with the ward personnel, discussing with
them my hours with John and expressing my feelings of hopefulness or
despair. We tried to make sense of what we observed, and in attempting this came to know and respect each other more, and to appreciate
the nature of the task in which we were engaged. The stereotyped
picture of John now faded as we spoke of him as a man of anxiety, or
fear, or anger, or hatred, or affection and disappointment, or
whatever.

After a month some changes were noteworthy. Restraints
were required only during occasional outbursts of panic, and the
patient ate well, gaining weight, appearing to be in good physical
condition, and showing no residuals of the trauma to his head. In
about two months he was no longer incontinent, and he came regularly
to my office, sitting or standing in silence, his back partially turned
to me. After four months he spoke, at first hesitantly and in low
tones, but gradually with increased conviction and forcefulness.
Although I had looked forward to his speaking, I discovered that I
had become accustomed to the silences as well as to his vocalizations.
His voice startled me, and I briefly experienced a wish for him to
stop speaking and to return to his former ways. The dramatic quality
of his vocal behavior was lost in the more conventional speech which
he now used. I wanted John to change, but I found change disrupting to
the routine set of our meetings. It is useful for the therapist to note
any tendency on his part to become attached to the psychotic behavior
of his patient, or to the at times comfortable regressed form of their
relationship, and out of his own necessities to cling to the past and
resist change.

In reviewing the first six months of our meetings, the following
observations seem particularly relevant to our general concerns with
psychotherapeutic principles:

1. To function as a therapist it is often useful to modify
   certain preconceptions of disease and treatment, and
   to seek divergent ways of looking at things. The old
   ways need not be summarily abandoned as "wrong,"
   and the new ways are not necessarily "right"; one
   tries shifting about to achieve differences in perspective.
   The contours of a mountain must be studied from

different approaches lest the subtleties of its form
escape one. To the therapist (and others) the patient
must become a person; he cannot remain a "case" of
dementia praecox or of anything else. In intensive and
prolonged treatment programs one will find theoretical
formulations of value; consciously or not, one always
works with some such formulation, and one's theory
should be readily available to awareness, or its
operation will be covert and less directly subject to
correction. A theory must be subject to change; otherwise it may become a rigid form into which patient and
therapist are fitted, rather than a flexible instrument
for their use.

2. In order to carry on treatment the therapist must spend
time with his patient. Although this observation may
seem obvious, the accomplishment of the task is not
always easy. During a therapeutic session the ordinary
concept of time, and the customary goals demanding
quick and direct attainment, may often be put aside.
One sits, and listens, and observes--the other, himself, and in time the transaction that is the resultant
of the being together, discovering in so doing that a
personality does not exist of itself, but is an expression
of past, present, and anticipated social fields. Therapy
is done in the here and now, not in the past, in the
future, or the elsewhere. There may develop many
"reasons" for not being with the patient. It is the
therapist's task to take a look at such reasons; in
them he may discover evidences of his own anxiety
and evasiveness. If you are to be your patient's
therapist, you must find ways to be with him--despite
objections raised by him or by yourself. If the
objections are too great, someone else must do the job.

3. The therapist wishes to learn how his patient views the
world, himself, and others (among whom is the therapist).
He wants to know what is "in the mind" of his patient,
and in stating this he suggests that he is willing to hear
"all." He soon discovers that there are limitations to
what he can endure. Some of what he hears and sees
may repel him by its strangeness and incomprehensi-
bility; some matters may be offensive in terms of his
own ideals and values; others may be experienced as
an attack on his own self-esteem, being especially
painful when searchingly near the truth. For example,
I often find that I do not listen with ease to accounts of
despair and loneliness, these reminding me of my own
aloneness and the indeterminacy and uncertainty of my
existence. It is difficult for me to grasp the idea that
there are occasions on which I can help only by not
helping, that I then have no power except in my ability

to continue in my being with another. Whatever the subject may be that increases anxiety in the therapist, he will react with some form of withdrawal, becoming angry, contemptuous, depressed, discouraged, overly talkative, or whatever, and thereupon his patient will likely feel puzzled or confused, if not rejected and unaccepted. Should the therapist be unaware of his own anxiety or deny it, the patient may come to feel that the physician is a blind fool or a hypocrite, or that he (the patient) grossly misperceives reality and is irretrievably crazy. In any case, the outcome is not likely to advantage the treatment procedure.

In brief, the psychotherapist is required not only to know something of his own major attitudes, motivations, values, and the modes of his behaving with others, but he must be able to learn ever more of himself, even though such increase of knowledge may be markedly disconcerting. The therapist will do well to seek greater knowledge of himself in personal therapy and in consultation with colleagues about the obscurities of work in progress.

4. In the course of treatment the therapist searches for evidences of anxiety in his patient and in himself--or, to put it more precisely, in the social field in which they both operate. As anxiety-laden areas are identified, the modes of expression of the anxiety, the defenses against it, the events leading to its increase and decrease, and its origins may be explored. One learns to respect the painfulness of anxiety, its function as a disrupting agent in interpersonal affairs, and its effectiveness in interfering with learning, accurate perception of past and present, and the exercise of foresight. Recognizing the above, the therapist will move, not with apprehension but with a certain circumspection, avoiding those increases of anxiety that threaten to disrupt the growing communicative process.

5. Although the therapist properly hopes for favorable changes in his patient, he cannot usefully approach the patient in the guise of one who observes behavior only to effect its alteration. To do so would be to devalue the patient, seeming to say, "I cannot accept you now, but only when you are different." Thus it is that one becomes concerned with acceptance and understanding, eschewing for a time at least, interpretation, judgment, valuation, and even salvation, being confident that the human organism tends to adopt more efficient and satisfying modes of behavior as anxiety subsides, communication increases, and opportunities for simpler goal-directed action are made available.

6. Although one is often moved to interpret some aspect of a patient's behavior, this should be done only within the limitations of the patient's tolerance of anxiety. It is useful to keep in mind the idea that no interpretation of human behavior is likely to be "exact," and that for each one offered, there may be alternative explanations to be considered as indicated. It is also well to attempt to distinguish the simply communicative from the obscurely communicative, and these from the incomprehensible. For example, it is often confusing and a waste of time to deal with the latter as if it were the former.

7. The therapist is not expected to be somehow perfect, completely self-knowing, totally accepting of the other, an unending source of love and understanding, or endowed with extraordinary wisdom. However, it is useful if that which he does is congruent with that which he feels and thinks, consciously or otherwise. That is, a persistent marked discrepancy between the therapist's attitudes and behavior will be experienced by his patient as a repetition of an all-too-familiar situation in which the words "I love you" are not in accord with the behavior which says, more or less clearly, "I love you not."

8. Although we seek to communicate in the abstract symbols of speech, in doing so we should observe that much-- perhaps the greater and most significant portion--of what goes on in the therapeutic exchange is nonverbal. The word gains its full meaning when supported by the act, and he who has endured the vicissitudes of life leading him to become a psychiatric patient has of necessity become extraordinarily attentive, not only to speech, but to its vocal and other gestural accompaniments. The patient in the hospital loses contact with others. As we seek to renew that contact we may reach out to the patient with our words and ideas, and also with sound and gesture. We touch the patient with words, with vocalization, with visual stimulation, with bodily contact, and so on, suiting our actions as best we can to the needs of our patients and ourselves.

CONTINUANCE AND ENDING OF THERAPY

Let us now return briefly to my work with John. For some months our relationship seemed to prosper. His confidence in me increased, and he haltingly told me something of his past. Although he hesitated to speak critically of his parents, I gained some idea of their chronic unhappiness together, and learned that John was subtly encouraged by his mother to disassociate himself from his father's allegedly wicked and worldly ways and to abandon himself to the emotional support of this anxious, dependent, and discouraged woman. John acted as if becoming an independent man was to deny the needs of his mother, whereas remaining bound to his home was to deny his own growth. Fearing both relationship and its apparent alternative, isolation, he became preoccupied with vague concepts of good and evil and salvation, seeking some way in which to grow without modifying or disrupting familial attachments. If the dilemma seemed insoluble, the psychotic reaction was not an adequate solution.

In these remarks I do not intend to specify a "cause" of this man's behavior. I do wish to indicate that the family scene was markedly different from that described in the hospital records, and was viewed differently by each of the participants in it. John acted as if he could not exist within his family or outside of it. He seemed to fear that in becoming independent he would remove his mother's only emotional support, abandoning her to the father for whom he felt both fear and contempt, and in whom he had not found a masculine model suitable to himself or his mother. His own moves toward self-realization were equated with the destruction of those upon whom he continued to be dependent. It became evident that John's growing separateness in adolescence was experienced by him and his parents as a threat to the integrity of the family social field, and, as is commonly the case, his advances toward health and assertiveness were met by anxiety and the subtle resistance of all concerned.

As the work progressed, John became more openly and directly expressive of his feelings toward me. Patterns of relatedness developed within his family became manifest in our relationship. At times he was assaultive, to which behavior I set limits for his sake as well as my own. He also expressed, often hesitantly, regard for me, and I showed my liking for him. Our relationship was marked by approach and withdrawal, acceptance and rejection, promise and disappointment, and at times I found my feelings of discouragement and frustration almost intolerable. John seemed to fear that his growing independence might be troublesome or destructive to me, but I was unable to develop this subject with him to any great extent. I wanted to learn more about his ways of thinking, his growing up, his views of me, and so on, but my questioning usually increased his evasiveness and withdrawal. In seeking understanding I frequently felt that I met obduracy that could not be penetrated, and at such times I felt anger and resentment. Sometimes we seemed to be engaged in a tedious, unending struggle leading nowhere.

Then there came a change in the relationship that heralded its premature and perhaps unfortunate termination. John insisted that he wished to convert me to his religious convictions, a fundamentalist variant of Protestantism that I found peculiarly unappealing. Feeling dominated and pressured, I tended to oppose and argue with him rather than to listen and attempt to comprehend what he was trying to do. He withdrew from me increasingly and finally insisted on terminating therapy, eventually returning to his home to live with his parents—to their stated pleasure and my dissatisfaction.

He would not discuss his leaving in any detail, and angered at his aloof attitude, I said, "You are trying to control me by forcing your religious views on me." To this he replied, "Look to yourself. I've had enough of being controlled," and we saw each other no more.

I regretted this separation from the man whom I had often thought of as "my patient" without having any clear awareness of the possessiveness thereby implied. As a therapist I was discontent with the incompleteness of the work, and as a human I felt hurt by this rejection of myself. Much of what had gone on was obscure to me. I sought for understanding in a consideration of transference counter-transference involvements, and in a continuance of personal analysis. There being a limitation of space--and perhaps of usefulness--I can present only some of my speculation regarding the therapy reported here in fragmentary form. It is well to remember that I cannot "prove" what I say; there are complex patterns of experience reflected in behavior, and I am hesitant to designate one or the other as "cause." What we can do is observe, formulate, report, and seek for patterns that may be shown to have some predictive value. Nevertheless, although experience may be felt as personally unsatisfactory or some-how unrewarding, the physician should attempt to learn from it. Certain of my observations of the work with John relevant to our interests are as follows:

1. As John's behavior grew more conventional, I had taken great pride in his accomplishments, looked upon in part as a reflection of my efforts. I belatedly became aware of my fantasy concerning him. I pictured him as completing his work with me, returning to college, getting married, raising a family, leading a somewhat conventional middle-class life, and on appropriate occasions extending to me due credit for his betterment. In having such ambitions for him I did not discover their acceptability to, or suitability for, him. In other words, I forgot my patient's goals in a preoccupation with my own. He spoke of converting me to a certain religious view, and in resisting this I failed to recognize that I was attempting to convert him to my idealized and mundane concept of American middle-class living without due regard for his own wishes, past experiences, and capabilities. In this odd and obscure struggle therapy did not prosper. I learned (as I might have known) that the therapist's ambitions, goals, and values cannot with profit be forced upon the patient. Many of us have had enough of such forcing in our lives, and do not respond favorably to those who speak of freedom and self-determination while more or less covertly they exert their domination.

2. I realized that despite my "good intentions" as a therapist, I had entered into a "power struggle" with the patient, the motives for my own behavior being obscure to me.

John brought into our relationship emotion and determination originating in his experiences at home, but now directed at me. Apparently he resented me and wanted to change me as he resented and wanted to change or "save" his father. I made efforts to interpret this "transference" distortion, but was unsuccessful. The patient's anxiety increased as I sought to increase insight, and often we lost sight of the transference aspect of the relationship. Certain of my own goals, needs, and values were unclear to me, and their covert operation in the therapeutic field proved to be a handicap. The therapist does not work outside of his own system of values; he has his own needs. It is important that these needs and values be readily available to his awareness so that their function in the therapeutic process can be openly identified and dealt with as necessity dictates.

3. It seemed clear to me that the therapeutic relationship is not a static affair, but is a dynamic field, moving more or less clearly in the direction of the facilitation of efficient human performance, or in the direction of restriction and cumbersome complexity. That is, I do not think we can say that "nothing is happening" in some therapeutic intervention. In my opinion, there is no standstill; despite appearances the patient is getting better or worse, whatever the definitions of these terms may be.

4. I think that a therapist must have a confidence and faith in what he does, and in the essential worth of the human being. That which he comes to know in himself and others he may like or abhor, but none of this can he deny or turn his back upon as somehow more or less than evidence of humanity. The therapist must persist in what he does, seeking knowledge however labeled as good or evil, being, perhaps, of the opinion that man, the creature of both his biological and cultural heritage, is not born to be destructive, although destruction may be his end.

5. In reviewing my association with John and others of my patients, I think that a major source of a therapist's distress arises from his lack of confirmation by the patient. Often he feels inept as a therapist, the exhibition of his technical skills may not lead to rapid or demonstrable favorable change, and there may be little evidence that any benefit derives from exposure to the therapist's benevolence. In brief, the therapist may question his adequacy as a physician and as a human, and in doing so despair about himself and his work.

There is reason for such sentiments. Early in our lives we learn the need to give and receive affection and tenderness. In our development we require a response to our own behavior --a response of recognition, acceptance, reciprocation, or even rejection. Without such responses we tend to feel lost and uncertain. From our patient's recognition that what we do may for long periods be minimal--apparently lacking -- we may grow uncomfortable, feeling alone, unwanted, useless, or simply insignificant. It is in the face of such slight and obscure feedback that the therapist must persist, refusing to retreat from a situation seemingly so lacking in significance that one's identity and self-esteem become threatened. It is well to remember that the therapist's feelings of loneliness and isolation may be the beginning of communication with the patient; as he can accept such sentiments in himself as hints to what the patient may experience, the way can be opened to a more conventional and symbolic exchange of ideas.

6. Of particular significance to me--as emphasized in my work with John--is the concept that the psychotherapeutic process is one of mutuality, in which the growth of both participants is involved in varying ways and degrees. Although we may desire and praise personal growth and development, most of us have learned to resist change. Change often implies anxiety. The therapist who successfully encourages growth in his patient will himself grow. Should he find the possibility of such personal alteration intolerable, he may unwittingly attempt to prevent change in his patient, thus defeating therapeutic ambitions in efforts to allay his own anxiety. In more fortunate circumstances the therapist will accept growth in both himself and his patient, and in so doing may discover unexpected rewards in the reciprocal nature of the therapeutic adventure.

ADDENDUM

Q. Did you formulate a specific diagnosis before you began phycho-
therapy, or was it made after psychotherapy was in progress?
Do such pre-therapeutic diagnoses inhibit or facilitate taking a
patient into treatment? Are your diagnoses subject to revision as
psychotherapy proceeds, and do they vary depending on the way
the patient responds to the treatment? Do you distinguish between
diagnosis as such and simple spontaneous diagnostic reflections?

A. The patient was diagnosed as schizophrenic before psychotherapy
was begun. Hopefully, a diagnostic label carries with it implications for prognosis and therapy, in which case it can be useful.
In all instances, however, one must search for the person who
bears the diagnosis, else the human may be lost in a name. The
name dementia praecox has a meaning of disaster for many, and
for those it unfortunately would prejudice the therapy. I may
revise diagnosis during the course of treatment as new data
become available. The patient's response to treatment is not
a major factor in such revision. For example, someone
diagnosed as schizophrenic may do well in therapy, whereas
another with the same diagnosis does poorly. I may discover
that the life experiences of the two patients have differed markedly,
despite the diagnosis. In brief, at present the diagnostic label is
not refined to the point of very useful precision. The diagnosis is
what I report for general statistical purposes. Diagnostic reflections are my private and public attempts to formulate in a
communicative fashion a grouping of clinical observations.

Q. Did you approach your patient with a consistent and verbalizable
theory or set of hypotheses on personality structure and/or the
genesis of psychic illness? Was such theory used directly (or
indirectly) in selecting the patient for treatment? How was it
applied in the treatment and how effective was your theory in
reaching the goals of treatment? What do you see as the function
of such hypotheses or theories?

A. I do approach my patient with a certain theory of personality
structure and of the genesis of psychic illness. In the work with
the patient reported here I had some familiarity with personality
theory, but was particularly interested in him because of his
history of improvement and relapse and his appearance of profound
despair. A theory of schizophrenic disorder was somewhat
developed and refined in the course of the work reported here,
but was not a major guide in treatment, as it had not been
formulated as it came to be in later years. I think that a theory
is potentially useful. We all have such theories, more or less
formulated, learned in more or less formal.experiences. Some
may have a theory of human development learned from a book;
others may follow a theory actually reflecting teachings within the
family; in some instances one may preach one theory and
unconsciously follow another. Whatever the theory, it should be

readily available to the therapist as a guide, as a background against which to check data, and as a subject for revision.

Q. What did you think of the prognosis of your case before you accepted the patient for treatment? What did you think during the first several interviews; and during the latter stages of treatment? Do you feel prognostic judgments about ultimate health or ultimate illness are useful? Can we dispense with a prognosis as a formal event in clinical treatment?

A. The prognosis of the case reported was poor in terms of diagnosis, response to treatment, prolonged hospitalization, and learning defects dating from childhood. In general I felt optimistic about the patient's outcome, but I was held to a sober outlook by the course of events and the supervisory comments of colleagues. At times I am required to give a prognosis as an aid in attempting to estimate the duration of treatment, to decide how to expend available funds, and to guide the nature of the therapeutic intervention. I favor making statements about prognosis, as it is useful for us to attempt an exercise of foresight. However, we need not be bound to our prognostications; they should be subject to modification.

Q. What particular therapeutic techniques did you apply in this case? Which of them were most effective and which ineffective, and for what reasons? Did you attempt any technical innovations on an empirical basis? When did you feel that a "peak" experience or turning point occurred?

A. The primary emphasis in this report was on the psychotherapeutic process. It was useful to be present with the patient--that is, to be available to him. The effort to deal with the patient "entirely" through verbal symbols was not useful; there was a need for greater use of nonverbal approaches. There was a turn for the better when it was evident to me--and I think to the patient--that I intended to be available to him. Matters did not go well when I became more concerned with "producing a result" than in simply trying to understand something more about the patient's mode of living.

Q. Did you feel that Freud's formulation of transference and counter-transference were sufficient to account for the therapeutic encounter with your patient? How would you describe your encounter?

A. The concepts of transference and countertransference are useful, but have required expansion beyond their original formulation by Freud. I prefer to think of involvements within a social field, the perceptions and behavior of the participants being influenced by past and current events as well as by anticipations of the future. With the patient in this report there was usually lacking a feeling of closeness and of the breaking down of interpersonal barriers. There were prejudices on both sides that interfered with the forming of a workable relationship. The beginning of change in these prejudices is the subject of this account.

Q. It has been said that psychotherapy is a white, middle-class, urban phenomenon which does not necessarily apply to other social stratifications or cultures. In what way did your patient's cultural background influence his illness and treatment? In what way did your own cultural background assist or deter the treatment?

A. In other circumstances this patient would not have been in psychotherapy, his home being in a small town where such services were not available. I discovered that I had some prejudice against the patient's fundamentalist religious views which I thought of as narrow and outmoded. It was difficult for me (from the western mountains of this country) to "empathize" with this man from a small southern community. As time has gone on I have become less provincial in my views to the benefit of my therapeutic endeavors.

Q. There is an increasing tendency for neo-analytic thinking to ascribe the genesis and treatment of psychic illness to the social psychology of the family. How did this apply in your case?

A. I think that to a large extent the patient's difficulties were expressions of family disorder. However, this observation could not be proved with the data presented. Of particular interest is the observation that the patient's behavior in therapy frequently seemed to reflect (in the transference situation) distortions of family relationships. In this case the "transference relationship" was not "worked through."

Q. If your treatment was concluded what criteria did you use for terminating it? If it is still in process, what guide points would you use to determine when your patient is sufficiently improved to discontinue treatment? Do you feel that a patient should be seen as long as he feels he needs it and is willing to pay the fees?

A. This work was interrupted prematurely by the patient's withdrawal from it. The criteria for discontinuing treatment cannot be discussed in the brief space available. I consider a practical criterion to be the ability of the patient to live effectively outside of a mental hospital and to derive some satisfaction from his relationships with other people. I expect that in the course of treatment we shall have reviewed many of the significant experiences of his past life in an effort to get some understanding of the sources of his identity. The major transference or parataxic distortions will have been revealed and modified, and a more dependable and predictable view of the patient, the therapist, and others will have emerged.

I do not think that therapy should be continued simply because there is money to pay for it and the patient says that he needs it. The patient's expression of need may be a defensive maneuver on his part that requires analysis rather than prolonged action. One must be careful that the therapist's own needs do not serve to prolong treatment unnecessarily.

Q. Did you make any mistakes in this case--in the sense of "if you had to do it over"?

A. Yes, I made mistakes in this case. Some of them have been reported in the account, and very likely others have escaped my memory, or were not recorded in my notes, or were never in my awareness.

Q. In treating your case did you perhaps feel that the classical distinctions between psychoses and neuroses were breaking down? (This question may apply even if your case represents neither a psychotic or neurotic.)

A. I find it useful at times to make a distinction between neurosis and psychosis in terms of "ego structure." However, the distinctions have not been dependable in many instances, and I have no great confidence in them. The patient reported was "psychotic" in the usual sense of that term. Had he improved further I think that he would have appeared increasingly more "neurotic." I think that the neurotic person and the psychotic person are very likely much the same except for the nature of their life experiences and the patterning of their modes of dealing with these.

Chapter II

THE PSYCHOTHERAPY OF A SCHIZOPHRENIC PATIENT *

by Gaetano Benedetti

INTRODUCTION

In this paper we attempt to describe briefly the psychotherapy of a schizophrenic patient whom we treated in 1953 for six months. The patient was a fifty-four-year-old woman whose psychosis had been preceded by an imperceptibly slow character transformation covering a period of years, only to become acutely manifest in the end. It had rapidly developed into a set of symptoms which led one to suspect dementia.

We should like to present the following data as background to the anamnesis:

1. The personality contours of the patient in the family milieu have been established in part on the basis of our own personal interviews with the relatives in question, but mainly by means of the findings emerging from our analysis. Brief interviews with the relatives helped us to rectify or to supplement the life history outlined for us by the patient herself. For the understanding of the dynamics of the illness, the patient's "internal" image of her parents seemed to us to be even more important than the marshaling of "objective" information supplied by members of the family. However, the question of the causal significance of the social environment in the genesis of the schizophrenia is not the actual subject of this paper. If, nevertheless, our description at times creates the impression that we regard the psychogenesis of the illness as proven, it should be expressly stated at this point that our manner of presentation expresses merely the manner and the style in which we spoke with the patient and lived through her psychosis with her.
2. The statements of the patient herself recorded here and there in the text were not taken down stenographically (which in fact would be impossible in this direct type of psychotherapy); hence they do not represent verbatim citations. However, since I wrote up the most important parts

---

*An abridgement of this paper first appeared in German in <u>Psyche</u>. Published in translation with permission of the copyright owner.

of our interview, after every session, the citations as they stand can be relied on as reflecting the sense of what was said; they also reflect rather faithfully the patient's style of expression. But in their subsequently recorded form, true as it is to the meaning of what was said, they seem much less confused than they were in reality. I am perfectly well aware that something is thus lost--what is lost is precisely what is "incomprehensible" or what is to be understood in another way. However, even a stenographic record of the entire treatment (in many respects even a tape recording) would hardly be capable of reproducing anything really essential: the mimicry, the attendant demeanor, the intonation of the voices, the whole atmosphere of the personal encounter, all of which, after all, constitute the most important aspect of the psychotherapeutic event. Our account, then, must omit important data and be restricted to showing the guiding principles controlling the actual course of the therapy.

3. The psychotherapy of our schizophrenic patient lasted six months. It was carried out within the scope of a series of psychotherapeutic tests which I undertook at Burghölzli, the Psychiatric Institute of the University of Zurich, in 1953, after my training with Dr. J. N. Rosen. The patient was continuously hospitalized during the six-month treatment. All the clinical measures connected with the care of the patient were decided on by the psychotherapist himself regardless of the ward the patient was on at any given time. The psychotherapist, then, in the eyes of the patient, stood for the authority of the clinic; whenever disciplinary steps had to be taken, he assumed the full responsibility for any eventual decision. During the first two weeks I treated the patient two to three hours a day; for the rest of the period--except for some days of more intensive therapy--one to two hours daily. Moreover, from time to time I employed her, by way of occupational therapy, in my own office, without allowing myself to be distracted from my other work by the patient's presence. The patient was immersed, as it were, in the atmosphere of my workaday routine. In all other respects her social contacts remained within the scope of the psychotherapy on the ward.

BIOGRAPHY AND FAMILY HISTORY

At the outset of the treatment we knew little about the family and life history of the patient who was already fifty-four years of age and living almost completely alone. Her parents had long been dead; the confused patient could tell us practically nothing about her childhood or youth; her only sister (who lived far away and for years had kept up almost no ties with the patient) maintained her inner distance beneath a semblance of superficial friendliness; what is more, she visited the patient only some months after her admission to the clinic. Thus, at the beginning we had to rely solely on what the patient told us in her confused state.

Later on, the following picture of the family milieu could be reconstructed: The patient's mother was a quiet, pious, reserved woman, to this day surrounded, in the eyes of her children, by a cool aura of austere saintliness; glorified and yet an alien distant figure with a nimbus of holiness, almost devoid of any personal physiognomy, resembling rather an inflexible Byzantine Madonna on a golden ground. In her psychosis the patient whould often say: "My mother was a saintly woman...." "My mother had no breasts..." "No woman in our family had breasts."

Her father was an accountant by profession; a kind, peaceable, industrious man, who, however, was not much of a success socially, was something of a failure in financial undertakings, and for a time was unable to support his family. The patient's relationship to him was at all times one of tenderness. Her sister, about ten years older than the patient herself, was characterized for us by her own son as a vivacious, easygoing woman, who never let anything worry her. At the age of sixty she still liked to go dancing and was diametrically opposed in temperament to our patient with her almost cramped conscientiousness, preciseness, and strict diligence.

Her nephew strikes us as perhaps the most significant person in the patient's life. To this day he is attached to her with almost the touching love of a son. For years on end, up to his rather late marriage, he lived alone with his aunt as her lodger. The patient at that time cared for her unmarried nephew just like a jealous mother; she would become tense and uneasy when the young man sometimes came home late in the evening. The separation following upon his marriage seems to have deprived this socially isolated, "schizoid" woman of her mainstay; closely attached to her nephew as she was, nevertheless from then on she kept all further relationships with him to a minimum.

The patient herself was her parents' last child. She was born fifteen years after her brother and ten years after her sister, when the parents were already at a fairly advanced age. She came into the world - - as she put it once in the psychosis--"by accident," at a time when the parents were in grave financial straits. She often felt that basically she was an unwanted child. She never developed a warm-hearted relationship to her elder brother and sister. She was not in their age group and could hardly talk with them; however, she envied them. Her brother was their mother's favorite; the elder sister grew up when the family was prosperous and therefore had a far happier childhood. The more the elder sister went her own way, drawing away from the parents, developing into a gay, easygoing girl, the more anxiously did the mother keep her youngest child at home. In the eyes

of her brother and sister and their friends she was "only a child."
For her nephew, fifteen years younger, however, she was later an
"old aunt." Shy and unsure of herself, she stood "between two gener-
ations." "That was my fate, to have dropped in between two genera-
tions. Today I still sit and knit as in school. My inside pockets are
empty. In the end I have remained the old aunt." These were the
words used by the patient in the restitution phase of her psychosis in
describing these tension-laden conflicts.

Our patient, as far as we know, grew up normally without
ever causing any particular trouble. She successfully completed
secondary and commercial high school and then worked as an accountant. She worked with exemplary diligence and conscientiousness in
the same job for twenty years, and her daily round was in all respects
like clockwork.

In her youth she was in love with a flier, who later crashed;
she idealized him and from then on did not want to marry anybody.
However, she had never formed a really concrete relationship with
this friend of her youth before his death; relatives reported that she
had imagined this friendship. Perhaps she needed this image of the
fiancé killed in an air crash in order more easily to evade her real
role, which was to become a woman. Throughout her days she went
strictly her own way; went alone to concerts and plays; went alone on
holiday trips; her cultural interests--and she is very intelligent--
were varied, but were satisfied on a decidedly intellectual plane,
outside the realm of social relationships.

The only breach in the armor encasing her vitality was effected
in erotic experiences: that is to say, in eroticism that was for the
most part casual, mainly interested in bodily contact without the
formation of any really vital partnership that involved her deeper
feelings. From the social standpoint, this eroticism of hers, involving free change of partners and the flouting of conventional mores,
constituted a certain contrast to the patient's rigidly correct workaday
pattern of behavior, which seemed almost compulsively neurotic.
Among her partners we found, in the main, considerably younger or
more or less helpless men (e.g., a Jewish refugee, a poor hypochon-
driac, who finally committed suicide), whom she looked after, helping
them financially as well. Her nephew reported that this erotic activity came to an abrupt end when this woman, now approaching her
fifties, suddenly "discovered that she was an old maid"; she then locked
herself up and immured herself entirely within her private life. From
now on work was her sole aim.

At this point, the patient's character began to undergo a
transformation. She became increasingly insecure and anxious.
She was obviously looking for a psychic compensation--she suddenly
developed ardent religious interests for the first time in her life.
As a Protestant, however, she hardly found any satisfaction of her

religious needs in her own Protestant tradition. Rather, she became
sentimentally enthusiastic about Catholicism, about the Catholic way
of looking at things, and Catholic modes of feeling. She was smitten
by the "beauty of the Ave Maria," and the confessional. On the other
hand, she tormented herself with remorse "as an upright clean Protestant." She formed strong attachments to pastors, her attitude
having a markedly deranged quality. There also developed a tender
relationship to another woman, a divorced colleague; but our patient
was outraged when she noticed that this woman at the same time
flirted with men. Then she became increasingly perturbed and suspected her boss and many male colleagues of having intimate relations
with this woman. Only six months prior to the manifest outbreak of
her schizophrenia she complained to an aunt that a woman in the office
was having an illegitimate child and that she herself was somehow
mixed up in this affair. The psychosis then began suddenly with an
acute agitation in which the patient accused herself of the embezzle-
ment, in fact, of the theft, of around 16,000 francs from the firm,
and threw her month's pay out of the window with the declaration:
"The money has to be clean! I don't need any man!"

Thereupon the patient was hospitalized in a mental clinic and
after a brief psychopathological examination was given electroshock
treatment. This resulted in total amnesia for the psychotic event.
Then the psychosis rapidly improved, so that her release after one
month was deemed feasible. At that time the patient displayed no
further gross symptoms of schizophrenia. However, what was noticeable was her autism, her fixed and occasionally anxious expression,
and a certain inner malaise. Moreover, the patient displayed a complete amnesia for her psychosis. She would ask anxiously what exactly
had happened to her and would stare pensively into empty space for
hours on end. She would also say her "former immoral conduct" must
have been in fact the cause of her illness. Only a few days after her
release she again began to have hallucinations. On her holidays she
heard "the snoring of a lascivious faun" in the night and became afraid.
She was tormented by a "mental reservation" to the effect that she was
carrying Christ in her womb. For this reason people would think she
was a great saint, the Mother of God. She wanted, however, to remain
Protestant. The patient refused to eat, shut herself up in her room,
and became increasingly disturbed, for which reason--only a few
months after her first release--she had to be committed to our clinic.

THE PSYCHOTIC SYNDROM

In our clinic, for months on end, she displayed all the symptoms
of a chronic, distraught, perturbed schizophrenic. The following
excerpt from the clinical report throws some light on the syndrome:

> The patient is lying in an isolation room on the floor,
> dressed only in a blouse, almost naked. Does not allow
> herself to be dressed despite all the efforts of the nurses.

In a loud voice she recites the Lord's Prayer in
French adding biblical citations. "Christ," she syas,
suffered on Golgotha and not in Burghölzli." "Il est mort,
il est mort, il est mort. Il est ressuscité, il est monté
au ciel." ("He is dead, he is dead, he is dead. He has
risen, he has ascended to Heaven.") What does the doctor
advise? Burghölzli? She has already been in Burghölzli.
"J'ai été en prison." ("I have been in prison.") (singing
again) "But that makes no difference. The nurses are
angels in Heaven, not yet, but if they behave well, or saints,
because they work, it's a miracle the way they care for the
patients and the way they obey their God, the ones who
believe in God." She is Mademoiselle J. A., she was taken
away from home last Saturday and she was... (distinct block).
In between, the patient looks at the doctor strongly eroti-
cized. "Voulez-vous continuer votre métier de dentiste?
Seulement vous n'etes pas dentiste, c'est ça." ("Do you
want to go on being a dentist? Only you're not a dentist,
that's what.") It has been such a long time since she last
saw her dear brother-in-law; her brother-in-law was a
dentiste. On the ward she claims to be a dancer, a film
star, a goddess of love; then, again, she is the saint, she
prays aloud, sees derisive whores about her. Speaks confusedly of a poodle and a cat that love each other. In the
center is her mania, her delusion that she is the Mother
of God.

We are confronted here by a woman who, at the age of fifty,
on the threshold of old age, with final solitude closing in on her,
suddenly awakes from an immured existence with the longing to be
allowed at long last to live. The longing for the confessional, for
the embracing Father, for the tender confrontation with Mary, for
the pure experience of motherhood brings a new resonance into her
life, strips off the veil, as it were, from an immured world and
opens up hitherto unknown affective perspectives and horizons. It
is a kind of break-through, which, however, is effected not in freedom but in psychosis. There is no freedom here. The striving for
new, vital, hitherto blocked possiblilities does not emerge here from
a basis of self-determination, but in the face of the now all but in-
eluctable fact of old age. The schizophrenic psychosis comes to a
head in the polar tensions which are structured in immediately
experienced fantasies. On the one hand: I am redeemed, I have
become a woman and a mother; on the other hand: now I am fifty
years old, now the end is coming. In the psychosis the patient once
said: "My one real guilt is that I bore no children." She saw in her
books and notebooks "the journeys that she had never made." Here
something fundamental has been missed, something that can never
be made up for, not merely the actual experiencing of becoming and
being a mother--this is the fate of so many healthy women--but,
rather, the basic underlying experience of a knowing-oneself-to-be-

prepared for such a vital possiblity. As long as the patient was still young, the future was spread out in panorama before her eyes. Now the future no longer possesses any dynamic--it presents its final face that will not change, and that means only one thing. And even the sole breach in her life, her erotic nature, is walled in. Old age, as inevitable fate, seems here to determine the time for this psychosis to commence. The psychosis appeared like a frantic rebellion against this reality, like a primordial cry: "After all, I am a woman and a mother!" The mania appears as a manifestation of her female nature, which finally wants to assert itself, which dances wild dances of love, represents itself as the nude Aphrodite, wants to embrace and clutch everything and be at once holy and profane, and would like to contain within itself both the depths of the wildest instinctual behavior and the heaven of maternal transfiguration--indeed the entire range of female existence.

This abrupt despairing attempt to take possession of the plenitude of existence, all social conventions and traditions notwithstanding, this monstrousness, means but one thing in the eyes of the conscientious aging cashier (the figure that never entirely vanishes from the scene even in the midst of the psychosis): "Theft." "You have stolen 16,000 francs--an enormous sum. Throw away this unclean money. You don't need any man." The strait jacket, to some extent broken out of in her mania, encloses her anew in the mania itself, exalts the prison walls in which the patient now feels herself to be immured, into the all-embracing experience of godlike motherhood. "I am in prison." "I shall never get out of this prison." The breakthrough no doubt had occurred "in God's name," and with these words the patient begins every sentence. However, it is to no avail, the invocation becomes a compulsively reiterated, empty incantation expressive of desperation: the patient need only stand before a mirror to see herself there as devil. "If I look at myself in the mirror, I see a devil in the mirror." She is now at once the Virgin Mary and the Devil, the Saint, and the Whore. In the center arises the experience of a "sacred" womanliness only just achieved. All round there is heaped up, all the more overwhelmingly, the "filth" which is only postponed and with which she has in no way come to terms. This "filth" always accompanies all compulsive purity like a shadow. The "Virgin Mary" complains that the bed linen is dirty. She, on the other hand, does not want to put on her clothes either, because they too are unclean, "because a filthy human being is inside them." She complains of having become ill because she "wanted to celebrate orgies with her father," and she groans that her apartment has "become a brothel." Her gay sister, "with her beautiful vivacious eyes," the obverse of the "Holy Mother's" would have turned the apartment into a brothel. Whores lie in the beds all around, whores whom she would like to "convert," but whom she cannot convert; whores who repeatedly make dirty comments on her "holy words"; and even her own mother--"the most holy thing I have"--appears on the ward as a whore. The patient is suffocating in such filth. She resists desperately. "I am not ashamed to be Aphrodite, for I have never really been such a one and, what's more, I cannot be such a one, my breasts, after all, are dried up." Or again: "A whore is not dirty; she may have a warmer heart than many other people." But this protest does not help her. She feels "guilty and depraved." Also horrifying to her is the contrast between her eroticism and the age of her body, and she is ashamed.

However, in the midst of this hell of torment there extend oases of ecstatic schizophrenic experience, for which she takes into the bargain, as it were, the whole psychosis. In these oases, removed from all humdrum reality, she elaborates herself into a woman. Her inner horizon expands beyond all the limits set by reality into a visionary infinity, and that in three directions. These we should like to designate by the key terms "Aphrodite," "the Holy Virgin," and "Mother Nature."

As Aphrodite, Josephine is a young goddess of beauty. Her dry emaciated legs now gleam in the full ripeness of youth and arouse admiration and astonishment on all sides. They want to launch the patient on a career as a "star," and the theaters of Paris are awaiting the renowned dancer. In her cubicle on the ward she frisks between beds and benches, she elaborates in her dance "all the amorous pranks of her poodle"--"a poodle has unbalanced me, a poodle that I was so afraid of but was so fond of." Soon she is seized by anxiety; Aphrodite cannot deceive herself for long. She looks with fright at her miserable scrawny legs. She cries out for food; her body is shriveled. "The people think I am a saint, a desiccated, dry saint that I am not, do not want to be!!" At this juncture, however, there opens up a second perspective in her mania: "Other mysterious things have happened that brought on my sanctification..." The patient smiles silently to herself, speaks of wondrous signs proclaiming: "I am the Mother of God."--"Too late no doubt to have a child! But--who knows God's ways? After all, what wonders God can work!" She lay utterly forlorn in her bed, frightened by the condition of the world, then she heard knocking on the wall: "Awake! Your Father is here. I tell you, Christ has not died. He is among us..." "I, then, am Mary ... I have borne Christ in my womb!"

She once explained the Josephine-Mary equation as follows: "Just as Mary bewailed her Son, so my mother wept inconsolably over the death of her beloved son..." She, as Mary, took over the "position" where her own "Holy Mother" stood; she was now her mother.

As such, she was now allowed to be with her father. "Here I move about in the blooming garden of my father; here I am quite alone with him... and thanks to God's power, wonderful flowers grow in my womb." She has a child from her father, an age-old dream comes true. The union with her father, however, means both happiness and peril: "Because I wanted to celebrate orgies with my father, I have become ill."

The father theme in many variations dominated the entire development of this psychosis: The father enters the patient's world now as God Himself, then as an elderly friend and doctor, Dr. R., then again as a Dominican Father with whom she is infatuated. She would like to follow this Reverend Father into his hermitage like a faithful little dog; she listens in the night to the wonderful music which her Reverend Father conjures up out of the organ, and the whole room becomes a temple. She is the second wife of Dr. R., and, like his first, deceased, holy wife, wants to be a mother to the poor...

The mother theme develops in a contrapuntal relation to the father theme. If the father is God Himself, then she is Mary; if the father is Dr. R., then she is his wife, etc. The father and the mother imagos emerge, however, in the tension of opposed representations and possibilities of being. The father appears to the patient not only as the protective, fructifying God that brings happiness, but also as a faun which snores in the night, invisible, untamed, and lascivious. She herself as mother appears at times to herself in the guise of a "rapacious wild cat," which wounds and tears. Again and again, even in the transfiguring wish-fancies of the psychosis, this woman comes up against limits that cannot be crossed without danger: untamed, instinctual figures lurk about, ready to devour her. She repeatedly has to retreat to lines of defense. Just as she morally justified her former eroticism in the role of the welfare worker, now, even in the psychosis, she is the mother of the poor, of the harried Jews. Her former loves appear to her as sparrows which she feeds. If she is the food-giving Virginal Mother, she may also without peril call herself Aphrodite. As patroness of the poor, as saint, as "the plain woman from the country," she tries to approximate the maternal model, but in vain. Voices proclaim mockingly that she is the false saint, the Eva Peron exalted by the masses while remaining only a doll. In the face of such derision, the patient gets into a state of extreme, often aggressive excitement. Yes, she is the false saint, because she simply cannot want without ambivalence that which the mother wanted and which imprisons her in the strait jacket of her existence. The adored mother image that she strives for holds no promise: "My mother had no breasts! I want to remain a Protestant, I protest!" Or again: "This mother, this saint, appeared to me today as a whore!" And once her avowal was like a deep groan of despair: "My mother never loved me!"

The patient explores a third path in her mania: If she cannot be the Holy Mother of God, she is "Mother Nature." As almighty Mother Nature she lies in her bed, filled with ecstatic happiness. She unites in her womb all the opposites of life, before which she no longer need fear anything, seeing that she is the mother that brings forth everything. "I could roll about naked on the dark earth, in the open air, under a fir tree, without fear!" She is now outside the categories of guilt and innocence, of pure and impure; she is the primal source of life which gives rise to everything. Here being a mother is no longer purified by holy virginity and lived out on the religious plane, but it is something that is immediately aspired to as the plenitude of being. This mania can therefore be called the patient's most magnificent attempt to break out of the prison of her existence. However, in the long run, to be sure, it does not constitute any protection against anxiety. Mocking derisory hallucinations break forth: "It is"--complains the patient--"as if my tongue had to say 'merde nature' ('excrement nature') instead of 'mère nature' ('mother nature')." 1. The merde - mère play on words is lost in translation. --Trans. Voices call out whorish words: "A torrent of dirty words pours from my mouth at night, an unceasing stream, until I am exhausted. I can do nothing against it." Disgusting figures force their way into her bed, in fact even into her very body: "There are in me persons with whom I don't want to have anything to do, inside here in my body, everything stinks here." The unity of nature falls asunder; the patient has to pay a heavy price for her attempt as Mother Nature to achieve such a unity of opposites: The dirty, the whorish aspect she sought to absorb, transcend, and redeem, she being the universal matrix, the primal source of all life; but this low aspect was in her attempt brought all the more forcibly home to her in the body--it now soils not only her linen, as formerly, when she was the saint, but it even rages in her very body as an alien presence. The "other face" of natural being discloses itself in naked openness, which gives the patient the lie for her deceitful delusion.

This psychosis thus appears as the reflection of a veritable catastrophe in the patient's life. The patient's main problem: "How can I become a woman?" is not resolved in the psychosis either. (How could such a fundamental vital problem be resolved by the psychosis!). In her role as Aphrodite, as the saint, the Mother of God, Mother Nature, or, vice versa, as the whore, in fact as the devil himself, in all these distorted roles she is never the woman, the self-consciously feminine woman which it is her mission to be. Her roles are masks, and behind these masks is a demented woman who does not know herself. On the one hand, these masks help the patient somewhat, otherwise she would not need them. Between unfulfilled mission--fulfillment in fact being a sheer impossibility--and dementia there lies a realm of psychotic self-deception where the patient, thinking in terms of dynamic opposites, defends herself on two fronts. If a voice addresses her with: "You are a whore, you dirty lump of offal," she can reply with a saintly dictum. If, on the contrary, the voices deride her as a "dried-up saint," as "the silly goose that has missed her chance really to live," she then replies as Aphrodite: "Love is my nature." It is by means of these alternating prevarications that she shuns her true mission and, on the other hand, flies from any consciousness of guilt and breakdown, as far as this is possible. But the dementia threatens to progress more and more, and the patient herself, in the midst of her confused state, senseless, mincing, and affectively unmodulated as it is, now and then briefly glimpses the danger: "Now I am finally going soft in the head." "A bell has tolled, a woman has died, she has died forever."

THE PSYCHOTHERAPY[2]

At the beginning of the treatment the doctor, it would seem, was nobody in the eyes of this confused patient. She did not appear to be aware of him at all. He spent many hours a day with her; he put the spoon in her mouth when she did not feed herself; he himself put her to bed when she stood there as helpless as an infant; he addressed her as a child, took her in his arms, held fast to her when she screamed, "Don't touch me, I am God." After her recovery the patient retained but a very dim, blurred memory of this period which had lasted a number of weeks; she would then say: "It was like a prodigious battle, you fought it out for me. I could not believe it..."

Gradually the doctor began to be perceived as a person, but never as a specifically real person. From the beginning until approximately the end of the therapy the doctor represented in this patient's world an imago: as father, devil, and God he filled the patient's horizon. His task at the outset consisted simply in being there, in giving concrete, interpersonal reality to shapes which were otherwise empty figments of her mania, flitting spectrally through the sheet lightning of the psychosis. Thus, his task was to give the psychosis its interpersonal tension, the structure of a meaningful dialogue. There loomed up, for instance, the figure of a fatherly friend: "His eyes have followed me everywhere. There is reflected in his eyes all of nature, the vastness of the sky. He gave me champagne to drink at Christmas, and I had never drunk wine; he did everything to free me from the prison. But he could not do it. The prison was too strong."

The doctor now represented this picture. He, however, introduced into it a personal way of behaving that confronted the patient with new situations other than those from which the psychosis had emerged. The psychotherapy consisted of both personal involvement and direct interpretation. The patient would complain, for instance, "If I say something holy, there is always a whore near by in this cursed house who adds something dirty to my words, a whore who uses foul language and mocks and tempts." I replied: "You yourself are this supposed whore! When you were hungry, when you wanted to love, that mother, whom you call the 'saint without breasts,' always regarded you as a whore! This whore that you hear has to complain of the sanctimoniousness of a mother who did not give her child a

2. We discuss in a separate section the treatment of the psychosis, after having described the psychotic syndrome, with a view to making the psychotherapeutic problem more concrete. To be sure, the syndrome depicted above does not as such precede the therapy, but it emerges in outline only from the dialectic and the inner dynamic of the therapy itself. This case of schizophrenia would perhaps have revealed to us another facet if it had not been treated psychotherapeutically. Mental illness always takes shape as an interpersonal reality.

single drop of milk and only wanted to have it parched and dry!"
Thereupon the patient screamed that I was the devil, turned her back
on me, hid her face from me, and prayed aloud: "In the name of God!"
An hour later, however, she remarked to a visitor: "I am under the
devil's protection. The devil brings me food." For weeks on end,
the patient kept asking me for food so that, as she put it, she would
have milk in her dry breasts. Memories floated up; for example,
those from her childhood, when she secretly masturbated in bed,
fearful that her mother might notice it. Toward me, the devil, the
patient developed an uninhibited, at times aggressively erotic approach
which, in the absence of natural feelings of shame and differentiated
impulses, could be quite coarse and revolting. It was often only
necessary to lay a hand on her brow and let her feel a trace of sympathetic tenderness to mollify her erotic frenzy. Then the excited
aging woman could fall peacefully asleep like a child, or weep. As
to her alleged theft of 16,000 francs, I told her that she had been in
the position of a hungry child, one who would like to grab many things
for itself that a cold mother never gave and that it bitterly needed.
She was perfectly right to take what, after all, belonged to her! The
patient listened without comment. From that time on she never again
mentioned the theft, and when I reminded her of it, she shook her head,
although in the midst of her psychosis, saying: "That was just a crazy
idea, a delusion."

Even in the early weeks of the therapy there were moments
or entire hours of clearer awareness, following the direct interpretation of a demented figment or hallucination, in which one could
sense that the patient was now near to, at close quarters with, reality.
Such situations soon unleashed violent anxiety and motor disturbance,
which were calmed if the dementia re-emerged. "Am I to return to
reality," she once asked me bitterly, "to this hell which I have been
tasting like a condemned woman for fifty-two years on end?" (For
reasons that evaded us, the fifty-four-year-old patient often said in
the psychosis that she was fifty-two.) Her anxiety was frequently
expressed in the shape of immediate aggression. We controlled
outbreaks of violent aggression and destructive rage by means of
physical force; as far as possible, in such situations, we preferred
a direct personal confrontation to any kind of technical clinical procedure, such as drugs, isolation, etc. By this direct approach,
expressing more than mere words because it impinged bodily on the
patient, the demented woman obtained the man, the father, she was
longing for, of whom she was afraid. She would say softly: "My God,
now you are my father." Sometimes she was also afraid of me. But
how redemptive was the excitement when she noticed what the doctor
meant by proceeding in this way. Immediately after such a confrontation she would say: "I cannot bear you any grudge for I sensed the
pain you felt in your hands." As God, the doctor appeared to her at
times as a figure of frightfully cold purity, and then again endowded with
the features of devilish sensuality. However, he increasingly personified a loving and priestly solemnity in whose dazzling light she

immersed herself as "Mother Nature." For weeks the patient remained
in a felicitous ecstasy detached from all reality and wholly given
up to her hallucinatory experience. She was in her father's garden and
gorgeous flowers grew in her womb. As long as she was in this condition, interpretations for the most part proved ineffectual, at least
in terms of their immediate, palpable effect. From the long-range
viewpoint not one word was really spoken in vain. Yet, we ourselves
did not wish to interpret such ecstatic states too precipitantly with a
view to uncovering their real content because as symbolic realizations
of long-repressed, unfulfilled wishes they were making possible an
inner development which could hardly have occurred by way of mere
interpretive logic. [3]

We suspected that the patient could arrive at maturity only by
drawing on this realm of dementia. [4] On the other hand, we did not
let up with our therapy for one moment so that the total inadequacy of
the dementia as a protection against her anxiety became palpable to
herself. Once she awoke from her ecstasy in great anxiety and agitation. She had felt an inclination, quite alien to her, to caress the
patient sleeping next to her. She spoke confusedly of strange voices
and odors which disgusted her. Doctor: "Anxiety is getting you
confused. Let's simply put it this way: You would like to sleep in
the bosom of a loving mother! Everything would be so easy if your
mother had just not been a desiccated saint." At this point the patient
became agitated. After some resistance, however, she admitted her
wish to lie with that woman. She stressed, to be sure, that it was not
her wish; it was only her urge. Doctor: "And what will you do as
Mother Nature if your urges, your own children, knock at the door?
You will turn them away unquestioned like a mother that is, in fact,

---

3. In another case I succeeded within a few hours, thanks to an exceptionally strong transference, in doing away with a similar ecstatic
mania by direct interpretations. The result? The patient was, to
be sure, entirely in the sphere of reality, but she fell prey to
melancholy, treatment proving to be all the more difficult because
the previous transference to me had vanished with the mania. In a
third case of precipitant interpretation and dissolution of the mania
there followed a phase of confusion--fortunately brief. Above all,
delusions which grow out of a strong transference to the doctor
should for a time be respected as attempts at important symbolic
realization. Here we can only confirm the experience of
Mme. Sechehaye. There are often fluid transitions between
symbolic play and mania.

4. Let there be no misunderstanding. Of course, the mania per se
has no curative effect. It remains wholly sterile if it develops as
a desiccated monologue in the solitude of the psychosis or, in
induced insanity, infects others. Symbolic realization is possible
only in the milieu of an encounter with the doctor thinking wholly
in terms of reality but understanding and experiencing inter-
personally and acknowledging the meaning of the mania.

not Mother Nature! You are acting now in the way your mother treated you! No wonder if these urges which you despise, these hungry children, who also want to have a right to live and who are banished and disowned by you, avenge themselves on you when they turn into alien powers, voices, and spirits that terrify you in the night."

The patient (listening in astonishment, shattered, and suddenly no longer distraught):[5] "Can you really accept all your children equally? Can you also love your ugly children?" Then the theme of "ugliness" was discussed. The patient repeatedly came back to an important cause of her conflict--senescence: "When I feel within me, within me, an old woman with white hair, childishly erotic impulses, when my body against my will produces childishly erotic movements, then I go crazy, then the others say I am crazy." Among other things, she could be shown that her white hair would not necessarily have been an obstacle to the experience of her own womanliness if it were not for her a symbol of the "Holy Mother" averse to all naive childish experience. Above all, with me the patient could have the experience of being a child, my child. And in truth there were hours when we both became aware of the timelessness of the unconscious. This woman, twenty years older than myself, was my child. And now--only now-- did the patient begin to be a person. The previous despairing question was silenced: "Who am I really? Am I a saint, a devil, a Mother of God, a whore? I have no right to be anybody, I am falling apart..."[6]

The patient became a person by again becoming, and entirely so, a child. This may sound like a mere formula. However, the following psychotherapeutic episode may briefly exemplify how this experience exhausted itself in hundreds of concrete individual experiences:

---

5. This episode can stand as an example of a rapid analytical dissolution of schizophrenic experiences of depersonalization.
6. This fragmentation of the personality in opposed irreconcilable figures and impulses and the consequent loss of a unified ego consciousness was once expressed, in the case of the patient, in the shape of hallucinations revealing phenomena of a double life. "Am I about to vanish?" the patient asked in terror. "When I was in the real world, everything was good, now I see everything double; I am falling apart, my right eye is separated from the left--what is this spectacle? Why are you putting on this comedy with me?"--Doctor (with feeling): "Go to hell with this comedy of yours, you're putting it on yourself! You see everything double and separated because you want to be the saint and the whore at the same time, and you will never manage this lie. I have more respect for your vagina than you yourself have. You are the only woman in the world who does not know what her vagina is worth." Then the patient said: "Now I understand. When you talk that way, you are in me and then I don't have to justify myself." Her seeing double disappeared at once after this confrontation.

The patient was acutely excited and aggressive. She complained that a piece of bread had been thrown to her to gnaw on as if she were a dog. She had been given a dirty rag to knit on. I asked her why she so depreciated herself, why she thought she was a dog. The patient replied that she had always been a bad child. At the age of four she had got a skin disease--scurf; she had scratched herself raw, so that her hands had been tied. (A few days before, she had spoken of herself as of a wild cat which scratches and lacerates everything.) She then added: "My mother told me that." I was struck by the connection: The patient connected the tormenting idea of being a dog, to which a scrap of bread is contemptuously thrown, with the memory "I was a bad child." Both negative ideas unleashed aggressive impulses. The impulse to scratch herself raw[7] is associated with "childish badness," and this emerges through the medium of the mother: "My mother told me that; I learned about my badness from her lips." To all appearances the infantile aggression was directed originally against the mother (and, moreover, a large number of other associations and symptoms speak for this), that is, against the "saintly woman" in whose eyes she appears as the wild cat. The child, however, whom the mother would like to destroy, bites into its own flesh. It is bad; it does not get good milk, but rather scurf; it would like to scratch, and its own skin is scourged. It would like to devour the mother, and it has dry bread cast before it like a dog. Here I attempted a direct interpretation in Rosen's sense: "No wonder the child would like to attack its mother savagely and devour her if no milk comes, if the mother is 'a saint without breasts.' Then your mother says that you are a dog." The patient looks at me attentively: "Yes, scratch her to bits, eat her up--and that hurts Mother." I asked her whether she expected to hurt me when, on the ward, she spits on the floor and in people's faces? She replied that here, as in those days at home, she was probably the only one to behave so horribly. When I asked, in turn, why she did not want to accept food from me which I would like to give to her, to her alone, why she would still like to be a dog, she averted her face and began to weep.

After about five months of treatment the patient's underlying delusions entirely faded away. She no longer had hallucinations, or almost none. Then she displayed a motor disturbance lasting for days and weeks, combined with utter intellectual incoherence and

7. When the patient in another connection would complain of fellow patients sleeping next to her that they "scratched themselves so disgustingly," she was referring beyond doubt to masturbatory manipulations. There was concentrated in the image of the fierce, scratching cat seemingly feminine impulses charged with aggressivity.

sudden aggressive outbreaks. [8] From the clinical standpoint we could not exactly rejoice at this turn in her behavior because it made her one of our most difficult inmates. Her care was a very great burden, and some of the staff were even expressing the wish that the psychotherapy be halted. In reality, I had no reason to despair, for a phase had begun in which, despite all her distraughtness, the patient was looking reality in the face with ever more resolution and directness. For the first time she began to talk of going back to work, of going home; that was, of course, just more nonsense of hers, but it was a new approch from which it could be felt that the patient was learning how to come to grips with the world, and even her aggressions were to be understood in no other way than as an expression of a preliminary turbulent encounter with her real environment, now looming ever nearer and assuming increasing reality.

The present behavior of the patient was, however, sharply distinguished from those earlier aggressions that had characterized the first phase of the illness, and that mainly with regard to the transference situation. At that time, at the beginning of the therapy, there was as yet no real transference; the patient behaved with indifference to her surroundings. Now it was quite otherwise. The excited raging patient became quiet as soon as she came near me, in fact, as soon as I appeared quite by chance on the ward. The storm at times subsided so suddenly that observers would talk of "magic." In the presence of the doctor the patient could, in the midst of her distraction, remain still like a contented child. It was also noticeable how the intellectual

---

8. Seldom have I ever experienced in a therapeutic case how clearly a whole series of schizophrenic behavior traits -- negativism, catatonic disturbance, delusions, hallucinations could always be understood as the desperate wish of the patient to see reality as it was not or to remodel it in the direction of her instinctual tensions. Even on days when I still regarded the patient as very ill, I was surprised to notice how, for instance, during a visit she could suddenly be normal. Then she would say to the nurse: "I have been in reality for a long time now, but this is still too hard for me." Sometimes the clinical syndrome alternated from day to day under the effect of the interpretations, as if the patient was having to resort to ever new delusions, ever new "security operations," to avoid a reality that was still felt to be unbearable.

incoherence changed in connection with the social situation and the topic of conversation. We now tried to harness therapeutically as much as possible the patient's obviously increased capacity to make a transference, and we replaced the therapeutically rather neutral ward milieu by a private attendant who now devoted her entire attention to the patient from morning to night. Her reaction to this change was at first entirely negative. She became only more wrought up. She demanded that she be left alone. She felt that she was being persecuted and spied on by this attendant. She threatened to put out her eyes, to strangle her; she struck her and spat on her. The attendant, undeterred, stood by the patient; she wept, but she displayed no hostility. I noticed that the patient was enormously jealous of this nurse. She was old and the nurse was young; she was single and the nurse was married. She had the idea that the attendant was engaged or married to a lover of hers. This gave me a chance to work therapeutically on the patient's strong unconscious jealousy of the young woman who had once "taken away" her nephew from her. I stressed in the therapy that I loved her, the patient, and not the nurse, but very decisively protected the latter against her aggressions. I believe that I am justified in assuming that the crux in this phase of her development was whether the "saint" would yield to the "young woman" --the possibility of inner womanliness now personified by the nurse. This final dramatic showdown, which lasted about a week, represented the climax of the therapy. The patient had to experience this: The young woman must not be destroyed.

I repeatedly compelled the patient to apologize to her attendant. If she did so in a derisive manner, if she slammed the door behind her, I would seize her, drag her back, and implacably order her to apologize. I declared solemnly before the patient and her nurse that I had no intention of ever seeing the patient again if she attacked her nurse who loved her. After two days the patient was practically no longer psychotic. To everyone's amazement the transition to health was swift. The patient's intellectual incoherence also disappeared, as it was apparently closely tied in with her emotional relaxation. Then we could quietly discuss the contents of the psychosis.

The patient's most important pronouncement at the end of this phase was: "My vagina is now healthy; it's functioning wonderfully." From this time on, the patient's condition improved from day to day so rapidly that she could be released after two weeks, and after a month and a half she could resume her work as a cashier.

The patient's psychosis thus ended with an avowal of her own femininity. It shows us that the problem lying at the basis of these psychotic events: "How can I be a woman?" had been resolved. To be sure, the patient knew that she would never be a mother, or even a happy woman. For the first time, however, in the psychosis she had experienced an authentic inner readiness to become a woman as well as a symbolic fulfillment of this demand on her.

In looking back we should recall the beginning of the psychosis. We come upon a picture which by its simplicity and clarity leads us back into the midst of the psychotic event. "I had bought a children's book and there I saw the affectionate antics of a poodle and a cat. But when I showed the book to my friends, they were all against me; in fact, all of mankind was against me. And I was so fond of my poodle, and at the same time I was so afraid of him." This story sounds to us almost like an allegorical parable. We sense here the patient's attempt to obtain from a sphere of naive childlike play the possibility of a more profound, more tender interpersonal contact, as well as her fear, in so doing, of falling prey to the demonic, the "unholy," the instinctual forces. Faust recognizes in the Devil "the heart of the matter."[9] The demonically instinctual sphere here allows the patient to discover herself before the mirror as the devil. But the heart of the matter in this case[10] is basically a childlike hungering that only needs to be satisfied in order to lose all its devilish features; a childlike hungering which appears, only in the eyes of a cold saintly mother, in the guise of a cat's claw, but which in her own old age can turn into a contented childlike smile.

FOLLOW-UP

Six months after release from the clinic the patient is in the best of health. On her old job as cashier she works with tireless diligence, competence, and a sense of responsibility. After release from the clinic she required no further treatment; she saw us only very occasionally but maintained a confiding relationship to the doctor and to the clinic. She remembers former fellow patients with touching sympathy, and she can talk to me about her past psychosis quietly, frankly, and without inhibitions. She regards nothing as trivial. Her

---

9. In the German original there is a play on words which is lost in translation--Trans.
10. Word play continued in German. -- Trans.

ffectivity, thought processes, and social behavior give an impression
f complete normality. The patient displays no ascertainable schizo-
hrenic defect.

Information obtained in 1963 revealed that the patient was
vell for eight years after her recovery. Her affectivity, behavior,
nd way of life were completely normal. The patient did not show any
chizophrenic defect.

Trouble did occur in 1961. During the previous two years
1961-63) the patient had three psychotic episodes. Because of the
act that I do not work in Zurich anymore, intensive psychotherapy
vas not resumed.

It is not known whether any change in the course of life of the
atient during the past two years could explain the relapses after
ight years of good health. Now, a recovery is reached every time
hrough pharmacological treatment. However, the recovery does
ot seem to be so profound as in the year 1953.

ADDENDUM

Q. Did you formulate a specific diagnosis before you began psychotherapy, or was it made after psychotherapy was in progress?
Do such pre-therapeutic diagnoses inhibit or facilitate taking a
patient into treatment? Are your diagnoses subject to revision as
psychotherapy proceeds, and do they vary depending on the way
the patient responds to the treatment? Do you distinguish between
diagnosis as such and simple spontaneous diagnostic reflections?

A. I formulated a diagnosis of schizophrenia. Such diagnosis facilitated taking the patient into treatment, because we had a program
of research in the psychotherapy of schizophrenia. Clinical diagnoses are made very carefully, but then they are not subject to
revision as psychotherapy proceeds and do not vary depending
on the way the patient responds to the treatment.

Q. Did you approach your patient with a consistent and verbalizable
theory or set of hypotheses on personality structure and/or the
genesis of psychic illness? Was such theory used directly (or
indirectly) in selecting the patient for treatment? How was it
applied in the treatment and how effective was your theory in
reaching the goals of treatment? What do you see as the function
of such hypotheses or theories?

A. A consistent and verbalizable set of hypotheses on the partial
genesis of schizophrenia did help me in approaching my patient.
This theory was not used in selecting the patient for treatment
because the patient was selected by the Clinical Director (Professor M. Bleuler).

Q. What did you think of the prognosis of your case before you
accepted the patient for treatment? What did you think during
the first several interviews; and during the latter stages of
treatment? Do you feel prognostic judgments about ultimate
health or ultimate illness are useful? Can we dispense with a
prognosis as a formal event in clinical treatment?

A. The prognosis of my case before accepting the patient for treatment was severe because of the tendencies to relapses. I think
that the treatment changed the course of life in this case. During
the treatment I didn't think anything about prognosis. Prognostic
judgments are useful because they permit us to compare the results and the catamnesis of the patient with these judgments and
to evaluate the effectiveness of psychotherapy.

Q. What particular therapeutic techniques did you apply in this case?
Which of them were most effective and which ineffective, and for
what reasons? Did you attempt any technical innovations on an
empirical basis? When did you feel that a "peak" experience or
turning point occurred?

A. Direct analysis and symbolic realization. Turning points were reached only as I could reach deeper identifications with the patient and feel what she felt.

Q. Did you feel that Freud's formulation of transference and countertransference were sufficient to account for the therapeutic encounter with your patient? How would you describe your encounter?

A. No. Freud's formulation of transference and countertransference were not sufficient to account for the therapeutic encounter with my patient. My concept of encounter in psychotherapy with schizophrenics cannot be given here. A formulation is given in my book, Klinische Psychotherapie, Huber Verlag, Bern, 1964.

Q. It has been said that psychotherapy is a white, middle-class, urban phenomenon which does not necessarily apply to other social stratifications or cultures. In what way did your patient's cultural background influence his illness and treatment? In what way did your own cultural background assist or deter the treatment?

A. I don't think that the cultural background in this case had a relevant importance in the genesis of the psychosis and in its treatment.

Q. There is an increasing tendency for neo-analytic thinking to ascribe the genesis and treatment of psychic illness to the social psychology of the family. How did this apply in your case?

A. In this case the social psychology of the family had importance in forming the character structure in infancy but not in determining the psychosis in later age.

Q. If your treatment was concluded what criteria did you use for terminating it? If it is still in process, what guide points would you use to determine when your patient is sufficiently improved to discontinue treatment? Do you feel that a patient should be seen as long as he feels he needs it and is willing to pay the fees?

A. The determining criterion for terminating the treatment was the full clinical recovery. If the patient is a psychotic one, I feel he should be seen as long as he feels he needs it, even for years after the recovery from a psychosis. This patient did not, however, need this after treatment.

Chapter III

A CASE OF POSTPARTUM SCHIZOPHRENIA

By C. Peter Rosenbaum

In this chapter, concerned with the treatment of a young woman who became severely disturbed and schizophrenic after the birth of a child, I will discuss first some theoretical formulations which have relevance to her situation, second, her illness and its treatment, and finally, certain questions about diagnosis, prognosis, dynamic formulation, etc., and their pertinence to treatment.

Views on the etiology of postpartum schizophrenic reactions vary. Some authors feel that the unique hormonal and physiological changes of childbirth are largely responsible for the symptoms. [1,2] Others feel that childbirth, like many another event in life, imposes psychological stress on the individual, and that psychotic reactions to it, like those to being drafted, graduated from college, having a broken love affair, etc., are best understood as failures of emotional adjustment. [3,4] Evidence is not clear about how much either of these factors (or others), separately or in conjunction, is implicated in producting postpartum schizophrenia; such clarification is a problem for future research. This discussion follows the latter, more psychologically oriented, thesis.

SOME RELEVANT CONCEPTS

The human organism, from birth (if not before) and throughout life, performs, usually with increasing complexity and skill, a number of operations in sensing, identifying, abstracting, and giving meaning to events in itself and its environment.

There is evidence to suggest that maintaining an optimum level of sensory input, and among those inputs certain special kinds, is a

1. Bower, W. H. and M. D. Altschule. Use of progesterone in the treatment of post-partum psychosis. New England J. of Med., 1956, 254, 157-160
2. Hamilton, J. A. Postpartum Psychiatric Problems. St. Louis: C. V. Mosby, 1962.
3. Fondaur, M., C. Fixsen, W. Triebel, and M. A. White. Postpartum mental illness. AMA Arch. Neurol. and Psychiat., 1957, 77, 503-511.
4. Seager, C. P. A controlled study of post-partum mental illness. J. Ment. Sci., 1960, 106, 214-230

necessity. In infancy and childhood, general lack of stimulation, and especially lack of the kind best described as consistent loving and mothering, can disastrously affect the development of the child. [5, 6, 7] Similar findings prevail in young monkeys and rats. [8, 9] Likewise, children who are constantly overstimulated become disorganized and can neither play with pleasure nor sleep with tranquility. In adults, those who are deprived of waking perceptual experience in sensory deprivation situations, [10] or of dreaming perceptual experience in dream deprivation situations, [11] respond with an increased generation of their own internal experiences.

The child soon comes to name such experiences. Labeling and identifying experience is among the earliest of social language functions to develop. One important group of experiences the growing child tries to label, and one which is a good deal more elusive than the objects in the physical universe, is that of the various emotional states encountered in themselves and others. Just as the labels of the physical world are learned from parents, so also are those regarding emotional states and interpersonal relationships. In either, the manner in which the parents respond to the attempts of the child to label can have profound influence on the development or distortions of conceptual modes in the growing child. [12]

The ability to label and form early abstractions starts at around one year and reaches a high level during the second and third years of life. [13] The ability to use such abstractions in communication, the use of metaphor, is something that comes later in life; every

5. Spitz, R. A. "Anaclitic Depression." In The Psychoanalytic Study of the Child, Vol. 2, New York: International Univ. Press, 1946.
6. Spitz, R. A. "Hospitalism." In The Psychoanalytic Study of the Child, Vol. 1, New York: International Univ. Press, 1945.
7. Bowlby, J. Maternal Care and Mental Health. Geneva: World Health Organ., 1952
8. Harlow, H. and M. Harlow. Social deprivation in monkeys. Scientific American, 1962, 207, 136-146.
9. Levine, S. Stimulation in infancy. Scientific American, 1960, 202, 81-86.
10. Leiderman, P. H. and P. Kubzansky. "Sensory Deprivation-- An Overview." In Soloman, P. (Ed.), Sensory Deprivation. Cambridge: Harvard Univ. Press, 1963.
11. Dement, W. "Experimental Dream Studies." In Masserman, J. (Ed.), Science and Psychoanalysis, VII. New York: Grune and Stratton, 1964 (in press).
12. Wynne, L. C. and M. T. Singer. Thought disorder and family relations of schizophrenia. AMA Arch. of Gen. Psychiat., 1963, 9, 191-206.
13. Gesell, A., et al. The First Five Years of Life. New York: Harper and Brothers, 1940, pp. 212-237.

adult uses it automatically in expressions like "get off my back, " "putting the bite on someone, " "a hot situation, " etc. The manner in which a child's questions of "how" and "why" are handled: the discrepancies in which are answered openly and on a level of abstraction appropriate to the child's understanding, which are answered evasively or on inappropriate levels, and which are anxiously avoided, supply to the young seeker-after-meaning information of a different order than he had anticipated. Implicitly, he comes to learn that there are classes of experience which mean either parental encouragement or parental disapproval--and sometimes parental disavowal and extreme anxiety. Such formulations, when they deal with interpersonal relationships, correspond to Sullivan's divisions into "Good-me, Bad-me, and Not-me."[14] Making such attitudes and categorizations explicit is frequently an essential task of psychotherapy.

If the continuous interaction of the growing child and his parents and the world around him proceeds harmoniously, he is able to assimilate the sensations that come from within and without, and he matures in the process. Some investigators believe that if this interaction is disrupted sufficiently early, sufficiently frequently, and sufficiently continuously in life, some people respond to a later demand for growth, change, or adaption in a peculiarly childlike or primitive way: they regress to very early modes of thinking. They become schizophrenic. [15, 16, 17, 18, 19]

The appearance of a classical schizophrenic episode satisfies many of the psychological needs described above and provides a reparative and restitutive function,even in the face of its apparent maladaptive features. The preoccupations, delusions, and hallucinations of schizophrenia provide a level of sensory stimulation when environmental stimulation is avoided because of fear and disappointment. The psychosis provides meaningful human relatedness with imaginary

---

14. Sullivan, H. S. The Interpersonal Theory of Psychiatry. New York: W. W. Norton, 1953, pp. 161-165.
15. Wynne, L. C. , I. Rykoff, J. Day, and S. Hirsch. Pseudo-mutuality in the family relations of schizophrenics. Psychiatry, 1958, 21, 205-220.
16. Wynne, L. C. and M. T. Singer. op. cit.
17. Lidz, T. , A. Cornelison, and D. Terry. Intrafamilial environment of the schizophrenic patient: VI. The transmission of irrationality. AMA Arch. Neurol. and Psychiat. , 1958, 79, 305-316.
18. Hill, L. B. Psychotherapeutic Intervention in Schizophrenia. Chicago: Univ. of Chicago Press, 1955.
19. Rosenbaum, C. P. Patient-family similarities in schizophrenia. AMA Arch. Gen. Psychiat. , 1961, 5, 120-126.

personifications when the real ones have been shunned. It organizes and limits a welter of chaotic sensations and perceptions into manageable classes. (In fact, the heightened need to ascribe particular meaning to events considered trivial by others is frequently one of the first symptoms of a developing psychosis.) Finally, it provides a rationale for action.

In the present case the patient had indeed these kinds of disruptions of her ability to know about, give meaning to, and act effectively toward a contemporary world whose events had left her mystified about herself, her husband, her baby, and the other people in her life. Many of the aspects of her treatment were directed toward a clearer understanding of these events and of her readiness to respond to them in the psychotic fashion that she did.

CASE PRESENTATION

The patient, who will be called Sylvia Tilman, was a twenty-three-year-old white, Protestant woman. Her husband, Paul, two year her senior, was a design engineer for a local space industry company. The patient's admission to the hospital took place a month after the birth of their first child, Susan.

Six weeks before Susan's birth, the Tilmans moved from the South to the West Coast because of Mr. Tilman's promotion and job transfer. Two weeks later they were established in their apartment, and Mr. Tilman was already working late hours on his new assignment. Three days before the child was born, Mrs. Tilman's mother came to help out during the next two weeks. The child, a normal baby girl, was born by routine delivery after a trouble-free pregnancy.

Mr. Tilman was operated on for acute diverticulitis three days after his wife's delivery; he came home a week later. Ten days after his return, old friends of the Tilmans, George and Marianne, came to visit; the Tilmans took them sightseeing after Mrs. Tilman's mother reluctantly agreed to baby-sit. Marianne and George had been close friends of Paul and Sylvia since high school. Mrs. Tilman's mother returned to her home in Connecticut a few days later.

About then, Mrs. Tilman first began to have periods of distraction and moodiness. One evening, while her husband was working late, she went to the back porch of their apartment and shrieked that she was having a nervous breakdown. Friends quieted her and called Mr. Tilman. The following Sunday she insisted on going alone to a Catholic Church and then spoke to her husband about the beauty and importance of the Catholic faith. She said their daughter had to be baptized before she was a month old, and that he must convert to Catholicism for their marriage really to exist. For the rest of the day she was very much in another world: confused, lost, and preoccupied.

The next day Mrs. Tilman felt convinced that a laundryman who came to their building was there to deliver some important papers to her husband from his old office. She was persuaded that this was not the case. That evening when her husband got home she again appeared preoccupied.

The next day she called her husband at work and told him she was sure that the background noises in his office meant he had discovered a rocket fuel which would take a rocket to the moon and back, and that his discovery deserved the applause of scientists and statesmen throughout the world. He would be an international hero. Her only fear was that his supervisor might turn out to be a Communist and steal the discovery for Russia. That afternoon local police found her walking the streets, looking dazed and carrying the child precariously. She was brought home and her husband summoned. He finally recognized that the situation was more serious than he had allowed himself to see; arrangements were then made for her admission to the psychiatric section of a local general hospital where I became her psychiatrist.

At our first meeting, Mrs. Tilman clutched my arm in a childlike gleeful-but-scared way. Her eyes were huge, saucerlike, and vacant. Her face, wreathed in a beatific smile, made me feel bathed in the warmth of an Earth Mother while at the same time I was not really apprehended as being on this earth. She was confused, having difficulty comprehending that she was on a hospital ward or in believing that various persons were doctors and nurses. At various times she thought her child was alive, dead, or had not yet been born. Her statements were frequently cryptic and symbolic; her gestures tended to be manneristic, though obviously filled with private meaning for her. At times her thoughts took on the reality of voices, and she frequently asked me if I had just sent her such-and-such a thought message through telepathy.

LIFE HISTORY

This history is an amalgamation of information obtained from both Mr. and Mrs. Tilman at the time of her acute break and afterwards.

Mrs. Tilman was born in 1938. Her father left home a few months thereafter, and her mother went to work as a secretary. A divorce finally ensued. While her mother worked in various places in the East, the daughter spent a good deal of time-- fondly remembered--with her maternal grandparents in Ohio. Eventually her mother settled down to work in Connecticut, and here she grew up.

The patient characterized her mother as being in many ways a very helpless, anxious person. For instance, every time they took a trip to New York, her mother on the way to the station would fumble for her tickets, and the patient would always find them for her just in time to make their train.

When Mrs. Tilman was ten her mother remarried. The husband, whom the patient called "Uncle Frank," had once been her father's best friend but had come to hate him for what he considered criminal desertion of wife and child. Uncle Frank had a bad temper and was quite restrictive with her, and she was constantly afraid of him. In later years he suffered from a chronic lung disease which aggravated his temper. He died when the patient was sixteen.

In high school Mrs. Tilman dated only one boy with much regularity, and this over her stepfather's objections and her mother's passive acquiescence. She also knew Paul, her husband-to-be, in high school, as did her mother who thought highly of him and his family. They did not allow her to do any baby-sitting in her high school years.

After high school the patient went to a women's college, from which she was graduated. Her social life was active and she was a quite attractive, vivacious belle. She and Paul saw a good deal of each other during their summer vacations. Eventually they decided to marry, although she vacillated. Finally, when Paul delivered an ultimatum, she acceded to his wishes. They were to marry just before his second year of graduate work, but the week before the wedding George came to Connecticut to discuss his sexual problems and fears about marrying Marianne. Mrs. Tilman later interpreted this trip, probably correctly, as an attempt to stall the wedding: none of the four had had extensive experience with the opposite sex, and George's trip overtly echoed their worry about the dissolution of their adolescent relationships in favor of marriage.

In June, ten months after the marriage, she had a brief period of extreme panic and was hospitalized by Paul in the psychiatric ward of a Connecticut hospital. She signed herself out after three days. The diagnosis was acute anxiety reaction.

Otherwise, the next few years were relatively pleasant. Though she and Paul had many petty arguments, they also had many things in common. They enjoyed going together to plays and other events. While he studied and worked, she busied herself with friends, and came to be fond of his parents and Roman Catholic grandparents.

She was not sure that she truly loved Paul or that he truly loved her. She occasionally wondered if she had married him because he was one of the few men who had gained her mother's approval. She sometimes had difficulty accepting him during sexual relations. The use of contraceptives further marred her sexual pleasure. She wondered if he married her only because she was attractive and decorative; such doubts increased when he insisted on trying to tell her about engineering in technical terms which she could not understand.

Her love for and acceptance of Paul increased considerably when they decided to have a child and deliberately stopped using contraceptives. Susan was conceived shortly thereafter. Her pregnancy was uncomplicated. She did not attend maternity classes during her pregnancy, but depended instead on Dr. Spock, whom she read faithfully. She could barely confess to herself, and not at all to Paul, that she felt she had to be a "perfect mother" and yet felt miserably unprepared.

DYNAMICS OF THE POSTPARTUM REACTION

In attempting to understand the reasons for Mrs. Tilman's decompensation, we must examine her personality structure, the external events of her life at the time, and the meaning of these events at both superficial and deeper levels.

Throughout her life she had feared she was not likable or desirable. She handled these fears by compulsively seeking out company and being an apparently gay and frivolous belle--social graces she doubted would be useful to her in caring for her new infant.

Chronologically, the external stresses on her were the following: the move to a strange part of the country, her husband's investment in his work and his resultant withdrawal from her, the presence and departure of her ambivalently-regarded mother, the birth of the baby and the consequent challenge to her mothering abilities, her husband's further withdrawal because of diverticulitis, and the emotionally charged visit of George and Marianne. Had she had to cope with only one or two of these situations, it is conceivable her decompensation would not have been nearly so severe.

Her past had not led toward particular trust in men. Her mother's and stepfather's comments about her father were most unflattering, and her stepfather's opposition to her dating (which she secretly defied) implied danger in involvement with men. The idea that men were an alien breed was furthered by her marriage to an aspiring engineer whose work left her mystified, but in which she felt compelled to be interested to preserve his interest in her. She feared she would become physically unattractive because of childbirth and that her husband would lose interest in her. She had little experience or training in child-raising and yet felt compelled to be a perfect mother to meet her husband's presumed expectations.

On a deeper level, she may have thought of herself as poisonous to men; had her birth driven away her father? As she herself mentioned, her separation from her mother was still incomplete psychologically. She felt that her anxiety about her own and her mother's helplessness was communicable and destructive to anyone who had dealings with her.

Thus the concatenation of events surrounding the move and the birth had stirred up grave fears. The birth of the girl baby signified many things to her. Mrs. Tilman, as therapy proceeded, expressed fears that her own childhood was ended, that her husband would now desert her as her father had deserted her mother, that the child would grow up to have the same anger toward her as she had toward her mother, that the physical changes of childbirth would make her unattractive to her husband, that she had lost something from inside her which was truly her very own, that her commitment to heterosexuality would forever estrange her from the intimacy she had known with Marianne, that her ambivalence about the child and her incompetence as a mother would become obvious and invite general disdain.

At first she attempted to cope with these feelings by over-dependence on her husband; later there were transient episodes of depersonalization with awareness of her distress, as when she called out from the back porch. Ultimately a full-blown schizophrenic reaction developed, with hallucinations, delusions, and frequent misinterpretations of events. Her preoccupation with Catholicism seemed to answer many of her fears in a magical way. It would forbid divorce, i.e., desertion by her husband. It would help her defend against her murderous impulses toward the child: if the child were baptized, it would be a human being and therefore she would not be allowed to harm it. It would provide her with at least two fathers besides her husband: a local priest and God. It would forbid contraception, thereby allowing increased sexual pleasure and feelings of feminine competence. It would promise her the long, happy marriage of Paul's Catholic grandparents.

Similarly, her thought that her husband had discovered the rocket fuel repaired her severely damaged self-esteem. It would mean an end to his long days in the laboratory and more time at home. It would mean a hero's reception for both of them; his achievement would show her competence as a wife.

HOSPITALIZATION AND TREATMENT

The patient was hospitalized two weeks. The general hospital psychiatric ward was organized as a well-staffed modern therapeutic community. Ample group and individual contact afforded social support and restraint. The ward attempted to minimize the gulf between the community and the mental patient.

Within this context the treatment plan had two major aspects: tapping available sources of environmental, pharmacological, and social support; and individual psychotherapy.

Among the sources of environmental support was the psychiatric ward. It was there that an important part of the hospitalization--

her continued nursing of the child--took place. Mrs. Tilman had breast-fed the baby prior to hospitalization and, at her request, continued to do so. Mr. Tilman's supervisor encouraged him to take needed time off during the emergency, a generosity which Mr. Tilman found very supportive. Mr. Tilman brought the baby over at least twice a day for feedings. He or a nurse remained with the patient during the feedings to make sure that no harm befell the child. It was impressive and gratifying to all to see Mrs. Tilman, floridly psychotic and at times not sure whether the baby had been born or was still alive, maintain a vital bond by nursing the infant, at first awkwardly and then more gracefully.

After I had come to some appreciation of the factors which led to Mrs. Tilman's psychosis, I spent time with her husband discussing certain forces involved. Talking about it considerably softened his intolerance for his wife's dependency and helplessness, and as he became much more sensitive to her needs, he took a major role in encouraging her recovery and her return home. He could reassure her that he did not expect her to be the perfect mother nor did he have the slightest intention of leaving her. When he first suggested that his parents come out to help, she was afraid they would woo him away from the baby and her. At first she expressed these fears symbolically through increased demands on him to become Catholic, share in the baptism of the child, and form a magically invulnerable trinity. When she came to see that the fears were unwarranted, she could discuss them more logically and ultimately assented. It was an excellent example of a too infrequently reported phenomenon: the constructive mobilization of a family.

Finally, among the important environmental factors was chlorpromazine. Mrs. Tilman wandered off the ward into other parts of the hospital, where her obviously psychotic appearance and statements caused considerable concern, and she frequently had to be retrieved. After trying to manage her solely through social and psychological means, I started her on oral chlorpromazine, with intramuscular doses when the oral doses were refused.[20] We told her the medication was to help her confusion and to keep her on the ward. At first she refused it, fearing it was poison, but when she saw our determination, she took the medication willingly. Her response to the drug was gratifying. Her sorties off the ward stopped, and her ability to synthesize her thoughts and test reality improved.

---

20. Research had indicated that very little or no chlorpromazine would be transmitted into her breast milk and therefore would not tranquilize the baby. Blacker, K. H. , B. J. Weinstein, and G. L. Ellman. Mother's milk and chlorpromazine. Amer. J. of Psychiat. , 1962, 119, 178-180.

The individual psychotherapy, both during hospitalization and afterward, was essentially threefold: (1) the prompt development of a relationship of warmth and trust; (2) the task of understanding the psychological factors in her break and the integration of such insight into awareness; and (3) an educative role in helping her assume gradually increasing responsibility for her home and family.

The development of a trusting relationship in the hospital came quickly, although it was tested repeatedly. The patient reached out for help and never seriously doubted my interest. I saw her daily and was available for impromptu visits or phone calls as necessary. She would ask periodically if I were a Communist or were sending her strange messages, but accepted my reassurances that such was not the case.

In dealing with her psychotherapeutically, I operated with three major assumptions. The first was that one major task of therapy was to try to help her decode and understand her symbolic thinking; the second, that many such communications could be interpreted as indirect commentaries of her perception of the immediate state of the therapy relationship;[21] and the third, that momentary intensification of the psychotic nature of her thinking signaled a rise in her anxiety and warranted attention to the events immediately preceding. For instance, at one point she started fingering a borrowed rosary, emphasizing in the Lord's Prayer, "Forgive us our trespasses as we forgive those who trespass against us." I asked if she thought that I had just trespassed against her. She said, "Yes"; something I had just said signified to her that I didn't like her and didn't want her ever to go home to her family. Once we had clarified this point she accepted my statement that I did like her and very much did want her to go back when she was ready.

To Mrs. Tilman's advantage, she was remarkably able to recognize, understand, and integrate the meanings of her psychotic thoughts into a conscious, useful, secondary process kind of thinking rather than having to cover them up. Thus, even months later, she recalled fairly well the content of her delusional thinking even though no signs of it existed. Her psychotic period had taken on the appearance of a fascinating, frightening, well-remembered, and well-analyzed dream. Treating her psychotic material as a second-rate way of trying to express first-rate concerns strengthened her gains.

At first in psychotherapy she used the facts of my different sex and religion and my inability to have a baby as bases for accusing me of not being able to understand her. On occasion I cited personal

---

21. Bateson, G. , D. D. Jackson, J. Haley, and J. Weakland. Toward a theory of schizophrenia. Behav. Sci. , 1956, 1, 256.

experiences that I felt were comparable and offered them in service of the possibility that we could make real contact. When we could agree on these as being comparable, rapport improved.

She asked from the beginning when she could go home. Her defensiveness about being psychotic made it difficult to answer her question. Her psychic state was quite fluid--she could drift into and out of a psychotic episode in minutes--and she soon learned to observe herself as she was doing so. We set the relative diminution of the episodes of "peculiar thinking" as the criterion for discharge, a criterion she accepted. At the time of her discharge there were certainly many areas of psychotic thinking. But she, her husband, and I were agreed that they were not so great as to keep her from going home and caring for her baby, and that work on her areas of confusion would continue in therapy.

During and after the hospitalization I saw the Tilmans periodically as a couple; she could then discuss with her husband some of the feelings she was afraid to voice outside the neutrality of the therapy situation. He, too, was more straightforward and treated her neither like a miscreant child nor a fragile flower, the two extremes he had felt pushed toward earlier.

Certain educative aspects of therapy were stressed. One was that mothering a child is a complex skill, and like any complex skill, takes time, trial and error, and good teaching. In learning any complex skill, the learner must go through stages of observation, imitation, and practice before the development of a successful personal style. When anxiety blocks acquisition at any stage of the process, therapeutic inquiry can be directed to the source of the anxiety in an attempt to facilitate learning. In this case, Mrs. Tilman's mother-in-law was present as a competent and well-intentioned practitioner of the art of mothering. Mrs. Tilman's fears about accepting her as one from whom she could learn had in part been based on her experience with her own mother, which suggested that the raising of a child was a perilous procedure which was fraught with hazard at every juncture. As such fears were explored in therapy, Mrs. Tilman made increasing use of her mother-in-law as a teacher.

Another educative aspect was the repeated discussion of ways in which roles change throughout life. Though part of Paul's original attraction to her was for her looks and frivolity, the birth of the child had not made her ugly; all was not over between them; growing to know and understand each other in their new roles as parents was a challenge that could be met.

Mrs. Tilman was discharged after two weeks of hospitalization. Her husband, baby, and mother-in-law were on hand to greet her. She continued on chlorpromazine. She came in for psychotherapeutic sessions five times a week in the month that followed and discussed various topics.

Mrs. Tilman's concern about being a good mother was expressed in at least two ways. At first she felt quite guilty if she did not spend twenty-four hours a day with the baby, and she interpreted the baby's every cry or shriek as evidence of poor mothering. We discussed this and, in the weeks that followed, she became a good deal more relaxed about letting the neighbors do some baby-sitting and about letting the baby cry for a while when there was no discernible cause for the crying.

Another concern was her fear that she could not make friends or that she would be an outcast because of having a mental illness. She made the acquaintance of her neighbors and found that they liked her much more than she had thought. She also admirably survived a company picnic given by Mr. Tilman's supervisor.

The flare-ups in her relationship with her husband mostly centered around his impatience with "having two children in the family" and his desire for her to be more self-sufficient and less clinging. For example, one day her religious preoccupations were considerably greater than usual, with fervent recitations of the Twenty-third Psalm. This event was traced back to an argument with her husband and her intense desire to have a shepherd watch over her. As it was clarified, her attentions returned to her relationship to her husband and left the theological plane.

By the end of the first posthospital month her husband was back at work nearly full time; he came home for lunch or to study. She took responsibility for the baby and the house, and drove to and from our appointments alone. Her husband, however, continued to make breakfast in the morning and give the baby her first feeding of the day. To assuage her loneliness she spent considerable time visiting her neighbors, watching T.V., or painting.

During the second posthospital month evidences of psychotic thinking appeared less and less frequently. Usually, simple confrontation and airing of the psychotic process was sufficient to cause it to disappear. Little by little, the things to which she had overreacted, such as not wanting to shop for groceries, to take Susan along on walks, or to pick up a set of car keys at the lock-smith, disappeared as they were discussed. By the end of the second month nothing further even had a psychotic flavor.

Toward the middle of that month Mrs. Tilman became increasingly prey to feelings of apathy, lack of joie de vivre, lassitude, and boredom. She could not fill up her time, reiterating the question, "I wonder what all these other girls do; they seem to be so busy with their babies and their homes, and yet I find nothing to do."

A urinary tract infection may have contributed to her general lassitude. She would also awaken in the early morning with nagging, unpleasant thoughts. The depression seemed to be a combination of a true post-partum depression (from which the psychosis had to some extent been a protection), the kidney infection, and a possible effect of chlorpromazine. When it did not lift after about a week, she was given imipramine. Her chlorpromazine was reduced, and she was also given an antibiotic for her kidney infection.

By the middle of the third posthospital month the depression began to lift significantly. This was probably a result of medication and of the psychotherapeutic discussion, including my suggestion that, despite her lack of motivation, she should carve out projects that needed to be done or that she would like to do, such as making a dress, and do them even if they were not gratifying. As the depression lifted, the imipramine was decreased and was stopped two weeks later.

She and her husband got along fairly well. She easily endured his absences from home, although she felt much better when he was around. They had an active social life. She found that she could carry off the duties of hostess quite well and looked forward to having people in. They squabbled very infrequently, in contrast to their first four years of marriage. In her period of apathy she had not cared enough about things to get excited, but the calmness persisted even after she felt better.

The therapy sessions became more and more prosaic. Mrs. Tilman often could not find problems to talk about, and we agreed to cut them down, always with the understanding that we could schedule additional appointments as needed. Three months after hospitalization she was completely off medication and was being seen only once a week. We took stock at that time and agreed to stop therapy. She was contented with the way she felt about herself, with her plans for her activities, with her use of time, and with her relationships with Susan, Paul, and her mother. I encouraged her to let me know from time to time how things were going generally and to call if anything came up which she wanted to discuss.

Eight months after the first appearance of her psychosis she called to say that she was having peculiar thoughts again and wanted to discuss them. At the interview she described a mystical experience of having been some kind of saint sent to earth to bring a special harmony to mankind. The experience came right after she and Paul had had an argument, another example of the relationship of precipitating factors and relevant dynamics.

She also thought she might be pregnant, a diagnosis confirmed medically some time later. The events of the preceding two weeks had been quite stressful. Paul had taken her and Susan with him to the East Coast where he was attending a convention, and she and the baby had been on constant display to old friends and relatives.

Mrs. Tilman did indeed show some psychotic thinking, though not enough to require her hospitalization. She frequently reasoned by predicate. For example, a group of experimental monkeys in the hospital had been written up in a local newspaper as giving birth in captivity. Since Mrs. Tilman was a mother and probably pregnant, did this mean I was experimenting on her? Again, as we discussed these thoughts, she usually accepted my reassurances that I was not experimenting on her. At one point, however, her suspicions about my intent grew to the point that she asked me to see her at home, where she felt safer than in my office. I did so. She proudly showed me Susan and their pleasantly decorated apartment, and we were able to resume office visits thereafter.

Daily psychotherapy and chlorpromazine were immediately resumed. After two months the psychotic thinking had vanished, the medication was stopped, and monthly meetings were set during the course of the pregnancy. She continued to do well, physically and mentally, throughout the entire pregnancy and delivered a premature infant girl eight months later. The baby was placed in a respirator the day after birth, and there was concern for the baby's life. Mrs. Tilman was told that the respirator and special attention were required for the baby. I saw her in the hospital and afterward.

She weathered the situation very well. Her concern for the infant was normal, as was her pleasure at taking the baby home two weeks later. Shortly after the baby had come home, Mrs. Tilman wryly remarked that she almost felt cheated--she hadn't even had a mild postpartum depression.

Two and one-half years have elapsed since her first psychotic episode. We maintain periodic contact. The Tilmans' children have been healthy and meaningful to them. Their marriage has gone well. They both have felt that the understandings they gained as a result of Mrs. Tilman's psychosis have helped them to be freer and more open with each other and that their lives have been a good deal more gratifying than they were before, although they would have preferred to have come by such improvement by a less harrowing route.

ADDENDUM

Certain questions proposed for this discussion involve matters of diagnosis, prognosis, and treatment as well as some theoretical topics.

Q. Did you formulate a specific diagnosis before you began psychotherapy, or was it made after psychotherapy was in progress? Do such pre-therapeutic diagnoses inhibit or facilitate taking a patient into treatment? Are your diagnoses subject to revision as psychotherapy proceeds, and do they vary depending on the way the patient responds to the treatment? Do you distinguish between diagnosis as such and simple spontaneous diagnostic reflections?

A. Mrs. Tilman's illness was incontrovertibly a schizophrenic one from the moment I first saw her: she had a thought disorder, confusion, ambivalence, delusions, and hallucinations. Knowing this did not affect my willingness to take her into treatment. When the psychosis cleared, signs of a classical neurotic depression developed: lassitude, boredom, psychomotor retardation, and unpleasant early morning awakenings. The diagnosis was changed accordingly. Several months later she again developed psychotic signs: thought disorder, delusions, and hallucinations, and once again the diagnosis was changed. In this case, therapeutic response did not affect diagnosis. Rather, treatment varied, depending on the picture she presented. When she was psychotic, a great deal of time and attention was spent trying to understand her communications; this ended as the symbolic statements disappeared. The depression required a different kind of treatment. Likewise, the almost symbiotic closeness of the earlier therapeutic relationship evolved gradually into one of increasing trust in the patient's ability to care for herself as a more self-sufficient individual.

Q. Did you approach your patient with a consistent and verbalizable theory or set of hypotheses on personality structure and/or the genesis of psychic illness? Was such theory used directly (or indirectly) in selecting the patient for treatment? How was it applied in the treatment and how effective was your theory in reaching the goals of treatment? What do you see as the function of such hypotheses or theories?

A. The hypothetical framework I used is set forth in part in the theoretical statements of the first section and in the diagnostic formulation of the case presentation. Such matters did not influence the selection of the patient for treatment. To recapitulate, Mrs. Tilman's psychotic thinking served certain important restitutive functions during her apprehension about and withdrawal from her real life circumstances. Viewed in this light, her illness, both in its form and its content, became more comprehensible. Such theories also helped me to label, abstract, evaluate, and find suggestions for the direction of therapy in the face of the inundation of sensory experience of the first and subsequent encounters with the patient.

Q. What did you think of the prognosis of your case before you accepted the patient for treatment? What did you think during the first several interviews; and during the latter stages of treatment? Do you feel prognostic judgments about ultimate health or ultimate illness are useful? Can we dispense with prognosis as a formal event in clinical treatment?

A. In the case of Mrs. Tilman there were a good number of firm, hopeful prognostic indicators at the very beginning; these were strengthened in the first several interviews. First, at least 30 to 50% of patients having postpartum mental illness improve.[22] Second, she had achieved a good level of functioning before her acute break; she had graduated from college, sustained a marriage that had been far from idyllic, and had made several major adjustments to help her husband's career. Thus there were solid areas of achievement in her past. Third, she obviously wanted to be helped. The speed and the tenacity with which she took to therapy augured well. Fourth, Mrs. Tilman was obviously intelligent and capable of verbalizing, certainly useful features in a verbalizing-conceptualizing psychotherapy. Finally, the fact that her psychosis was acute and in response to discernible sources of external stress argued for a favorable outcome. Her ability early in the course of therapy to relinquish psychotic thinking, or understand the symbolic meanings of her thoughts, reinforced my optimism about the outlook. Furthermore, the fact that we obviously very much liked working with each other gave the therapy situation natural warmth and trust.

Generally, when a favorable prognosis can be made, not for reasons of Panglossian positive thinking, but from sound clinical indications, it can and should be communicated to the patient and those concerned. The importance of warranted enthusiasm and hopefulness in influencing a favorable psychotherapeutic outcome has been widely noted.[23] Thus prognosis can frequently be a valuable part of treatment.

---

22. Madden, J. J., J. A. Luhan, W. Tuteur, and J. F. Bimmerle. Characteristics of post-partum mental illness. Amer. J. of Psychiat., 1958, 115, 18-24.
23. Lesse, S. Placebo reactions and spontaneous rhythms in psychotherapy. AMA Arch. Gen. Psychiat., 1964, 10, 497-505.

Q. What particular therapeutic techniques did you apply in this case?
Which of them were most effective and which ineffective, and for
what reasons? Did you attempt any technical innovations on an
empirical basis? When did you feel that a "peak" experience or
turning point occurred?

A. The techniques applied in the case have been described in detail
in the case presentation. I cannot divide them into those which
were effective and those which were not; all probably contributed
to the outcome.

An empirical, technical innovation was Mrs. Tilman's continued
breast-feeding of the infant when she was first admitted. She
requested it; I could think of no good reasons to refuse and
thought it might help. She was thereby able to maintain a
natural link with her baby for which no amount of psychotherapeutic
discussions could substitute. In addition to the natural gratification
of nursing, it symbolically represented our expectations that she
could indeed learn to be a good, nurturing mother. It furthermore
diminished her fear, first of being in the hospital, and then of
having to go home and meet a strange baby, already bottle-fed for
several weeks.

There was no peak experience or turning point that I can cite.
Her improvement was gradual and steady. She was not significantly
less psychotic ten minutes after she left the hospital than ten
minutes before, although her discharge did constitute an official
sign of the improvement she had made.

Q. Did you feel that Freud's formulation of transference and countertransference were sufficient to account for the therapeutic
encounter with your patient? How would you describe your
encounter?

A. Freud felt that schizophrenic patients were impervious to
psychoanalytic treatment because they were unable to form trans-
ferences, a result of their extreme narcissistic withdrawal of
libido from the outside world. [24, 25] Later psychoanalytic writers
felt that modified techniques sometimes were useful. [26] Recent
writings have taken the position that the apparent withdrawal is,
in reality, a defense against feelings of terrible vulnerability to

24. Freud, S. A General Introduction to Psychoanalysis. Trans. by
    J. Riviere. New York: Garden City Pub. Co., 1943, p. 364.
25. Ibid., p. 388.
26. Fenichel, O. The Psychoanalytic Theory of Neurosis. New York:
    W. W. Norton and Co., 1945, pp. 447-452.

engulfment or harm from people in the environment and to the inner chaos of not being a stable person through changes of time or situation.[27,28,29] In particular, the presence of the therapist may call forth extremely strong impulses for incorporation, destruction, and the like, and leave the patient at the mercy of a too strong, not too weak, transference.

Work with schizophrenic patients, therefore, demands that the therapist be sensitive to the patient's fears about the potentially damaging effects of the therapeutic contact. Frequently the therapist's first recognition of such fears occurs when he finds himself feeling anxious, aroused, angry, etc., presumably in response to a similar but hidden state in the patient. He should be free to recognize such states in himself when they arise, and they arise frequently. He should be free to comment on them to the patient when he feels such comment might be useful.

Mrs. Tilman was obviously quite involved in the therapy situation, although she had to guard against her fears of involvement through symbolic expressions at first. A good deal of our encounter was spent in clarifying our attitudes toward each other and our expectations of the treatment situation.

Q. It has been said that psychotherapy is a white, middle-class, urban phenomenon which does not necessarily apply to other social stratifications or cultures. In what way did your patient's cultural background influence his illness and treatment? In what way did your own cultural background assist or deter the treatment?

A. The many similarities between patient and therapist favored a good outcome. Both patient and therapist had been brought up in middle-class homes, in which education, reading, thinking, and talking were valued. It is no surprise, then, that we were able to engage successfully in a talking, thoughtful, educative psychotherapy.

27. Hill, L. B., op. cit.
28. Fromm-Reichmann, F. Principles of Intensive Psychotherapy. Chicago: University of Chicago Press, 1950.
29. Searles, H. F. Integration and differentiation in schizophrenia: an over-all view. Brit. J. Med. Psychol., 1959, XXXII.

Q. There is an increasing tendency for neo-analytic thinking to ascribe the genesis and treatment of psychic illness to the social psychology of the family. How did this apply in your case?

A. Mrs. Tilman's experiences with her mother and stepfather, I believe, contributed to her predisposition for a schizophrenic reaction at the birth of her first child. Mr. Tilman's temperament, his commitment to his work, the presence of Mrs. Tilman's mother, etc., influenced her illness. Had Mr. Tilman been able, for instance, to recognize more quickly and responsively the kinds of distress his wife was feeling, much of her reaction might have been avoided.

In the context of the importance of the family in the genesis of psychic illness, I would like to add some speculations about her initial appearance as a sort of Earth Mother. Her bestowal upon all, when she was first hospitalized, of a kind of radiance and care is a phenomenon I have seen more vividly in schizophrenic patients than in others. There may be a childhood precursor for this: an experience of mothering the mother, to develop an idea of Searles. [30] Evidence from studies of families of schizophrenic patients suggests that one or both parents invested the existence of the child who later became psychotic with a special meaning. A great deal of energy was spent trying to make the child conform to a particularly rigid, often unconscious, set of parental role expectations. [31, 32, 33] When the child failed to conform, the parents became anxious, and so the child modified its behavior in an effort to reduce parental anxiety. In effect, the child had to do psychotherapy with the parents to save them from their own fears of alienation and abandonment: the child mothered the mother. Because of this I suspect the early seeds of needing to mother the therapist, as well as her fantasies of being a savior, were planted in this fashion. In Mrs. Tilman's case, mention of her having to help her mother with railroad tickets on every trip to New York supports such a speculation.

30. Searles, H. F. The evolution of the mother transference in psychotherapy with the schizophrenic patient. In Burton, A. (Ed.) Psychotherapy of the Psychoses. New York: Basic Books, Inc., 1961.
31. Wynne, L. C., I. Rykoff, J. Day, and S. Hirsch, op. cit.
32. Brody, W. M. Some family operations and schizophrenia. AMA Arch. Gen. Psychiat., 1959, 1, 379-402.
33. Lidz, T., op. cit.

Q. If your treatment was concluded what criteria did you use for terminating it? If it is still in process, what guide points would you use to determine when your patient is sufficiently improved to discontinue treatment? Do you feel that a patient should be seen as long as he feels he needs it and is willing to pay the fees?

A. The conclusion of treatment in this case was based on three criteria: the disappearance of symptoms of disorder, i. e., psychotic thinking and depression; evidence that the patient was functioning at an even better level than before the illness; and her contentment with the way her life was going. This last represented no more than ordinary amounts of denial and repression of conflict, and therefore did not warrant attempting to prolong the treatment. The decision to continue therapy is better based on an estimation of the likelihood of benefit from further treatment than on the patient's willingness to pay fees or simply to keep coming to sessions. [34]

Q. Did you make any mistakes in this case--in the sense of "if you had to do it over"?

A. One important mistake in the treatment was withholding chlorpromazine for a few days longer than necessary. In retrospect I ascribe this to a peculiar form of professional narcissism to which I and others have succumbed. Something in the lore of dynamically-oriented psychotherapy claims a victory for a psychotherapy practiced without recourse to such artifices as drugs. Yet many who are tempted to scorn the use of drugs are only too willing to make use of a well-run psychiatric ward for the acutely disturbed patient. What a peculiar and snobbish hypocrisy about the use of adjuvants to therapy! By withholding something which may be useful to the patient, we are treating our own narcissism, not the patient's anxiety. All the more strange is this in that it runs counter to the views of two highly respected psychiatrists who worked extensively with schizophrenic patients--Harry Stack Sullivan[35] and Frieda Fromm-Reichmann[36] Both have warned against the production of anxiety which causes psychotic fragmentation of personality: from such a distressing experience the patient learns nothing. Whatever the therapist can do to minimize such anxiety is in the patient's interest.

Withholding the chlorpromazine let Mrs. Tilman have several days more than necessary of disorganized thinking and desperate excursions off the ward, none of which helped her. Her response

34. Rosenbaum, C. P. Events of early therapy and brief therapy. AMA Arch. Gen. Psychiat., 1964, 10, 506-512.
35. Sullivan, H. S., op. cit., p. 152.
36. Fromm-Reichmann., F. op. cit., pp. 126, 185-6.

to the drug, namely decreased confusion, agitation, and psychotic
thinking, and increased ability to gather her thoughts and express
them, was gratifying. That I changed my views is obvious from
the ease with which I suggested (and she accepted) a resumption
of the drug when she had her second episode of psychotic thinking.
Were I to do it over, I would start promptly with appreciable
doses, cutting back if and when undesirable side effects became
apparent. Drugs, like psychotherapy and hospitalization, are
useful parts of a comprehensive treatment program.

The home visit was certainly no innovation, but it would have
been a mistake and an unfortunate turning point not to have made
it. The strength of the therapeutic relationship was strained at
that point, and an insistence on my part that Mrs. Tilman conform
to the role of the "good" psychiatric patient by coming to the office
could have been quite destructive. My reluctance to make the
visit came from a fear of establishing a precedent, with all further
sessions conducted in her living room. Discussion with my
consultant on the case brought such a fear into the open; ways of
exploring it with the patient in terms of a temporary need for a
visit and appreciation of what she had been able to do with her
home made it possible for us to arrange for future sessions in
my office.

Q. In treating your case did you perhaps feel that the classical
distinctions between psychoses and neuroses were breaking down?
(This question may apply even if your case represents neither a
psychotic or neurotic.)

A. The classical diagnostic distinctions between neurosis and
psychosis are still fairly useful, though in recent years there
has been increasing recognition that many patients are neither
purely neurotic nor purely psychotic, or that a classical picture
of psychosis at one point does not preclude presentation of a
classical picture of neurosis at another. As indicated,
Mrs. Tilman was psychotic when first seen; later she had a
neurotic depression; later she became psychotic again. It
would have been a mistake to let one or the other label so
confine my thinking as to make treatment stereotyped along
inflexible lines.

As the tenor of this discussion suggests, current statements of
theories of emotional life, and of diagnosis, prognosis, and
treatment, are useful guides in psychotherapeutic work to the
extent that they suggest, not direct, the treatment. They are
far from complete and are in constant need of revision and
addition. The complexity of human behavior exceeds by far
our current understanding.

Chapter IV

CONJOINT FAMILY THERAPY AS AN AID TO INTENSIVE PSYCHOTHERAPY

By Don D. Jackson and Irvin Yalom

INTRODUCTION

In the past two decades the basic focus and format of psychiatric therapy has undergone significant change. The classical intrapsychic focus has been infinitely enriched by the cultural and interpersonal contributions of such innovators as Adler, Horney, and Sullivan. The classical one-to-one doctor-patient format also has been enriched by the rise of such new formats as milieu therapy, group therapy, and more recently, conjoint family therapy. At this stage of our knowledge, it is sagacious to consider classical techniques as being enriched by newer approaches rather than being challenged by them. Not only may different approaches be the therapy of choice for different individuals but several different approaches may be indicated in the treatment of one individual. These different approaches may be utilized concurrently or sequentially. This paper will present an example of the latter instance in which conjoint family therapy was utilized as one of a sequence of therapies. In this instance family therapy was particularly efficacious in abruptly motivating an apparently chronically hospitalized schizophrenic to leave the hospital, to find a means of supporting himself, and to involve himself meaningfully in further individual therapy.

The drama of sudden improvement can obscure the heuristic aspects of such cases and leave us with anecdotes rather than therapeutic insight. We present the case, however, not as a claim for the efficiency of conjoint family therapy but as an illustration of the basic theory behind family therapy.

Our basic theory stems, in part, from two observations made many years ago by innumerable therapists who came into contact with the families of hospitalized schizophrenic patients. One observation was that the families almost deliberately seemed to sabotage the treatment of the ill member. A harsh, even cruel charge, to be sure, and yet the behavior seemed so gross that no other conclusion could be reached. The other observation was that there occurred not infrequently an alternation or substitution of illness in the family. The patient's improvement was accompanied by the appearance of severe mental illness in some other family member--often the mother, less frequently a sibling or the father. What conclusion could be drawn from these two observations? It would seem that, despite the family's natural concern for the ill member, there are strong forces operating in the family to keep the patient sick.

Our major assumption, therefore, is that the family is a homeostatic system inextricably involving and influencing the patient. [1,2] Specifically, the family context of the schizophrenic is one in which the patient and only the patient has difficulties; and conversely, his position in the family is to be the problem. In addition to this we see the peculiar absence of personal problems in the cases of other family members. This assumption, of course, has many implications for therapy. The attempt to effect therapeutic change in a patient closely involved with his family without recognizing and dealing with opposing family forces is often foolhardy as well as futile. In fact, an important method of instigating some change in the patient is to tamper with the family system. Admittedly the schizophrenic family system is often ossified, and even when change occurs, it may be evanescent - the complex family forces quickly reinstating the status quo. [3]

The present case illustrates both the long-range use of family therapy and a specific technique for tampering with the family system in a crucial interview which appeared to be a turning point in therapy. We wish to call attention not only to the changes in the patient but to the changes in the family as well.

THE PATIENT

The patient, David Brown, is twenty-five years old, unmarried, and when therapy was first begun by one of the authors (I. Y.), had been continuously hospitalized for one and a half years. Although in retrospect there were many ominous signs adumbrating his illness for a period of six years, he was first officially labeled a patient while in the service at age twenty. At that time, shortly after induction and assignment to Alaska, he was noted to appear confused, preoccupied, and withdrawn. He was unable to perform his work, had repeated episodes of extreme anxiety, and several inexplicable outbursts of anger and melancholy. The main thought-content involved the recent termination of a (largely autistic) relationship with a woman and marked indecision about future occupational plans. The confusion and withdrawal progressed to catatonia, and the patient was hospitalized and four months later medically discharged.

---

1. Haley, J. The family of the schizophrenic: A model system. J. Nerv. Ment. Dis. , 1959, 129, 357-374.
2. Jackson, Don D. The question of family homeostasis. Psychiat. Quart. Suppl. , 1957, 31, 79-90.
3. Jackson, Don D. and J. Weakland. Conjoint family therapy. Some considerations on theory, technique, and results. Psychiatry, 1961, 24, 30-45.

He returned home to live with his parents and his only sibling, a brother seven years his junior. His life pattern here consisted of numerous social and occupational failures. He dated often but characteristically misjudged the nature of the relationship and on several occasions made a premature and inappropriate proposal of marriage. Despite a high level of intelligence and a two-year college education, he was unable to negotiate even the least demanding jobs (janitorial work, messenger, etc.) and was invariably discharged because of his confused ineptness. He was seen by a psychiatrist in therapy during this time, but treatment was ineffective and hospitalization was advised.

The patient presented himself as an attractive, well-groomed young man, who, on casual examination, appeared to be in no distress. On thorough psychiatric examination, however, major impairment was obvious. His affect was peculiar--often indifferent, occasionally saddened, with periodic outbursts of inappropriate laughter or loud singing. He had had auditory hallucinations since the onset of his illness, chiefly derogatory, and resembling the voices of his family members. Present also were ideas of reference as well as bizarre somatic delusions that various parts of his body were decaying or vanishing and that maggots were infesting his blood stream. The chief impression one obtained from talking with him was one of vagueness, indecision, confusion, and a tendency to agree with everything the interviewer advanced. Because of his intelligence, attractiveness, good grooming, and presumably good potential, he elicited much interest and compassion from the ward personnel and on several occasions was involved in individual therapy. President of the ward community, editor of the hospital newspaper, he functioned well in the hospital setting, and the staff, like his family, tended to underestimate his inner turmoil. Student nurses and medical students identified with him, often vociferously taking issue with the diagnosis and ominous prognosis.

SUMMARY OF THE FIRST 18 FAMILY INTERVIEWS

Since individual and group approaches had failed to help, it was decided to involve Dave and his family in conjoint family therapy. His father and mother together with Dave were seen once a week in ninety-minute sessions. Because of school pressures, the younger brother, Charles, could attend only a couple of the sessions. (The meetings, incidentally, entailed some sacrifice on the part of the parents, since they lived over two hours away from the hospital.)

In the initial sessions the therapist attempted to orient the family to the rationale of family therapy. He expressed the opinion that the other family members are invariably troubled, although the obvious distress of the identified patient tends to overshadow their pain. The family expressed a great desire to help and accepted this orientation albeit tenuously and quizzically. During the early sessions much historical data was discussed, developing the history of the family from its origins (the first meeting of the parents) as well as the early histories of each parent. These accounts, though seemingly complete, were strangely impersonal. Conspicuously missing were mentions of the typically human as well as the idiosyncratic problems of living. Aside from the appropriate concern for Dave's illness there was only happiness, cooperation, love, and inexorable social and financial success. Dave's response to this was, at one point, to pound on the table and shout, "My God, I come from a perfect family!" Mother answered, "Dear, have we said anything that wasn't true?" Dave replied, "No, but now I see what a goof ball I really must be."

Also absent was the occurrence of any "give and take" between the parents. They seemed to function as a single person or system. It was not until the sixth interview that the first semblance of individual differences occurred. Father, during the session, informed Dave that on his last job, he (father) had actually been paying Dave's salary and Dave's employer retained him only as a personal favor to father. Mother wept at this, saying that father shouldn't have told Dave. The first overt disagreement occurred much later when father accused Dave of not working because of laziness. Mother disagreed, gently serving as a peacemaker between father and son. It was especially difficult to obtain a multi-dimensional view of mother. A shadow figure, she smiled bravely and endlessly coined Norman Vincent Peale-type cliches. When the therapist commented thereupon, the family responded with disbelief or utter incomprehension, leaving the therapist with the maddened feeling that he had been the fall guy for father and sons, all of whom withheld their true feelings. (The bewildering experience of the therapist who treats this type of family is graphically described by Schaffer, et al.)[4]

Despite statement of the therapist's theoretical position, it seemed impossible for the family to grasp that they were coming to help themselves as well as the patient. The feeling prevailed that they were there for Dave's sake, and the burden of keeping the discussions going fell on his shoulders. The parents after approximately eighteen sessions felt all "dried up"; there was nothing more to say. The sessions became increasingly unproductive, with all participants including the therapist growing discouraged.

---

4. Schaffer, L. et al. On the nature and sources of the psychiatrists' experience with the family of the schizophrenic. Psychiatry, 1962, 25, 32-45.

CONSULTANT'S INTERVIEW

Because the family was losing interest and the therapist felt conjoint family therapy was still the patient's best hope, he asked a consultant (D. J.) to interview the family, primarily to get a feel for them, but in addition to behave therapeutically if the opportunity offered itself. The consultant felt that like many of the families of chronic schizophrenics, the Browns were well defended and most of their energies were focused on maintaining the patient in the sick role, as well as maintaining the <u>status quo</u> of the family inter-relationships. He decided beforehand to see if the family could be moved by placing them in a particular therapeutic bind; namely, they would be asked: "<u>What problems might arise for the family if Dave improves</u>?" Apart from that question, the interview was not structured.

The usual framework for psychotherapy is a restorative one; that is, we presume to remove the presenting complaint so that the patient and those close to him can go about their lives without this handicap. Clinical experience, however, often argues against this view. The evidence concerning relapse and/or psychopathological repercussions among other family members has led us to suspect that we have tampered with part of an ongoing system and altered its "normal" state in removing the labeled symptom of one member. Thus, the usual assumption that things will somehow get "back to normal" if the identified patient improves can obscure the possibility that the symptomatic behavior of the patient has a vital <u>present function</u> in maintaining the balance of family relationships.

In this case of a rigid family system, the physical presence of the other family members in a psychotherapeutic setting had not aided their understanding of their interlocking roles in Dave's schizophrenic symptoms. Indeed, these occasions only seemed to verify their myth that the family would be ideally happy but for Dave's misfortune, to which other problems could be traced with a truly remarkable consistency. The authors were in agreement that such a context was not likely to help the patient, and that family therapy was not going to succeed until each family member sought some help in it or himself. And no one at this point was even admitting to a problem.

The consultant felt that the situation warranted a sharp reversal from the prevailing view of Dave's psychopathology as aberrant behavior, and decided to use his authority as the consulting expert to focus the family's attention on their investment in Dave's illness. This was done by placing them in a particular therapeutic double bind. The question "What problems might arise for the family if Dave should improve?" is particularly forceful because it is a paradox in which the family as presently organized "can't win." The question encourages problems in a framework of help. Rather than arousing their guard by indirect probing, the consultant takes advantage of the family members' view of themselves as helpful individuals and implies they would be uncooperative if they did not produce some difficulties to discuss with him. Backed as it is by an expert, the question is heavily weighted to evoke at least token answers. Yet any indication of family difficulties which might be caused by Dave's remission can be amplified as barriers to his recovery and, hopefully, force the family to consider, at some level, that they must change before recovery is possible. If such a small dent can be made in the family's present rigidity, then further steps can be taken to get family members to assume some problems of their own.

This session was opened after polite formalities by the consultant's asking the above question. The family was incredulous at first, but the patient seemed intrigued by the question. The first break-through occurred when father admitted that if the patient improved and came home, he (the father) would be embarrassed socially. The mother was terribly hurt by this admission on his part, and the parents' usual coalition began to come apart at the seams.

Dave was helpful in suggesting several difficulties which might follow his improvement. He suggested that if he should fall in love and want to marry, it would be a problem for him to present his intended to his parents. Mrs. Brown said, on the contrary, she would be delighted, but qualified her statement by adding: " 'Course, I would always hope it would be the right one." The consultant agreed that this was a chancy thing, that every mother who loves her son is troubled by such questions as whether the girl is good enough for him or whether she might be too good for him. But while the mother agreed it was a "gamble," the rest of the family joined in to table this discussion on the grounds that it was a "natural" problem and, at any rate, "not that big of a problem."

The parents maintained that it was the opinion of many doctors that Dave should become "independent" of them if he were released, so therefore no problems for the family would arise. In the following example the consultant pressed them to admit that their plan for complete separation was neither practical nor desirable, and the patient attempted a rescue. Note that nonverbal intervention such as laughter is effective as interpretation while avoiding the sort of discussion in which the therapist must digress and risk becoming quite legalistic to make his point.

Dave: Wh-What if it goes completely the opposite, what if I don't even wanna see them? (pause)

Consultant: (laughs)

Dave: (laughs)

Mother: (joining laughter) What's happened...?

Consultant: Mhm!

Dave: (still laughing)

Consultant: How far away would you have to get ---

Dave: (interrupting, laughs)

Charles: Tahiti or some other ---

Consultant: (interrupting) Yeah, I-I was wondering - I was thinking of Timbuktu... (Dave, still laughing) Ah, you don't think that wouldn't cause a problem.

Dave: Sure it would. But uh, I would... (sigh) I don't know what -- there's a - there's a problem in family relations that goes something like this: Unless you're actually in a psychiatrist's office you never want to hear - if you're on your own -- I don't -- I feel you never want your family to know just exactly how y- how bad things are or maybe... how... uh... realistically what things are really like. At least - I think you put up a front in both lines -- especially if y- the more you get independent and away from your family, the more you're likely to be like this. At least this is the way I see myself... So I see.. uh.. as I get well I see associations with my family more or less going down the drain.

Consultant: Mhm.

Mother: Well, other people's [relationships] don't.

Mrs. Brown's comment illustrates a typical double bind which rvades the schizophrenic family: While he is instructed, on great thority, to be independent of his family and thus avoid causing them buble, he is told at another level that if he improves and breaks me family ties, he is behaving unnaturally and unlovingly.

In addition to this "stay away closer" position, the parents maintained that if difficulties ensued from Dave's improvement, they would be problems for Dave alone and not for the family:

Dave: What if- what if by some-some chance I should become more successful than my father, then how would my father feel about it?

Consultant: Well, predictably, he would say 'Great going!'

Dave: Mhm.

Consultant: But how would he feel about it?

Dave: Yeah.

Father: If you want an answer... from me; I'd be thrilled.

Dave, Charles and Consultant laugh.

Such a patently superficial answer illustrates that not only Dave is trapped by his role as receptacle of the family problems. The others are as obligated to feel and speak only the positive aspects as Dave is to accept the negative aspects of a given situation. Once this system is set into motion, the others cannot admit to "bad" feelings in the many situations where this is appropriate or even necessary. Here, by laughing, however good-naturedly, as the consultant did earlier, the sons indicate some preverbal understanding of the untenability of their father's position. Lest we be accused of advocating filial impiety, let us hasten to add that laughter often serves as a synthesis and release of paradox, as in formally labeled humor, and here, when family members have been forced to realize that something is vaguely amiss in their usual patterns of inter-action. Further, laughing together is a vital form of interpersonal confirmation, which the consultant used frequently to ally the patient while forestalling distracting symptomatic behavior.

During the discussion of the drawbacks to Dave's improving, the younger brother had been silent but interested. When asked about Dave's weekends with the family (from which the patient usually returned quite agitated), Charles withdrew and relabeled Dave: "Before he comes home I'm a little nervous because I never know in what mood or how he'll be." The consultant pointed out that it seemed as if Dave were being asked to bear the intolerable burden of the whole family's solicitation. He was the total barometer of how well or how poorly things went on the weekend. Surprisingly, the patient burst in on this with:

Dave: Well, I feel that sometimes my parents
and Charles also are very sensitive to how
I might feel, maybe overly sensitive about
how I feel, 'cause I don't -- I don't feel I
raise the roof when I go home, or...

Mother: Mhm. Dave, you haven't been like that
either since you had your car, it's just --
but before you did.

Dave: Well, I know I did...

Mother: (overlapping) Yeah, but even -- yeah,
lately, twice since you had your car.

Dave: Yeah, OK, anyhow, ah, (sigh) that's-ah,
I wish I didn't have to be that way, I guess,
it'd be nice if I could enjoy myself or
somethin' ... (sighs, pause)

Consultant: You change your story in mid-stream when
your mother is nice to you, you know. Which...
is understandable but in your position you
just can't afford to do it. (Dave: Mhm.) It
makes you kookier. Then you don't even
know what you're thinking.

Mother: What did he change?

Consultant: That-ah, I can't read his mind so I'm just
going by - I don't know what he was going to
say precisely, I have a general idea, I think,
just from experience --

Dave: Well, it's just, just the story that I'm the
sick one in the family and so this gives everybody else a...a chance to be a good Joe and
pick up Dave's spirits whether Dave's spirits
are necessarily down or not. That's what it
amounts to sometimes, I feel. In other words,
I can't be anything but myself, and if people
don't like me the way they am -- ah, the way
I am -- then I appreciate when they, if they'd
tell me or something is what it amounts to.

The patient's slip of the tongue captures the puppetry in
which he is entangled; although he says "I can't be anything but myself,"
the question remains: is myself I or they?

At this point the consultant decided on a second major tactic to tamper with the family system: to use as a foil Charles, the younger brother, who was insipidly polite, smiling, and much too controlled for a boy not quite eighteen. It was felt that his loosening up might be beneficial to him and also would not make the patient's behavior appear so out of line with the rest of the family. Further, the goal of this single interview was not insight, but to set in motion family forces which would alter the previously stable but unhealthy patterns of interaction. If Charles could be labeled as a problem, even if only to cooperate with the consultant, then Dave is not only somewhat relieved of his role but other family members must try new ways of coping with Charles, and those changes must have repercussions in other family relationships.

He was asked if he ever had any moods, which question elicited explosive laughter from the patient and his father. Charles carefully explained that sure, occasionally he had little problems, but in continuing in this vein he strained his father's patience to the breaking point. The father mentioned "slamming doors," schoolwork, and alluded to a rocky love affair mentioned earlier in the interview. This, it turned out, was a romance with a girl one year older than Charles, and though he had protested there was not much to it, the father had stated that he hoped Charles would not marry until he finished college. When the patient, in a brotherly manner, had asked Charles if he were thinking of marriage, father and mother had invoked the family rule that there were no problems and brushed the question aside.

In discussing Charles, Mr. Brown unexpectedly confessed his feelings of inadequacy as adviser to his sons. But before this could be explored, Charles sought to restore the family facade:

Charles: And I think, I think it's better that way, too, because you get y-you -- in other words, of course a big problem I'll take to my parents but smaller problems 'n things I try to solve myself 'cause that way, even if I do make a mistake I learn that way.

Consultant: I didn't know there were any big problems...

Charles: Well, I say "if."

Consultant: (laughing, with Charles) If there are none then you haven't had the...

Charles: (overlapping) Well, I -- I...

Consultant: ...experience of taking it to them.

Such examples illustrate the tenacity of the family rules even in the face of logical contradiction. Seeking to construct a situation in which it would be impossible to deny there were other family difficulties beside Dave, the consultant made a specific suggestion:

> ...there's something, Charles, that you could do that would be, I think, of immeasurable help to your brother. And I think of help to you, but I can't prove that to you. And that is that you would agree that you would become more of a problem, during the time that Dave wasn't coming home. (pause)...

Charles: You mean rebel against my parents, or...

Consultant: No... there are all sorts of ways of being a problem, what I mean is being a problem with a purpose, not just to -- not a troublemaker -- that's nothing -- but I mean you would be more of a problem in the sense that you would get a little more honest about some of the things that trouble you, or some of the uncertainties you may have, or whatever you don't share with your parents now because you don't want to bug them.

His father protested that Charles was already a problem.

Father: Well, ah, I'm thinking of Charles at home, though, it, ah, maybe you have a different idea of Charles than the way he is at home, ah, Charles, ah, yells and hollers around the house and there's no question about what it -- that something displeases him, you know it quick, and ah, he's very demonstrative, and ah, ah, ah, you sure do know what, what he likes and what he doesn't. He-he's not around trying to placate us.

Consultant: Do you -- are you aware of yelling, hollering around the house?

Charles: Well, sure, I mean, but this is my temper, I mean, just the way I am, you know, I -- I have a temper where -- it'll -- you know, fizzle out pretty fast and I'm all right again, you know, it -- it does -- it's not a lasting, you know, dislike...

Consultant: It -- there's no reason why it happens. It's just some kind of chemistry inside of you that. . .

Charles: No, no. There's something that certainly has to tee me off, but I mean, you know. . .

Consultant: Mhm. But -- you see --

Charles: Just a little thing --

Consultant: -- it's obvious, I would think, that what tees you off is something that the three of you don't have consensual validation about. You don't -- that, you know, there's no agreement; "Yes, this did happen, and this tees you off and it's going to continue to happen whether you like it or not, or we'll make some reparation. . ." It's treated as if you have a temper, not as if -- this is part of working out a relationship. If you're going to become more of a problem, in order to help your brother, then instead of just blowing up, you'll have to state, you know, what the problem is: "I feel unfairly treated," or "I'm not getting enough allowance," or whatever the thing, and have a discussion about it.

Mother: Well, it isn't those kind of things that --

Consultant: Whatever it is.

The only example the three could agree on was Charles' agitation at misplacing his glasses or keys. Charles agreed to become more of a problem, and the consultant ended the interview with the suggestion that unless they found some personal reason for family therapy, they should not burden Dave with their continued benevolence by attending sessions.

SUBSEQUENT FAMILY INTERVIEWS

The changes in the family following the consultation were dramatic; temporarily, at least, the therapist was able to break into the family system. Father began the very next session by stating that he had been thinking that he was tired of carrying all the family burdens and he would like to be a problem for a change. When he was asked how he might go about being a problem, he replied that he might come home late from the office one day without previously informing his wife. This opened up the crucial but previously unmentioned issue of mother's possessiveness, and immediately there was a deluge of pertinent and important material. The younger brother, Charles, commented that the family slogan or joke is

"Mother has to know!" Everyone knew that mother became upset and worried if some family member went almost anywhere without "signing in" with her first. The issue was treated as gently as possible by the family, mother's contribution being to point out all the ways in which she had improved over the past few years. Following this meeting mother became quite depressed, and in the following sessions for the first time really began to talk about herself. She brought up the fact that her first marriage would have failed anyway even if her husband hadn't been killed in an automobile accident, since he had been flagrantly unfaithful to her. Mother suggested that this may have destroyed her trust in men and might explain her intrusiveness into the lives of her husband and sons.

She also related that her mother, who died when Mrs. Brown was six, was a severe asthmatic and had become addicted to narcotics. After her mother's death she lived in terror lest her father remarry, bringing an evil stepmother into the house. Some of these facts and others were heard for the first time by the family, and the two sons were quite astonished to hear of the previously unsuspected unhappiness in mother's life.

Father continued to bring up things that had been worrying him. He mentioned, for example, that during the family sessions he had often been a "nervous wreck" because he felt it necessary to walk a tightrope to avoid on the one hand upsetting Dave and on the other hand wounding mother if phrases were not carefully chosen. Father again expressed his utter lack of confidence in himself as a parent and his reluctance to counsel Charles about almost any matters because of his total failure with Dave. On several occasions when father was trying to proceed, Dave attempted to focus the meeting on himself by direct request or by acting crazy in a fashion that demanded therapist's and family's attention. The therapist commented on these moves and in addition kept the family from focusing on them. Father told Dave that the fact he (father) liked peace and quiet and therefore kept things to himself was misleading. "If you think I'm superhuman, that I don't have feelings or hurts or problems, that nothing inside bothers me, then I've got news for you!"

And this was news for Dave as he began to see his parents with their frailties and disappointments in a way he had not previously perceived them. The parents became so involved themselves in the sessions that there was a marked de-emphasis of Dave's problems. He reacted to this at first with diversionary tactics as mentioned above and then with sadness and fear at being extruded from the family. He saw more clearly than before the dilemma which had perpetuated his illness: that getting well and relinquishing his function as the problem meant losing mother and father and facing the loneliness of life without them.

Charles was made an important part of the therapy by the prescription given him to be more of a problem so that Dave would be able to be less of one. Whereas previously he had attended only a couple of sessions and remained on the periphery, now he attended every one and was cast in a central role. His attempts to be more of a problem were at first feeble, and he was dealt with severely by the therapist and, surprisingly enough, by his parents, who objected he was not trying hard enough to be a problem. If, for example, he was able to tell his parents that he was worried about breaking up with his girl friend he was criticized for not bringing it up earlier. He was told that by waiting a couple of days and working it through, he was depriving his parents of a chance of worrying with him and helping him find a solution. Any protests by Charles were countered with, "It looks like you just won't let Dave stop being the problem in the family." Charles ultimately was helped to grow more spontaneous and honest with himself.

The third session after the consultation was an important one - - containing among other things, father's aforementioned "news" for Dave about his own problems, and including a detailed description of some of his early unhappy times. Immediately afterward Dave answered a want ad and obtained a job on his own for the first time in years. He worked at this for a month before being discharged because his employer obtained a skilled worker and possibly because of the patient's lack of manual dexterity (the job was making and installing awnings). When he lost this job the family response was appropriate and encouraging. When he expressed shame at failing them after all their effort in therapy, they all reminded him that they were also coming for themselves and pointed out to him the ways in which they had all benefited. It is of interest to note that once when Dave was working and could not attend a session, the family elected to meet anyway, an inconceivable proposition to them earlier in therapy. There was competition for the therapist's attention. After the brother's last session (before leaving for college) he privately expressed to the patient his annoyance at the parents and the therapist for not having devoted enough of the last session to him. Later the patient passed this confidence along to the therapist with obvious relish.

SUBSEQUENT INDIVIDUAL THERAPY

At the time of this writing the patient has been out of the hospital for a year, living alone and supporting himself. He held one job for nine months, and then graduated to a more responsible, higher paying position.

With Dave's gradual maturation and disengagement from his family, a new stage in therapy began and conjoint family sessions have gradually been replaced by individual sessions.

The family therapy context was directly pertinent to subsequent treatment and greatly enriched the scope of individual therapy. For example, Dave repeatedly created for himself a particular interpersonal dilemma. Early in a relationship he revealed everything about himself and later resented his friends for their premature intimacy and intrusiveness. The concept of roles was an utterly alien one to him. The idea that one has different roles (student, patient, employee, boy friend, etc.) and that one reveals different parts of himself in different roles seemed grossly dishonest and evil. However, when this dilemma was considered from the vantage point of the family and "Mother has to know," it became more comprehensible both to the therapist and to Dave. "Tell all to Mother" and "be strong and self-sufficient" were conflicting messages delivered to Dave all his life.

The examination of Dave's indirect methods of communicating with others was another crucial part of therapy. For example, one day he came to his therapy hour angry and discouraged. He had proposed marriage to a girl he had been dating and was rejected. It turned out, however, that the proposal had been far from a spirited one, and when he was asked what he would have done had she said "yes," he replied, "I guess I would've gotten the hell out of the state." Therapy then focused on the task of finding more adaptive techniques of learning whether one is liked.

Another example occurred shortly after the patient was officially discharged from the Veterans Administration and began paying a fee for outpatient visits. The therapist was late for a session and, although he denied concern about this, during the hour he reported hearing a voice within him say, "You are robbing me." The therapist helped Dave to understand both that he was angry at the therapist and that he could, with safety, openly say so without resorting to indirect, crazy devices -- in this instance, a fledgling hallucination. On several occasions the patient found himself in an inextricable bind. His boss disapproved of psychiatry and refused to allow him time off for therapy hours. The therapist, of course, strongly urged him to remain in treatment, but only rarely could he offer him evening hours. This bind, which was constructed by two important survival figures, was experienced by him as one which he could neither attack, avoid, nor comment upon. It is interesting that this "independent-dependent" bind was similar to the previous one mentioned in relation to his mother. Dave's repertoire of responses to this type of life situation was limited -- almost stereotyped -- and he resorted to periods of confused, bizarre behavior or inappropriate laughter. In therapy Dave was helped to understand the nature of the bind and that more adaptive responses were possible. A discussion of this incident led to the development of tactics to handle Mother (especially humorous overstatement), and the patient seemed to benefit from these discussions, although he is still far from adroit in handling his parents.

The paramount significance of all these incidents, however, is that the patient repeatedly gets into difficulty because of his inability to label situations and to comment directly on his affective responses -- especially when his feelings involve anger or love. This defect is, of course, glaringly present in his family, and comparisons were frequently made between Dave's communication problems and the pathological communication in the entire family. It was at this point that Dave stated he finally clearly understood the role of his family in his illness and the rationale behind the family sessions.

Another important double bind that Dave's mother, like so many mothers of schizophrenics, created was in the area of achievement. Fundamentally, the contradictory messages that Dave received were: "You shall be a very great man -- the man among men" and "You cannot attend to even the basic necessities in life and without me would not survive." Dave's mother, who was somewhat of a mystic and belonged to a group of glossolaliacs, cherished a prophecy made by her sect when Dave was an infant that he "would one day be in India with an eagle on his shoulder." This prophecy was known by all and formed part of the family folklore. While Dave was in the hospital he ruminated endlessly about what he should be in life and subscribed to many correspondence courses. This rumination disconcerted the family who beseeched him to stop. Mother reinforced the double bind by frequently telling Dave, "Stop worrying about jobs because when you get well you can be anything you want to be." When Dave obtained his new job (which happened to necessitate a move to another apartment), he called home to give his parents the good news. Mother's response, however, was "What did you do with the clothes you had in storage at the old place?" Dave's response to this was predictable -- a feeling of confusion and a diffuse anger, culminating in his shrieking, "That's personal."

DISCUSSION

The utilization of conjoint family therapy as part of intensive individual psychotherapy is in need of further exploration. We have used conjoint family visits in connection with the psychotherapy of college students living away from home where the therapist would ordinarily not have the opportunity to meet the patient's parents. Many other situations arise that seem tailor-made for family sessions as a part of ongoing psychotherapy. Occasions such as contemplated matrimony, discharge from a hospital, moving of a relative into the home, divorced parents who share child visitation, and many others need study and documentation. If the psychotherapist is flexible in his approach, we feel that he will discover many indications for implementing psychotherapy with family sessions.

SUMMARY

An increased flexibility of therapeutic approaches has been one of the concomitants of the developing maturity of the psycho- therapeutic fields. Not only may different techniques be applied to different individuals, but different techniques may be employed concurrently or sequentially with the same individual as he passes through various stages of therapy. A course of therapy is described in which family therapy was used to liberate a chronic schizophrenic patient from a restraining family system which operated to impede his efforts at individualization. A therapeutic tactic, designed to rupture the premise system of the family, was employed. Some family disorganization ensued at first, but eventually the patient was able (at least temporarily) to relinquish his obligatory role as the problem in the family. The patient subsequently engaged himself gainfully in individual therapy which explored in depth many issues which had been raised in the conjoint family therapy sessions.

Chapter V

EXPERIENCES IN THE TREATMENT OF DEPRESSION

By Florence Powdermaker

Inasmuch as the anti-depressant drugs are so widely used and temporarily ameliorate symptoms, there is some danger that psychotherapy for the depressed patient may be neglected, especially as such patients are often burdensome. But nevertheless one seeks for treatment which can bring about change.

Since Freud has so rightly said that psychoanalysis is not suited to the treatment of psychotics, methods are being evolved that use psychoanalytic concepts but avoid rigid methodology. Most important, a different patient-therapist relationship is established.

Many years ago a probably apocryphal story was going around the hospital where I was working. A resident was walking on the sidewalk of a bridge and in the distance saw one of his patients about to jump off. He yelled as loudly as he could, "You can't do this to me!" The patient turned around, saw the resident, started toward him, and they quietly walked together to the hospital. The patient did not make another attempt as far as I know. The episode seems to me to epitomize one of the feelings that can occur between the depressed patient and the therapist that is helpful in treatment. This paper, instead of formal case histories, gives brief summaries of factors that have been useful in bringing about a successful outcome of treatment and then discusses the relevant dynamics.

CASE 1: Mary was seventeen years old and in her last year of high school when I first saw her. At each visit she sat weeping quietly and saying nothing. She came somewhat irregularly at the start, and no pressure was put on her. Occasionally, I thought of something to say or a question to ask from the history given me by the parents, but it was ineffectual, and many an hour we sat with neither of us saying anything. I saw no point in talking when nothing occurred to me that could conceivably help the relationship or make her more comfortable. Eventually, however, after my summer vacation and ten months after she first saw me, she did tell me what had been particularly distressing, disappointing, and confusing in the last year of school. She was very intelligent, and the frustration of being unable to understand the paradoxes of her life was intolerable. She had always been a "good" girl at home, school, and church, very helpful and conscientious. Then why had she no friends and no dates? Where were the rewards of goodness? Also, there had been a lack of tenderness from the mother, and approval for being good had been an unsatisfactory substitute.

With the patient's approval, her feelings were discussed with the parents, and after some defensiveness on the part of the mother, both parents, to a degree, were able to meet her normal needs. When this and many other situations and feelings were talked about often with considerable feeling, there were no unusually silent periods. The depression diminished and she eventually graduated from college, though attendance was interrupted by three periods of depression and two manic phases. There has been no return of either to date (nine years since treatment ended). She has held a responsible job, married, and has had one child. It is significant that one summer when she was in a mild manic state, the family wanted her to be hospitalized and given shock. They consented, however, to her staying with a couple who had three adolescent children and who lived near my summer home. I saw her almost daily. Since this time she has called me Aunt Florence.

I saw her for a total of one hundred and thirteen sessions over a period of three years and eleven months. She and her parents now have an excellent, warm relationship in spite of their original disapproval of her marriage on religious grounds. Her mother took care of her after the baby was born and stayed until Mary was able to look after the house and the baby. Her occasional letters are casual and contented and give a picture of a quiet life with her husband, baby, and friends, with her interest in music and gardening filling her days easily and pleasantly.

CASE 2: John is an attractive, intelligent, well-educated man of thirty-five. He had been depressed for two years, beginning shortly after discharge from the Navy and his marriage. He was unable to work and refused any psychiatric help. His wife found the situation intolerable and came to me for help. After three months she asked if I would mind if her husband came and sat with us during her sessions. This was his idea, and she thought it might lead him to seek treatment. I said that I had no objections if she did not mind. He came and sat in a typically depressed manner, saying nothing while his wife and I carried on her therapy, very much as if he weren't there. I always spoke to him for a minute or two in a casual, friendly manner when he came and when he left. After four months he asked if he could see me alone, which he did. I also continued to see his wife. He talked freely of his conflicts and unhappiness and related them to the frustrations and conflicts of his early life, largely in relation to his mother. His dreams were very helpful, and there was more analysis than with other patients, as the depression seemed to be more of a neurotic than psychotic nature. He started to read at the public library in his area of interest, began to build radios at home, having fixed up a workshop, and later went to the university for an advanced degree. He obtained an excellent job, and has prospered. There has been no return of symptoms.

CASE 3: James was a sixty-five-year-old man, who had been depressed for about six months following his retirement and immediately following a rather brief physical illness of his wife on whom he was emotionally dependent. He was an unusually generous man of means. He took pride and was happy in his thoughtful benevolences. He was devoted to his children and grandchildren and gave a great deal of thought to their welfare. When I saw him in consultation at the request of the family, he had been given a series of EST which had been temporarily helpful and was then put on anti-depressant drugs and was in psychotherapy. He had made one suicidal threat and refused to go back to the hospital or to take any medication. He had had a good relation with his psychiatrist, but was adamant about not seeing him again, saying that what had occurred in his life was none of the doctor's business. He seemed to me to be lonely and unhappy, more than typically depressed. He was very angry at his wife but did not verbalize it to any extent. However, he made her life as difficult as possible. She had a genuine love for him but was a very undemonstrative woman. I suggested to her that it was possible he felt guilty and unhappy about his hostile feeling and behavior, and although she had not rejected him, he would feel that she should. In the light of his sensitivity and high degree of generosity, I suggested that she be completely uncritical and as giving of affection and a sense of closeness to him as she could honestly express, even though such expression had not been her habit. However, under no circumstances was she to overdo it or put on any kind of act (which she could not have done in any case). She carried this out in a real way, and he responded to it. He has had no medication and no return of symptoms. We also arranged that he would have some responsibility in his office that would not be exhausting but would keep up his former interests.

CASE 4: A woman, age fifty-five. went into a quite deep depression during and after a divorce proceeding which she had wanted for many years but did not seek until her children had grown up. She had insomnia and was unable to work, had some social life but did not enjoy it. She remained in this condition for six months before being willing to see a psychiatrist. It was evident that there was a sense of failure over the marriage, a great deal of anger that she could not make it turn out the way she had originally expected it to be, and this was consciously blamed entirely on the spouse. There was a strong need for support which she did not have, and that need had never been acknowledged. On the contrary, she was rejected and criticized. There was a period when I thought the patient might possibly be suicidal, although this was never verbalized and did not appear in dreams which she would occasionally describe. Nevertheless, I gave her Librium until the depression lightened. I was, however, as supportive as I could appropriately be, was available at any time, since I found that she did not take undue advantage of this, and gave her an opportunity of talking freely, being very careful that any interpretation was so put that it could not be taken as a criticism. She was very intelligent and had considerable ego strength which one could use constructively. Within a year she got a job in a field that had always interested her and in which she had had some previous training. She has been promoted, has a happy social life, has made a home for herself that she is pleased with. There has been no return of symptoms for the last two years.

CASE 5: A thirty-five year old woman came for treatment because she was guilty and distressed about her homosexual desires which she had not acted out. She was depressed but able to go on with her work. Eventually, she brought out a great deal of hostility toward her mother. One day in the office, without her ever having made any statement about suicide, I had an intuition that she was going to commit suicide and immediately. I asked my next patient to excuse me and continued with this patient who was talking at considerable length with much affect about her mother. At the end of about two hours she opened her bag and gave me a revolver which she said she had planned to use when she arrived home. Two weeks later she said to me that as soon as she had given me the revolver, she regretted it and planned to commit suicide by drowning. She then asked me if I knew why she had not committed suicide. I did not know and said so. She said, "When I left the office on the day when I gave you the revolver, you did something you had never done before. You walked to the outside door with me, shook hands, and then put your arm across my shoulder and gave me a pat. I felt that you cared about my living and I no longer wanted to die."

This gesture was made unconsciously. It came back to me after she told me.

CASE 6: This is a mild depression in a sixty-year-old woman who had recently left a fashionable sanitarium against advice. She thought the daily discussions were superficial, boring and silly, and unrelated to her actual difficulties. From her account, this was true. She was intelligent, thoughtful, not suicidal, and seemed to me to have a considerable ego strength. The anti-depressant drugs were not then available. Her two children were married happily, and she thought the prospect of life with only her husband was more than she could stand. He was domineering and arrogant, very successful in business, with few friends, and with little if any tenderness for her or the children. She did not want to be emotionally dependent on them. After considerable ventilation of her anger and disappointment in her husband, she was free to accept her warm love for her children and their love for her, her fear of inappropriate dependence left her, and she developed a freer friendly relationship with her peers. Her existing interests were encouraged. She became able to accept the reality of her situation and found it preferable to being a divorced woman, which was her alternative. In contrast to her previous experience in therapy, she trusted our relationship and was able to talk freely, and express feelings and act in accordance with her reality situation.

DISCUSSION

The therapy in each of the above cases was characterized by a warm, friendly interest by the psychiatrist and, where possible, by a member of the family. The patients have felt that in spite of the repressed, or not so repressed, hostility, they were loved, and the love and concern was real and generously given in a way that the patient found acceptable. It was spontaneous and not overdone. While EST and anti-depressant drugs were used in a few of the later cases, they were depended upon only to help the patient over the immediate situation. Psychotherapy was used for as much catharsis and re-organization as the patient had the ego strength to stand. Always, the personality and character and history of the patient in relation to the actual situation was the determining factor in the nature of the treatment.

When drugs were used, the patient was given the drug but only enough for one day. Then the patient came back the next day for perhaps five minutes, and another day's supply was given. In this way there was little likelihood of pills being stored up for a suicidal attempt, and the daily visit, no matter how brief the talk, was helpful.

NEUROTIC AND CHARACTER DISORDERS

Chapter VI

RELATIONSHIP THERAPY WITH A CASE OF IMMATURITY

By William U. Snyder

Rudolf Dvorjak was a twenty-three-year-old graduate student in psychology, the son of immigrant parents from Central Europe. He had lived in a large mining city in Pennsylvania all his life before entering graduate school. He had one sibling, a married sister several years older than he, who had not gone beyond high school. His parents' education had concluded with grade school. The family were members of a lower socioeconomic level; the father worked fairly regularly as a miner. The family life had been very unhappy, with almost constant quarreling, most of it revolving around the father's egocentric and overly dominating behavior. He was a rigid, ignorant, unlovable person who tyrannized over his family and resented all their attempts to adopt the typical American culture. Rudolf bitterly hated his father; toward his mother his feelings were more ambivalent. While she was at some times somewhat loving, or at least considerate of him, she was also petty and vindictive, controlling in a sometimes passive, sometimes aggressive manner. Like many such immigrant parents, however, the Dvorjaks eagerly encouraged their son's attempts to better himself educationally and professionally, even though they had little comprehension of the profession of psychology for which he hoped to prepare himself. Rudolf had a fairly good relationship with his four-year-older sister, although there had been some normal sibling rivalry.

Mr. Dvorjak appeared to be a student of average ability for graduate school. His work was undistinguished, and there was some evidence that this was partly due to a lack of effort. In personality, he was a nonmixer. His relationships with other graduate students were rather formal and distant. He was so unskilled in social graces that he tended to be one of the last to find friends. He also was naive about social interactions and unable to observe the typical amenities which facilitate interpersonal relationships. Physically he was unimpressive, although he did pay a lot of attention to his dress and grooming.

Mr. Dvorjak requested psychotherapy to help him establish better relationships with his peers and to become less sensitive and insecure. He was concerned about his feelings of hostility and his difficulty in suppressing rage toward his family. Somewhat later in therapy he mentioned a sexual compulsion which bothered him a great deal but which he could not discontinue.

DIAGNOSTIC TEST FINDINGS

  Two standard tests were administered to Mr. Dvorjak; once he took the Minnesota Multiphasic Personality Inventory (MMPI), and on seven occasions throughout therapy he was given the Edwards Personal Preference Inventory. Also, after each interview he filled out Snyder's Client Post-Interview Affect Scale, and the therapist likewise filled out Snyder's Therapist Affect Scale. On the MMPI Mr. Dvorjak had the following standard scores:

Table I

MMPI SCORES OF RUDOLF DVORJAK

	T-score		T-score
Truthfulness (1)	66	Social Intelligence	55
Validity (F)	58	Anxiety (A)	40
Defensiveness	70	Repression (R)	70
Hypochondriasis	60	Ego Strength	67
Depression	60	Dependency	40
Hysteria	69	Dominance	70
Character Disorder (Pd)	69	Control Problems (Cn)	45
Sexual Problems (Mf)	69	Responsibility	69
Paranoid	59	Status Problems	52
Psychasthenia	62	Anti-Semitic Prejudice	32
Schizoid	71	Role-Playing Problems	65
Hypomanic (Ma)	45		

  Although Mr. Dvorjak's defensiveness and truthfulness scores may indicate a slight amount of invalidity in his other scores, his profile is probably reasonably valid. His major problems were a schizoid tendency, dominance problems, repression, hysteria, character disorder (Pd) and sexual problems (Mf). Favorable scores were his elevations on ego strength and responsibility, and his freedom from anti-Semitic prejudice. In no case were any of his scores sufficiently elevated to indicate a serious deviation from normal.

  Mr. Dvorjak was administered the Edwards Personal Preferenc Schedule on seven occasions during the course of therapy. His high scor were on introception, exhibitionism, dominance, heterosexuality, autonor and orderliness needs. He scored low on needs for succorance, change, abasement, endurance, achievement, deference, and nurturance. The greatest amount of variability on EPPS scores occurred on deference, aggressiveness, affiliation, and autonomy. His most stable scores were on introception, exhibitionism, nurturance, endurance, and succorance.

After every interview Mr. Dvorjak took Snyder's Client Affect Scale and the therapist took the Therapist Affect Scale. These scales reveal the quality and intensity of positive or negative affect which the two persons in the dyad experience for each other at that specific point in therapy. General trends in affect are most apparent when the scores on these scales are grouped together in small groupings throughout the course of therapy. The Client Affect Scale also includes a score for client dependency on the therapist. The general trends in affect for the nine segments of the therapy process in groupings of five interviews per group were as follows:

Table II - Affect Trends

Interview Group	Client Affect Score	Therapist Affect Score	Dependency Score
1	27.2	-40.6	13.2
2	12.2	-109.2	12.0
3	24.3	-86.8	7.75
4	14.6	-52.6	11.6
5	26.0	-74.2	7.4
6	30.4	-19.0	7.4
7	39.0	-10.0	10.0
8	46.4	-51.8	9.8
9	47.6	+ 5.4	11.8
Average	29.5	-52.8	10.2

If these scores were plotted graphically, it would be observed that despite minor setbacks, there is a slow but steady trend toward an increase in positive affect on the part of both client and therapist throughout the therapy. Compared with other clients of this same therapist, the scores tend to be somewhat low, and the increase is not as great. The low scores for therapist affect are owing to the fact that the therapist scale also measures signs of maturity and of client affect as perceived by the therapist. Mr. Dvorjak was, of course, a very immature person, so this fact tended to depress the therapist's scores. There was not a very high level of client dependency revealed on this scale, and not much fluctuation in dependency, although there was a little. The mean dependency score of a research group of twenty similar clients was 21, or twice that of Mr. Dvorjak.

THERAPEUTIC APPROACH

A word about the type of therapy employed with Mr. Dvorjak is in order. It was an ego-oriented relationship therapy which was eclectic in character. Lying somewhere near the middle of a continuum of directiveness, its theoretical basis was the learning-theory oriented system of Dollard and Miller, but with a strong flavor of the client-centered approach of Carl Rogers. Very little use was made of the psychoanalytic theories of interpretation, even though there are apparent many elements in Mr. Dvorjak's dynamics which would lend themselves to a classical interpretation of an Oedipal problem. The therapist did keep constantly in mind the basic analytic description of the narcissistic character as he dealt with Mr. Dvorjak. But he paid very little attention to interpretation of unconscious mechanisms, and tended to treat the case at the level of reinforcement of learning of more mature behavior patterns on the part of a person whose libido-cathexis was primarily directed inward, because of a lack of "normal" affect-rewarding experiences. It was a case of training the client to experience and exhibit affection which he had not previously been able to display. The principal medium for this training was the person of the therapist himself. In this regard, the therapist attempted to fill the role of a benign father surrogate who could exhibit to Mr. Dvorjak the sort of loving and rewarding behavior which he had not experienced with either of his own parents. While this may sound like a classical transference neurosis situation, a strong effort was made to avoid interpretation of unconscious mechanisms and to employ more re-educative than reconstructive techniques.

The case is presented here in the form of a slight condensation of the therapist's case notes. The twenty-eighth interview is reported from a condensed transcript of the recording. Although the case was considered only moderately successful by the therapist, it was terminated after forty-five interviews because the therapist felt that all but one of the major problems (sexual adjustment) had been considerably improved, and there was evidence that the client had come as far as he was able at that time. Several follow-up interviews and a letter sent three years after the completion of therapy suggest that the case was more successful in the long-range perspective than would have been apparent immediately upon completion of the interviews.

CASE NOTES OF RUDOLF DVORJAK

<u>Initial Interview</u>. The client talked about a large number of items, mostly centering around his pronounced feelings of insecurity and inadequacy. He feels unloved by his parents, both of whom are very insecure persons. He also feels very ill at ease with authority figures and with girls. He cannot display emotion and feels very childish if he does. After some discussion he recognized that this was a cultural phenomenon within his family. He sees his father as hostile, aggressive, and immature; his mother is insecure and unhappy.

<u>Second Interview</u>. The client talked about his hostility toward authority figures and immediately criticized the therapist as being in that class. He spent some time on the concept of status hierarchies, which is very important to him. Then he moved to the topic of his

insecurity feelings with women. He wants to ask for dates, but is
unable to. He feels threatened and has feelings of physical and social
inadequacy. He would like to date younger, more insecure girls. We
discussed ways in which he might find such girls and the reason why
he never tries, i.e., his fear of failure. He then moved on to
discussing his sense of vocational insecurity, after which he returned
to the topic of status hierarchies; he wondered whether some people
are "better" only for the reason of holding a higher status. In this
vein he criticized me for asking questions on comprehensive
examinations about "which psychologists are located where." I didn't
try to defend myself, since he seemed to need to find reasons for
criticizing me.

Third Interview. Mr. Dvorjak had just had an interview with a
clinical faculty member and felt an intense sense of irritation,
because of his feeling that although Dr. S. had been trying to make
him feel at ease, he really felt patronized. I suggested that his
position didn't seem very defensible, and he said what he really
resented was the feeling that S. was "lecturing him." He then
said he didn't know what to talk about with me (Resistance), and
felt embarrassed because he thought that I expected him to "keep
talking." I directed him back to the topic of Dr. S., and then helped
him to see the similarity in the two situations (with S. and with me)
to times when he had been talking to his father. He recalled two
times when he had defied his father and wanted to scream, "F--k
you." But then he recognized that although he felt some relief to be
able to talk about this, "the catharsis wasn't really complete."
He mentioned some good things about his father; although the latter
is having financial difficulty, he gave him a thousand dollars in order
to come to graduate school. And recently he gave the client a tape
recorder. At this point I interpreted the client's ambivalence. He
indicated that he wasn't sure that telling his father off would be a
good idea. He would prefer a friendly equalitarian relationship with
his father -- not overly dependent, just one of friends and equals.

Fourth Interview. The client discussed his tremendous hostility
toward his father. This generalizes to all authority figures. It is
hard for him even to listen to me reflect a feeling, because he
resents the interruption it causes. We discussed the possible
effect of this situation on our relationship. The client felt there
were some things that were so bad about himself that he ought to
drop out of the field of psychology. We discussed this, and I gave
much reassurance and support, indicating that what he said would not
affect my opinion of him as a person and that I always refuse the
responsibility of making any decisions about a client's fitness for a
career in psychology. He then discussed masturbation, which he
engages in about once a day. I adopted a reassuring attitude. Then
he told me about a compulsion he has of going to various "lovers'
lanes" and masturbating openly in such a manner that a girl who is
petting can see him doing it. We discussed the social implications

of this behavior and its possible effect on a career in psychology. He doesn't think the behavior is unethical because he feels sure that the girls are never disturbed by it. He asked whether I thought he should drop out of clinical psychology, and I said that he should wait until later in therapy to decide that matter. He wondered whether I thought that engaging in intercourse would eliminate this compulsion, and I indicated that it would not necessarily do so, although it would likely reduce the frequency of the compulsion and <u>might</u> eliminate it. I praised him for being willing to tell me about the compulsion and for desiring to eliminate it.

<u>Fifth Interview</u>. Mr. Dvorjak reported experiencing some anxiety after the last interview, but it was combined with a sense of relief, and the anxiety dissipated after two or three days. He had a date last Saturday, and it went pretty well. He has had only four or five dates in his life and knows he wants to date more often. He then recounted three or four passive homosexual incidents which he had experienced in college. He reported that he had found the situation boring. He asked me whether I thought he could get into trouble for practicing his masturbating in public. I painted a pretty bleak picture of possibly being expelled from graduate school and perhaps even being sent to a reformatory (a typical handling of such activities by the local court). He stated that last week he had been able to masturbate privately without feeling too much guilt and marvelled that I wasn't rejecting him for it.

<u>Sixth Interview</u>. The interview started rather slowly. The client discussed his progress regarding possible dating; he had made two phone calls to girls, but had been rejected (for quite adequate reasons, actually). He then shifted to a discussion of his relationship with his adviser and his clinical supervisors. He considers any criticisms he receives as personal rejections. He could never see his parents' motives in criticizing him as being anything but attempts to frustrate him. We returned to the topic of dating behavior, and I suggested that in this regard he had advanced to only about the thirteen-year-old level of development.

<u>Seventh Interview</u>. The client demonstrated a tremendous need to express hostility this week. He wants to "tell everybody off," including me. He is anxious about the evidences of passivity in his personality and afraid it may mean that he is a homosexual, but he doesn't really think that this is true; he does know that he's not very masculine. He then expressed strong feelings of hostility toward his father, which I reflected. He knows he has generalized this father-hostility toward all persons in authority. I discussed appropriate versus inappropriate hostility display.

<u>Eighth Interview</u>. Mr. Dvorjak discussed his difficulty in working on a thesis. He feels compelled to resist all suggestions made to him but knows that he'll be "punished" if he doesn't get busy.

He considers the thesis a "pain in the neck, " a sadistic form of punishment unreasonably imposed upon students by the faculty. This topic arouses great anxiety for the client.

The client then discussed his difficulty in building relationships with people; he fears getting close to anyone. I suggested the interpretation that he may experience anxiety about being friendly because it would replicate the situation of his being criticized by his father for befriending his mother in family arguments.

Ninth Interview. The client is noticing some changes in his ability to handle his relationships with faculty members. He is still threatened by any requests they make for him to complete certain assignments. Some of this feeling is transferred to me also. He had a dream in which I put my arm around him and another student (Transference). He mentioned a situation when he passed me in the hall recently, and he felt that I was friendly and wanted to relate to him. But he is still afraid of the situation with his father; will he fight with him when he goes home for the Easter vacation? I described his reaction toward anticipated punishment as being similar to that of a frequently whipped puppy, and indicated that he needs to learn how to discriminate between punishing adults and nonpunishing ones.

Tenth Interview (Follows a three-week interval). The interview seemed very difficult for the client to start. He experienced some very lonely times since our last interview. Things went fairly well at home, but he was lonely and several times engaged in his public masturbation. He didn't enjoy this, though, and worried about having to tell me about having done it. We discussed this as a possible fear of punishment. He felt that in the last session I had manipulated him into feeling affection toward me and opening up and being spontaneous about himself; he said he was afraid to feel close to me, and then said he was worried because he felt like crying, which would be embarrassing. I reflected his fear of becoming vulnerable by showing emotions, and associated it to never wanting to show his parents how he felt, for fear he would be hurt.

Eleventh Interview. Mr. Dvorjak felt very good during the past week because of my acceptance of him in the last interview, and also because of his increasing ability to recognize the difference between benign authority figures and the kind of authority represented in his father's irrational behavior. Almost crying last week "loosened him up, " and he felt close to me. We then got into a discussion of his appearance, which is displeasing to him; when he thinks about this, he experiences an excessive need to eat and to masturbate. He thinks the eating behavior may come from his family's tremendous preoccupation with eating.

The client then discussed his desire to beat up his father, although he knows he would never be able to bring himself to do it.

He recalled how his father would punish him for crying; he considered this most unjust and irrational. He has lately been more friendly with various male peers and with authority figures. However, he hasn't done anything about a date for over a month. In one area he's showing some improvement; he's been able to work some on his thesis.

Twelfth Interview. The interview was mostly about being ill at ease in a recent social situation. He also recognized that our therapy relationship couldn't be the same as a deep interpersonal affection of the sort he would like to have with a girl. On the other hand, he feels deeply ill at ease with girls. We talked about ways to approach a certain girl in one of his classes whom he has found to be quite attractive. He can't seem to act in a natural manner. I encouraged him to plan his dating with girls with whom he has something in common, rather than with pickups and strangers he might see in the library. He discussed his resentment of people explaining anything to him or giving him advice (Resistance). Here there was, of course, some implied criticism of my advice-giving.

Thirteenth Interview. Mr. Dvorjak masturbated again publicly, and feels he is driven to do this because of lack of companionship and dates. We focused on lack of dates for the entire hour. He can't bring himself to try to get them because of fear of failure owing to not being able to interest a girl. Even when he receives obvious "come-ons" from them, he is unable to follow through. (I'm not sure that he is able to discriminate between real evidences of interest and mere casual conversation; he sometimes seems to over-interpret the significance of people's behavior). I pointed out some ways in which boys eight years younger than he build up their hetero-sexual relationships in a very natural manner. I asked him when he thought the desire for companionship would become so strong that it would finally overcome his fear of instigating dating situations; he said that he hoped it would occur by next year.

Fourteenth Interview. (Last interview before client goes on internship.) A desultory interview; the client seemed to have little to talk about. He admitted that he didn't want to "go into anything deeper" because of the impending break in therapy. He asked numerous questions about the internship situation to which he had been assigned. He asked whether he might take up therapy after his internship fifteen months hence, and I assented. He asked for my opinion regarding whether he had shown any improvement. I reflected his feeling, and then said I felt he had a long way to go in the question of heterosexual relationships; I indicated that he still showed some hostility and resentment toward people. He decided he didn't need to come for an interview next week, since he didn't want to start on any new topics.

Fifteenth Interview. (A special interview after the summer which was not recorded.) Mr. Dvorjak came in to tell me how much progress he felt he had made during the summer. He has started dating recently,

and while this is causing some anxiety, he feels that it is going
reasonably well. He entertained his family for four days here on
the campus last spring; the visit went well, and they "had some fun."
He sees his parents now as somewhat more understandable and even
somewhat pitiable at times. He now feels that therapy is an ongoing
process which continues after the interviews are over. Therapy has
shown him some of the deeper levels which he ought to explore. He
sees that there is nothing sudden about therapeutic change. His
greatest improvement has been in his own increasing sense of
self-worth.

Two months later he sent the following letter:

> I have been meaning to write to you for quite a
> while to tell you that I am having many experiences
> which are more meaningful and rewarding to me as a
> result of the insights into myself and the behavior of
> others that I achieved during and after therapy. I feel
> that I have more potential for understanding now, in
> my social, professional, and personal, and family life.
> In the beginning I expected to be able to change myself
> thoroughly and to be the perfectly adjusted individual,
> but now I think more in terms of understanding my
> limitations and assets and how these will interfere
> with and facilitate satisfying relationships. I realize
> now that I still have some areas of needs which I am
> not secure enough yet to take action to satisfy, but I
> am more tolerant of the anxiety that my inadequacy
> provokes, and am slowly beginning to accept the pain-
> ful process of trial and error or reality testing.

Sixteenth Interview. (First session after fifteen months of internship.)
Mr. Dvorjak reviewed his rather mild improvement during the last
fifteen months. Although he is more sure of himself, he still has
many feelings of inadequacy, especially in the presence of authority
figures. He discussed various difficulties in his home between his
parents, and how he finally almost single-handedly persuaded them
to get a divorce. He also discussed his relationship with the psychologists who supervised him on his internship; these went rather well
because both men were rather kindly people. However, he still feels
a bit of anxiety in his feelings toward Dr. G. and me, whom he sees
as powerful and threatening persons. He still has intense hatred for
his father and would very willingly beat him up. He very much wants
to have a close relationship with a girl, but fears the responsibilities
it would entail. He also wants to maintain his independence. He often
likes to be alone and wouldn't want to be obligated to do things for
somebody else, although he enjoys having others do things for him.

Seventeenth Interview. Mr. Dvorjak discussed his feelings of
hostility and aggression, and reluctantly admits that he knows he

feels more of these sentiments than he ought. He now has a clerkship working in a clinic, but he strongly resents the staff's efforts to get him to work with children. He resists this by performing so poorly that in desperation the staff assigns him to adult cases. He then discussed the question of whether it is possible to have a relationship with a roommate in which the appropriate amount of dominance and submission can be established; he thinks this would be very hard in the case of two males, because both should want to be dominant. In a marriage it should be more feasible. He seems very naive about girls and thinks they all prefer men who are rugged, dominant, aggressive, athletic types. Since he cannot be this dominant, he is afraid to establish relationships with them.

Eighteenth Interview. A very insightful interview. Mr. Dvorjak recognized the existence of his challenging behavior toward other people, and the fact that he tends to perceive the world, with the exception of three other graduate students, as being made up of competitive people trying to dominate him. He sees that he either tries to dominate people or feels depressed because he is not succeeding in doing so. He arrived at many of these insights as a result of an interview with Dr. G., in which he felt that the latter tried to give him the brush-off. Mr. Dvorjak challenged this, and he thought other students sided with him and were opposed to the view of Dr. G.

Nineteenth Interview. The client discussed his feeling of being threatened in the presence of any loud-talking older male, and analyzed it as a typical conditioned response, in this case the original stimulus being his father. He took up the matter of his need to eliminate his public masturbation. I expressed deep concern lest he be caught and his career ruined. He talked about his need to date; unfortunately, his usual approach is to seek girls who are out of his league. I pointed out how this was probably self-defeating behavior. He won't try to be friendly with the girls who have shown obvious interest in him, as in the case of several graduate students in the social sciences. Also, he doesn't attempt any natural ways of encountering the girls -- he simply calls up a strange girl and asks for a date. I asked him how long he intended to remain a lonely bachelor and suggested that maybe getting a wife might now be his major life task.

Twentieth Interview. Mr. Dvorjak discussed the hostility he felt toward me last week because I had been pushing him. But after a day of feeling hostile, he had had quite an effective week in general, and felt good. Also, he had fantasied making some approaches to girls he saw in various places. He was upset this week when a married friend was unable to play handball with him because of an engagement this friend's wife had made for them. He invited Mr. Dvorjak to join the group, but his feelings were hurt and he wouldn't go. I interpreted this as "primitive jealousy." Then we again discussed the loneliness of bachelorhood, as observed often

t holiday periods. I discussed my motivation in pushing him pretty
ard last time and indicated that it was a calculated risk I had taken.
also said that I want to see some results this year on the "dating
ront," and admitted this might actually constitute some impatience on
ny part. He stated that he felt very friendly toward me today, but last
/eek he had been quite angry with me.

'wenty-first Interview. This started as a rather depressed interview,
'ith a lot of resistance. He said he felt that he has insights, but
so what?" He has now had no dates in one and a half years, and
reviously had only about three dates in a three-year period. Naturally,
e is very lonely. He then discussed his relationship with men. The
nain problem seems to be that he can't give love or accept it with men
r women. He either has to exploit people or he feels that he is being
xploited by them. I suggested that before he can learn to like girls,
e may have to learn to like people in general. He has had no experience
1 loving or receiving love in his family, and is in a sense "love-
npoverished." He said he felt that maybe he should start trying to
nderstand other fellows and feel some affection for them, as a form of
ractice, so he can learn how to feel love for girls.

'wenty-second Interview. Mr. Dvorjak had analyzed the discussion of
1st week about his not being able to feel affection for people. He has
een trying to be more friendly toward his roommate. They have been
ooking dinner at home, but he really prefers to withdraw and not have
) commit himself to people. He helped another graduate student with
is moving this week, but then wouldn't stay afterwards for a beer. I
ommended him for helping, but said that he muffed the relationship by
ot staying for the beer. A girl graduate student whom he admires
ied to arrange a date with him, but he wouldn't take her up because
at would be allowing her to dominate him! He has been trying to
ractice participating in a mutual sort of relationship with his room-
ate but doesn't think he has been very successful; he always sees
imself as either dominating or submitting passively. Even listening
 his roommate talking, for instance, he considers to be "submitting."

wenty-third Interview. Mr. Dvorjak mentioned two events in which
 had taken a selfish course of action. In one case he was supposed
 get another student into a football game, using his own student pass,
it muffed the situation by not trying very hard. In another case he
ccepted kindnesses from a fellow student and his wife without repaying
em in any way. His parents always did things for him without expecting
iy sort of return, so he feels he never learned to do things for other
ople. I told him that I had found altruism to be somewhat positively
rrelated with maturity and health. But I reassured him that I didn't
ink he was a completely exploitative person. I also said it was
ossible to change these traits if one was not satisfied with oneself.
e mentioned a number of graduate students in psychology who believe
at anyone who is altruistic is a "schmuck."

Twenty-fourth Interview. A slow interview. The client has made no progress, except that he has been a little more friendly with his room-mate. He discussed his passive-aggressive tendencies, which take the form of stubbornly withholding himself from others. As a child he wouldn't go into a room if guests were present, but he resented being left alone. Recently, he wrote a friendly letter to his father, but the latter has not replied. However, the client refuses to "go asking people to be friendly" to him. He also has not attempted any dating. I suggested the possibility of my requesting him to attempt to get a date before the next interview, but said that I was not going to do so. Mr. Dvorjak said that if I asked him to do something he would feel compelled to resist the request; he said that he has made a resolution on his own to try to have a date before our next appointment.

Twenty-fifth Interview. (Follows a two-week interval, because of Thanksgiving vacation.) Mr. Dvorjak reported some progress for several days after his last interview, during which he felt that he was really living and interacting with people. Then he went into a period of depression following an interaction with a professor whom he sees as an authority figure. I asked him whether he could visualize any really kind father-figure, and he mentioned his former internship supervisor.

There has been no dating progress; I suggested several ways of becoming more socially adept.

Twenty-sixth Interview. Mr. Dvorjak started by discussing his perception of older males as threatening. Only his internship super-visor was truly kindly. He mentioned three peers who were not too threatening, although he still holds himself somewhat aloof from them. All girls are threatening. His father was a consummately threatening person; his mother he sees as patronizing, but sadistic in minor ways. She would order him to eat certain food, but then when he would finally start to comply, she would snatch it away from him in a vindictive manner. He sees me as somewhere in between these extremes -- not very threatening, but still he can't feel too warm toward me. He always has some feeling that we are competitors. It annoys him that I seem eager to understand him, because this either makes him feel obligated to me or else it gives him the feeling that I'm prying into his private affairs. I told him at the end of the interview that nothing else would be so good for him as to be able to find some person whom he could come to love, at least for a while.

Twenty-seventh Interview. A resistant interview. Mr. Dvorjak talked about his feelings of inadequacy relative to his relationships with girls. Even when a girl all but solicits a date, he retreats from the situation. Similarly, he fears the wooing process, although he could accept an invitation to "shack up" with a girl. He thinks he could even accept marriage if he could get over the initial "wooing

hurdle. " Also, he says he fears "the aggressiveness of the sex act. "
He fears he wouldn't know what he should do, although his friends tell
him that it would come naturally to him at the right time. I said that
this was true and that no intelligence is required; I inferred that
motivation was the absent ingredient in most cases like his.

Twenty-eighth Interview. This was a good interview. In all areas
except that of relationships with girls and with his parents, Mr. Dvorjak
has been able to feel closer to people. He has recently been truly
spontaneous and unguarded with his roommate and with several male
peers. The hostility and tension toward his family continue unabated.
His feelings toward me are more relaxed, and he feels now that most
of his hostility toward me has been of the transference kind and
undeserved. I indicated my basic feeling of empathy or sympathy for
him. He finally seems to be growing able to feel a bit of positive
affect toward people and to reciprocate their feelings toward him,
except for his family.

CONDENSED TRANSCRIPTION OF TWENTY-EIGHTH INTERVIEW

Cl. I guess I've been thinking about a lot of things
since the last time. Now I feel less pessimistic about my
ability to change my method of interaction with authority
figures. I've begun to think more easily about what my
responses are with them, and I'm able to say to myself,
"Now he's not yelling at me or forcing me into the submissive role, but he's telling me what he thinks. "
Wednesday, during the second week of Christmas vacation,
we went to H. Hospital (fifty miles away). Dr. T. took us
down there, and my relationship with him, I used to like him
very much, but I related to him dependently, and then I was
changing and I became competitive with him, and then I
began to feel like he had some of the same problems that
I did, but then during the trip, and in the car on the way
back, a discussion developed which turned into an argument,
and in that situation with two other fellows it was kind of
relaxed, and I was able to argue with him and raise my
voice and say what I thought, and nothing happened! (Laughs,
as though indicating great surprise.) We discussed things,
but he didn't get angry with me. And I felt, in the car,
though, whenever I wasn't talking, I felt angry whenever he
was talking to R. Somehow or other in my relationships with
authority-figures, if there's a good friend of mine present,
and possibly some other people, if this good friend begins
interacting with the other people, I get angry because I
expect the same kind of attention. My needs have become
very great from this person I like, and it's in a similar
fashion to authority-figures. I need acceptance and constant
approval, and I can't afford to give any of myself in the
relationship.

Th. It becomes a kind of competitive situation where you want the attention to be focused on you, and you think that you resent it when the attention is being focused on someone else or demands are being made upon you. (Clarification.)

Cl. I think when it is being focused on someone else, maybe it's like competition for parental approval, and I guess this is one of my troubles in getting along with people.

Th. They all become sibling substitutes, in a sense, and you're all competing for parental approval. You always feel as though you're sort of getting the worst of the business. (Clarification.)

Cl. And then I'm becoming a little more objective, like in my relationship with you, I feel that I have more neurotic hostility towards you now than I did before. Or I believed, then, that there were things that you did which justified the hostility, let's say. But now I'm beginning to feel that it's more just the fact that I simply can't tolerate your talking to me, for my own neurotic reasons. And I've been thinking also about -- we discussed the example of walking into a store, and somebody says something to me, and I get angry at that. I think that is just what it is; I have to keep my mouth shut in certain situations where I'm under stress or threat, and I just feel very inadequate and very angry, and I feel like I'm being dominated. And I guess, in terms of our relationship, added to the usual neurotic relationship there's the fact that I felt I had been competing with you in a lot of ways. I need your approval very much, but again I'm sort of poking at all these bad aspects of myself, so I sort of felt that my opinion of myself goes down, and I tend to become more hostile and aggressive than I want to.

Th. Um-hm. You want me to like you, and yet when you have to tell these bad things about yourself you don't like yourself very well, and you assume that I couldn't like you very well either, and this makes you sort of mad at me. (Clarification.)

Cl. Yeah. And I felt that I had been overlooking a lot of improvement that I was making because of this. I was always focusing on the worst aspects of myself and usually had the feeling afterwards that there are all these good things happening that you don't know about.

Th. Like you tell only one side of the picture, the bad side. (Restatement.)

Cl. Yeah. And then, after vacation I feel that I don't know what's happened, but I feel a lot closer to a lot of my friends. And I've made new contacts more easily, and things just seem to be improving in my relationships. I had dinner with G. (a married friend) one night during the second week of the vacation, and it was just a perfect evening. We enjoyed it, and it was relaxed, and I really felt like one of the family. And then, I've gotten to know L. and R. even better, because we've driven back and forth from the hospital. I don't know what's happened, really, but our relationship seems to be becoming more sincere, and I feel more accepting. There are some people who threaten me, and I feel that I've been able to say to myself more now, "Well, listen to what he has to say," even though I feel hostile at the time. And I've been able to manage some kind of interaction with them anyhow. Dr. E. is an example; I met him with R. one night, and he never really does anything objective to make me feel the way I do, and yet I've never been able to tolerate a word from him. I'm unable to tolerate my own aggressiveness in the situation, I think. I remember when you said I can't stand pushes or pulls; I thought that I can't stand the way that you talk to me, but at the same time I also feel guilty when I feel I'm being aggressive toward you. So, either response is unacceptable. (Laughs, with embarrassment.) At any rate, I feel a little more optimistic now.

I haven't made any overtures yet to any girls, but I feel that there are some girls that I know, that my relationship with them has developed, and it's gotten to the point where you can see that now rather than fearing to become even _more_ intimate with each other than we are, I've been able to leave things as they are, and I enjoy their friendship very much. I'm still afraid to _date_. (Laughs with embarrassment.)

Th. The relationships with the fellows have been improving a great deal, and you feel more at ease and more comfortable, and with the girls you're comfortable just the way things are, but you haven't allowed them to go any further than that. (Clarification.)

Cl. Yeah. I always block on this topic.

Th. I wonder why? (Question.)

Cl. I dislike talking to you about it. (Laughs.)

Th. Do you feel that I'll be critical of you, or do you feel that you'll be critical of yourself? Or both? (Question; relationship.)

Cl. I guess again, what I really feel is that action speaks louder than words, and just talking about it isn't going to do any good.

Th. You're saying to yourself that <u>having</u> dates would be more convincing. (Restatement.)

Cl. Yeah, instead of all this talking. (Pause; half-minute.) Another thing I feel now is that when I went home for the holidays I didn't see my father, but my sister was pressuring me to go and see him, and, of course, this incurred my negativism and made me not want to see him. The reason I give for not wanting to go to <u>him</u> is because, well, why won't he come to see <u>me</u>? And there's something about that -- if I alienate someone from me, or if someone disapproves of me, I feel that that's the end of the relationship. I can <u>never</u> regain the approval of that person. And I think maybe that's the way it is with my father, that I feel guilty about what I've done. There's something about going back, that if I'm wrong and I feel that I'm wrong, I become more proud, and I feel that I don't want to be submissive by going back.

Th. If you were to go back, this would be an admission of fault on your part, a humiliating experience; it would really be asking him to forgive you for something. It would be tantamount to conceding error on your part. Whoever makes the first concession is the guy who admits that he was in the wrong. (Clarification.) (Pause.) When did you last see him? (Question.)

Cl. Last March. And I guess I feel now that a more mature response would be to feel that, right or wrong, it's not the end of the world, and I can make a go of it anyhow. But in his case I don't particularly feel that I am wrong or guilty. With other people, sometimes I feel that I am. And then if they get angry with me it threatens me because I feel that I have no recourse with them. I still want their friendship, but I feel that I can't re-establish the relationship.

Th. In <u>his</u> case, do you <u>care</u> whether you see him age or not? (Question.)

Cl. I guess I do, but consciously I don't. That was the one weapon my sister had against me. She said, "You'll regret it." And the way I feel now, I won't. I don't feel good about the way I feel (laughs), but that's the way I feel.

Th. I have the feeling that in such a situation a father should be the _first_ to be willing to call it quits. According to my stereotype, he should be even more forgiving than his son. So I can't say that I feel that you're wrong. It would sort of be the Christian thing to go to him and say "All right, we've quarreled, but let's make it up." But I also have the feeling that he is a pretty inadequate father, even if this were all your fault, not to forgive you. (Support.)

Cl. I wrote him a letter, and I told him that.

Th. You made an overture, actually, which he didn't reciprocate. (Restatement.)

Cl. My sister said that he told her about the letter, but his response was that he doesn't know what to say. He refused to write me a letter.

Th. There're lots of things he could say. He could tell you that he was sorry that it had happened. He could tell you that he was fond of you. I guess none of these are things he was _able_ to say, so that's why he doesn't know what to say. (Information.)

Cl. I guess maybe that's why I feel guilty. I have the feeling that he does like me very much. I've heard from a friend of my mother's that he feels a greater loss about my leaving him than I do. People have the feeling that I've done him a great wrong because he really loves me very much, they say. I guess this has been a source of my real prog-ress. What I'm saying is that either he'll express some-thing of love to me, or I don't want to see him any more.

Th. You don't feel positive enough that you feel any great desire to do anything about it. Not to the extent of going to him. (Clarification.)

Cl. I think what really brought it about is that when I went home, I spent the first week with my mother, and I was just _seething_ with hostility toward her, and I feel better now, because I can see that even _she_ is like my father in her reaction to me. She still considers me a child. I didn't have too much money when I went home, and so I really couldn't make good excuses for not being home all the time during the day, so I had to submit to the regimen of the household. And I found myself at her disposal every day. She'd tell me all sorts of things to do, and I really had no good reason for refusing. I had to break my day up in terms of her needs, and I dislike that very much. And then while I was in the house she'd give me little orders like, "Take this box of tissues into the other room," and this really infuriated me. This seems to be the role that I'm given in the family; a symbol of what it's perceived I can do. And there's just such a complete difference in values now that I can't agree with anything that she says.

Th. Even if she said something that you agreed with, you'd be angry anyway. (Clarification.)

Cl. Yeah. And then I begin to feel badly, and I know that I'm all she has.

Th. When she says these things, does she say "Please"? (Question.)

Cl. (Laughs.) She gives me clipped orders.

Th. What do you do? (Question.)

Cl. I do them.

Th. But you get angry. (Clarification.)

Cl. Yes. Then I started something. We'd sit down and she'd start asking me if I wanted different things, and that always gets me very angry too, and I made a point of saying "No!" Then a half-hour later I'd get them for myself.

Th. Why do you think you did that? (Question.)

Cl. Because I wanted to train her to realize that I'm not helpless.

Th. She's oversolicitous. She's babying you. And so you just refused everything. (Restatement.)

Cl. Yeah. Something that makes it hard, too, is that I feel that in her relationships with other people, I can see some of the things in her that are in me. I feel that her relationships with other people are worse than mine were in the beginning. She really has very few gratifying outlets for herself, or significant interactions. That makes it even harder because I know that she has a lot tied up in me and my world. If I'm to do everything that she likes me to do, it means....

Th. A submerging of your real self. You know you're important to her, but this doesn't change the fact that you just become very irritated with the way she treats you. (Clarification.)

Cl. Yeah.

Th. What would she say if the next time she said, "Get me a lemon," you said, "Say please," or, "I will if you say please"? (Advice.)

Cl. Um-hm. I don't know. She'd wonder why I said it.

Th. I think what I'm asking is, do you let her know, directly, that you are now old enough to be treated like a man? Or do you just sorta sulk, and approach it indirectly? (Criticism.)

Cl. I guess I sulk. I've thought at different times at home, well, why don't I just bring everything up and start talking about it, but I find that when I do that I generally lose my perspective to the point where I begin doubting myself. She'll say, "No, I don't; it's really not true that I baby you," and then I think to myself that I know I'm right but I just can't convince her, but then I feel real intropunitive. But if I do persist, and just arbitrarily say that I'm not going to let her convince me the other way, because I know I'm right, and show her that I feel she's wrong, she'll become deeply intropunitive and feel very badly about it. And then my sister'll criticize me for being mean to my mother, and she'll say that it's all my fault again.

Th. And what does that make you feel, when your sister challenges you this way? (Question.)

Cl. Well, I can see now that although my sister doesn't bother me very much, I think that before when I was younger whenever there was any stress in the family, somehow or other I was the one who ended up with the hostility.

Th. You were low man on the totem pole -- at the bottom of the social pecking order. (Clarification.) What would your sister say if the next time she said, "See what you're doing to Mother," you'd say, "Oh, shut up!" or "Don't give me any of that stuff!"? (Advice.)

Cl. She would say all the old cultural clichés as to why I should go and see my mother. "Boys just don't do that," she'd say. And, "You'll live to regret it," and things like that. And I would just give her my reasons for not doing it, or use some psychology on her. And she'd say I sounded just like an old grandfather now, all-wise and all-knowing. Whenever I get into an argument I feel at a disadvantage because I feel things are said in an argument that are really true. I had a lot of cruel things that I could have said to her. During the separation (of the parents) she couldn't tolerate what I was doing, and my brother-in-law thought she was having a nervous breakdown. So I feel that I don't want to be aggressive with her, because I feel very badly if I am.

Th. They'll all get angry with you, and become extrapunitive toward you. (Restatement.)

Cl. No, if I do push, they'll become intropunitive toward themselves, and then I'll feel guilty.

Th. What sort of person is your brother-in-law? Is he reasonable? (Question.)

Cl. Well, I feel he's another me, in a lot of ways. He's basically a pretty submissive guy. But when he gets looped -- he gets drunk a lot -- then his hostility comes out. And although he supported me in the separation, he supported me even though he thinks it's wrong. You shouldn't break up a family. He was loyal, I guess you'd say.

Th. In the sense of being loyal to you, despite a conviction that you were doing a wrong thing. (Restatement.)

Cl. That's true. As a matter of fact, I know a number of people who haven't gone through the same thing I've gone through, and they feel the same way toward their father. (Laughs.) I guess eighty per cent of the male graduate students in psychology here have these feelings about their family. And I think with J. (roommate) that approach has paid off and we've become closer, and we had the usual long talk one night, and our backgrounds are so exactly similar in so many intimate ways that it's just fantastic. I mean it feels almost as though he was talking about my life to me, and somehow this was good for me; I just kinda felt, "Well, gee whiz, I'm not really that lousy."

Th. You found that others felt the same way. As if you were not the only neurotic around (both laugh). I think you're quite right; your figures might be a bit high, but the general principle is one that would be true. (Reassurance.) There is a lot of hostility toward parents in this group, it's true. I think there's a lot in many groups. It's almost, but not entirely, a universal phenomenon. I'm sure some young

men find their fathers lovable. But it's a cultural stereotype that there's hostility between sons and fathers.
(Information.)

> Cl. I had the idea that the reason why people go into
> clinical psychology is that they really want to compensate
> with paternalism. That they want to pat their little clients
> on the back and help them through life, and that also part of
> it was a reaction formation to the real hostility they feel.
> (Is this a possible criticism of the therapist?)

> Th. Well, this may be true of many cases. (Accepts.)

> Cl. I think it's true of myself, anyhow. But I guess a
> lot of times I generalize from myself to other people.

> Th. The things that I was suggesting doing were
> illustrations of straightforward but controlled aggression.
> What I was trying to illustrate was procedures which were
> not repressive, just expressed the feeling of aggression, but
> in a wholesome way, and didn't magnify it. Because I
> perceived this as an ideal way of handling the situation.
> (Pause.) (Information.) There's another side of the picture
> that bothers me; I think about the deprivation of positive
> affect that you've experienced, or even now experience, from
> other people, and that makes me not want to encourage you to
> do anything that would jeopardize even the slightest positive
> reactions that you might get from, say, your mother. But
> you don't have a father who gives you any love, and the
> relationship with your sister is dubious, or at least
> ambivalent in terms of affect, and that's true of your
> mother; it's ambivalent. You're getting some affection
> from your friends and your roommate, and also feeling some
> affection for them. (Support.) We may have to settle for
> that, and recognize that your parents are too old to change.
> I've had clients who thought that their idea of really getting
> this thing nailed down was to go and tell the old man off and
> beat hell out of him. And the recognition of their problems
> here has been such that when they really did encounter their
> father, it was unnecessary to do that. They were able to
> take a mature attitude of perceiving their father's weaknesses,
> and to some extent understand them, and interact with the
> father as an adult man would interact with another person,
> and the fathers in turn interacted with them differently.
> (Information.)

> Cl. I think the times when he came up here I guess
> I felt more like that, because I felt that up here I was
> the boss.

Th. He was on your ground, anyway. (Pause.) You've noted a phenomenon that you must be starting to be aware of, which is that as anyone grows older, as he passes middle age, he becomes less dominant and less aggressive, as a rule, and eventually he reaches the point where he becomes helpless. Then there's no question who's boss; the younger person is boss. The roles become almost reversed. What I'm trying to do in that illustration is to point out the perspective of the whole life period and show you that the relationship inherently must change, by virtue of the character of physical changes which occur. (Information.)

Cl. I think he would be willing to become very dependent. I mean, the last time I saw him was right after I'd taken my mother away from him, and I didn't know what to expect at that time, whether I would have to fight him, or what. But I felt some of that change that you've mentioned; that I was in the driver's seat now. But I don't like to think of myself as taking care of him for the rest of his life because it becomes a dependency that becomes too severe.

Th. I expect that happens sometimes. (Pause.) Well, you've been analyzing the relationships and studying changes in them, and in terms of all but those with girls you have noticed some changes in them. You talked about the relationship with me; you say that you're noticing some changes in that. You said that your feelings of hostility or irritation were perceived now as more neurotically-oriented or originating more in neurotic needs than as the result of being deserved. That you're projecting some kind of transference onto me in the situation. (Clarification; relationship.)

It's been a most unusual kind of relationship, and I've spent much time in trying to analyze it, because I have been aware of this intense hostility. I keep recognizing the transference element and keep telling myself that the hostility is not earned affect. I do this to keep myself free of developi negative countertransference, which is considerably over-powered by the predominant feeling of empathy or even sympathy with you. (Relationship.)

Cl. That is one thing I have some trouble with on the questionnaire. Up to this point I've felt that our relation-ship was to some extent unreal or entirely away from reality, and I always have the feeling that you do empathize with me. And I think also, speaking about my relationship with you, I never do ask you what you think, or how you feel about me; I just make an assumption. And probably I'm embarrassed by an expression of affect towards me.

Th. What do you think produces that? Why do you think it embarrasses you? (Question.)

Cl. I don't know. Maybe I also feel that I'm hostile. I think maybe to me positive affect means seduction and submission.

Th. That's what I thought it might be. Because there's a common stereotype in our culture that males don't show affect, either positive or negative. It's all right to show hostility, but they may not show grief, and they may not show affection. The cultural stereotype may have its own psychological reasons for existing. But I think some of it may be a rather direct response. To show positive affect breaks down defenses, doesn't it? It makes you vulnerable, and you can be more easily hurt. You're sort of compromised, in a sense, if you reveal affection, and then have it not reciprocated. (Pause.) (Information.)

Tell me more about the situation with your roommate. You said you were coming to feel more friendly with him and fond of him. Why do you think that is? (Question.)

Cl. Well, I felt before that evening that he was always fairly aloof, and also that there was an unreality to the relationship. I guess that we weren't being too direct with each other. (Client seems quite emotional now, and is repeatedly clearing his throat.) And I guess really, living with him, that he's become more relaxed and spontaneous. I think I've felt a potential to be that way with him, but he hasn't been able to reciprocate. And then this one night we were talking about things, and this one night I decided to take an arbitrary tack with him--I pushed with him, and also I related to him my own experience, and this had an effect. At least, at that point he seemed to respond to this aggressive interest that I had in him, and he became more responsive.

Th. So that there was a spontaneity and honesty in your level of interaction with each other such that you let yourself be unprotected and not withdrawing and withholding of affect at that point. Both of you. (Clarification.)

Cl. Um-hm. I also remember thinking that in a sense it was a rare experience for me, because I find that the older I get, the less easy it is for me to have prolonged interaction where I'm not actually analyzing every step of the way and thinking about the behavior, but where I can spontaneously express a very intimate value and have enthusiastic acceptance by the other person. And this seemed to be one night that we were just voicing our own intimate values and having them enthusiastically responded to by the other person.

Th. It was a kind of rapport, an honesty of interaction without subterfuge, a mutual appreciation which you
rarely experience. This is the kind of friendship I've hoped
you could come to experience with people because I've perceived this almost continuous guardedness in your reaction
to others. I've felt that you've needed to experience some of
these straightforward, open, undefensive feelings toward
another person. (Advice.)

Cl. I'm having this experience with L. as well, my
clinical supervisor in the clinic where I work. I think his
dynamics are similar to mine, and he's been on the verge of
a nervous breakdown a number of times. I look forward to
seeing him and working with him, and I seem to feel better
after I've worked with him for an afternoon. There are some
good things in _that_ relationship too.

Th. So you're really relating to people much more
intimately now, and openly, and in a much more healthy way.
(Approval.) _Men_, that is; with girls you still haven't been
able to feel that way, and you still have your guard up.
(Clarification.)

Cl. Well, one interesting thing about that, too, is
that part of that guardedness was rewarded by the very act
of analysis itself, because I know now that on my internship
I was beginning to become aware of this. I had made it
implicit with my own rules of interaction, in terms of
analysis of dynamics. And these rules of interacting were
actually aimed at giving me rules possible for keeping
myself as controlled as possible. I have kind of been pushing
the tendency even further since then, I guess. I had very
good rules, I remember. One of them was never at any
time to express any spontaneity because you always stand
to lose by it. I think part of my improvement is accepting
more aggressive impulses in myself.

Th. Um-hm. (Pause.) I see our time's up. I guess
we'll have to stop for today.

Twenty-ninth Interview. The client reported a lot of progress; he had
a date, and enjoyed it. Unfortunately the girl is a graduating senior,
and will leave the campus in two weeks! He has been having smoother
relationships with his peers, toward whom he has felt less competitive.
Also things have been going better in his contacts with authority-figures
He was pleased to be able to report his ability to argue with a professor
recently, and to uphold his own point of view without becoming hostile.
He tends always to see professors as "assignment-givers" rather than
as teachers. The client is bored with studying; he can't stand being
given assignments. I suggested that he consider them as _invitations_

to explore exciting new areas of knowledge. He has the feeling that no
professor has anything to teach him. I challenged this, pointing out
how he sees them all as advice-giving father-figures. I asked whether
this is really a transference reaction. He accepted this interpretation.

Thirtieth Interview. Mr. Dvorjak was quite depressed because although
his "girl friend" was leaving for Pittsburgh soon, he hasn't bothered to
get a date with her. He feels it would be too much trouble to maintain
the relationship when she is 125 miles away, although he feels that she
would be an ideal girl for him. I suggested that many young men would
consider it worth the trouble. I reviewed for him many of the ways that
men and girls can spend time with each other without necessarily
becoming involved in sex, which he finds pretty threatening to contem-
plate. I reflected his feelings and interpreted that his fear of marriage
might relate to his parents' poor marriage, and he accepted this.

Thirty-first Interview (Follows a three-week interval.) Mr. Dvorjak
was rather depressed; he has not had any more dates, and is tremen-
dously lonely. His girl didn't give him her Pittsburgh address. One
of his friends says he should go to Pittsburgh to visit her, but he knows
that he isn't enough committed to her to make the investment of time
and money. However, he doesn't do anything about more available
girls because they're not beautiful enough. I gave some advice about
having dates just to have fun. I also indicated that I thought he should
either visit Pittsburgh or forget about that girl. Again I asked him
for how many years he was going to be willing to tolerate the loneliness he now lives with.

Thirty-second Interview. A very good interview. Mr. Dvorjak
reported much progress professionally and socially. He has put
himself on a time schedule and feels that he's operating very
efficiently. He finds he can now somewhat depersonalize people's
remarks which he formerly considered as being personal criticisms.
He is also able to assume more of a role of leadership and to tolerate
actual criticism without feeling threatened. I gave him a lot of praise
for making this progress. Only on the "romantic front" are things
not progressing. He has now learned how to have a good relationship
with his roommate; he feels that he could do the same thing with a
girl if he could only find the right one. He has thought of a place on
the campus where he could meet some girls. We discussed the
importance of his taking active steps in this matter.

Thirty-third Interview. The client feels he has made progress
professionally and socially. Only the intrapsychic and sexual areas
of his personality still need attention. He can't get up enough nerve
to ask for a date. He is now able to see that people aren't always
criticizing him. He then said that he doesn't feel he has enough now
to talk about in therapy interviews every week, since the main problem
is lack of dating, and he isn't able to do anything about that. Therefore he wanted to start biweekly visits (Resistance). I discouraged our

holding biweekly meetings since I usually found this simply a form of tapering off therapy. I also pointed out that I probably wouldn't be able to continue with the therapy after the end of the semester. I admitted I would be bored if we had nothing to talk about. I also said that I was not willing to give him little dating assignments and tasks to perform, since I felt that the motivation for such activities had to come from within himself. He decided to continue coming on a weekly basis.

Thirty-fourth Interview. A very good interview. Mr. Dvorjak started by discussing the threat that he feels from authority figures. But he was recently able to argue effectively with Professor G. Also he argued with Dr. F., and talked him into giving him a summer position. He discussed the anxiety he feels whenever he visits my class. He felt especially threatened when I took a position which differed from his, but he realized that he shouldn't personalize this as being a criticism.

The client talked about girls; he almost called a girl for a date but got scared that she would turn him down. He doesn't want to put himself in a girl's power that way. I pointed out that it would be impossible to have dates if he wouldn't undertake some risks of this sort. I gave him some responses to try if a girl did turn him down ("Is there any other night when you would be free?"). Then he asked me whether a marriage could ever be really happy. I told him that many were significant and satisfying.

Thirty-fifth Interview. The client is making some progress. He spoke up very aggressively in my class last week, so today I commended him for his ability to hold his own in a difficult argument. He asked me for an objective evaluation of his general ability. I clarified his feelings here, and then asked him questions reviewing the objective data he has on this topic, all pointing to an average performance in graduate school. He hates to admit that this is true.

Regarding dating: he hasn't asked for a date, and isn't sure that his motivation is strong enough. I asked him how lonely he felt, and whether he felt less adequate as a male as a result of never dating. These things bother him. I suggested that he might try getting some help from his roommate, who might agree to keep reminding him to call up a girl. This is a supportive mechanism which would help reinforce the desire to date, but he thinks that he would resent it.

Thirty-sixth Interview. A slow interview. Professional things are all going very smoothly, and he is pleased with his progress in this regard; he feels much more in control of the situation. With regard to the girl situation, there has been little progress. He had coffee with one girl, but then at a party he watched another fellow hold hands with her, and this made him feel inadequate and furious; he felt that he had lost out in competition. Last night he became interested in a girl in the library, and talked to her. She seemed interested, but he failed to follow up on it and invite her to go out for some coffee. He felt very angry with himself for this; I commended him for making some effort.

<u>Thirty-seventh Interview.</u> This interview involved a rather profitable discussion of an interaction he recently had with a friend, who asked Mr. Dvorjak to evaluate his performance recently when he gave a lecture. Rudolf indicated that he thought it had been rather poor, and his friend was quite hurt by this and in turn criticized him. They had been quite cool toward each other for about a week, but both then took measures to bring about a reconciliation, and the relationship is now improved. We discussed the question of tact and the inherent hostility sometimes found in excessive frankness. He seems to enjoy being negatively critical; and he always feels competitive. However, in the case of his roommate and of the friend mentioned above, he is learning to give and accept affection.

<u>Thirty-eighth Interview.</u> This was a resistant, inactive interview. One sign of some improvement is that he has been paying more attention to his dress and grooming. I focused on the matter of body-image and its effect on the sense of personal adequacy, especially in things like dating. He feels very comfortable with his improved professional progress, and is not much motivated to do any dating; he does sit near girls in the library, but doesn't talk to them. He was hard pressed to bring up anything new today to discuss.

<u>Thirty-ninth Interview.</u> I am quite discouraged by the general lack of progress. We discussed his problem in terms of learning to cope with the anxiety feelings which people arouse in him; he didn't seem very interested. There has been no progress in the matter of dating, and I commented that thus far therapy had been quite unsuccessful in getting him anywhere with this problem. I asked him how he would feel about some more persuasive type of therapy, and he said he thought he would resent it and resist it. The only potent argument anyone could use would be to challenge his manliness, and he felt that he would resent this. I was discouraged today, and have given up any hope of getting him over this last hurdle. His resistance to dating is too strong to overcome. I don't suspect homosexuality; rather I feel it is a kind of pervasive narcissism.

<u>Fortieth Interview.</u> No very significant developments. Mr. Dvorjak had a pleasant visit with another graduate student last week and feels very friendly toward him. He does not tend to feel so hostile toward people now; he also feels less distant from me. He discussed several girls in whom he is mildly interested, but he is also threatened by one, who teases him a lot. I asked him if he had thought about double dating, as a more comfortable way of beginning the dating process. He took to this idea pretty well. I also suggested possible ways to contrive a situation for getting together with some of these girls, i.e., offering to help them with their work for some of their courses.

<u>Forty-first Interview.</u> (Follows a two-week interval.) Mr. Dvorjak beautifully described his childhood in a nonloving environment;

neither parent could give any affection, and both were jealous of any fondness which he displayed toward the other parent. He thus never learned to show affection, but he is still worried about how easily he becomes hostile in social or personal situations. He attempted to get dates during Easter vacation but was unsuccessful. He and his room-mate plan to double-date this weekend, but making the arrangements has been left up to Mr. Dvorjak, and he hasn't done it yet. I disclamed any intention of trying to persuade him to date, saying that I felt we had accomplished enough in therapy. He asked about having therapy next semester and volunteered to pay for it. I said that I now tended to feel we had accomplished about all we could in therapy. I indicated that I thought maybe at this point he should spend some time in reality-testing before going on with any further therapy. Today he said he was going to date this weekend, not to please me, but because he wanted to.

Forty-second Interview. Mr. Dvorjak gave a summary of the development of his ability to accept people more. Then he discussed his continuing difficulty in having dates; he knows now that it's due to a resistance on his own part, because several girls are "throwing themselves at him." He still masturbates pretty regularly. I suggested it might be good to limit the frequency of his masturbation in order to increase his sex drive.

Forty-third Interview. This was a good interview. Mr. Dvorjak gave a summary of his personal dynamics as being conditioned to a general defensiveness, hostility, and lack of love -- with a fear of interacting with people, and with no close personal relationships. Only one time did he feel close to his father -- the time the two of them brought his furniture up here to school and his mother was not with them.

We discussed his lack of generosity toward people and his lack of any long-term friends. There are hardly any people for whom he would give blood, or with whom he would even share a towel. Probably he would have done the latter with his former girl friend or with me. (Positive transference.) He and his roommate divide up the housework and minutely measure who has done the most; he wouldn't even like sharing a towel with his roommate. He now feels that all the hostility he directs toward me is the result of transference from his father, rather than earned by me. We discussed his deep anger with his father; there is an actual desire to annihilate him. I praised him for having been more compassionate in his actual behavior than in his thoughts.

Forty-fourth Interview. This was a very good interview. Mr. Dvorjak started by describing his anxiety in classes and group discussions and the conditioning factors in his childhood which produced this. His father had always considered anything but quick assent to be hostility.

Mr. Dvorjak then shifted to discussing three girl graduate students who particularly annoy him. He feels that they all show prejudices and strong masculine protest. After letting him express himself fully, I asked him whether his own attitude revealed any prejudice. He admitted he was quite prejudiced against competent women because he thought they were besting him in competition. He criticized one of the girls for making a trip to Europe, which he felt was an affectation. I challenged this and tried to help him contrast his own socioeconomic background with that of the girl mentioned. He admitted that in his own family a good meal and a Sunday ride were the prime cultural enterprises. He also recognized that his choice of possible dates revealed his social insecurity, but his criticism of girls for snobbishness seemed to be unduly pronounced. I discussed the problems inherent in the situation in which children who go to college grow away from their non-college parents, and the parents feel a real sense of loss as the children repudiate the parents' values. He left in a very friendly mood.

Forty-fifth (Final) Interview. This was a rather diffident interview. Mr. Dvorjak seemed to be struggling for material to fill up the hour. I found it a little hard to remain attentive. He discussed his difficulty in interpersonal situations and his fear that he carries a certain suspiciousness into these. He always considered it a sign of hostility when people smile, and realizes now that it may actually be a sign of friendly feelings.

He discussed our relationship. He feels that it has been quite warm in the last four interviews. Still, he believes that he cannot be totally spontaneous with me, and that if he were, a hostility would well up because he perceives me as an authority figure. Near the end, he raised the question of continuing therapy. He can't decide whether his desire for more therapy is an evidence of a compulsive perfectionism, but he does feel he still has a lot to cover. I questioned this, indicating my feeling that he has made marked strides and that he can't expect to overcome all anxiety. His remaining problem is in the area of dating difficulties, and we both seem to feel that he is not yet ready to do anything about this. The symptom of public masturbation is "almost entirely" eliminated; he finds that he can usually distract himself into other activities. Mr. Dvorjak accepted my interpretation that perhaps therapy had covered about all that was to be expected at the present time. He left in an apparently friendly mood, shook my hand, and thanked me.

Special Interview (six months after conclusion of therapy). This was a very intellectual discussion of some of Mr. Dvorjak's academic difficulties. He has been feeling very inadequate in this regard, although he has actually been working much harder in his courses. However, his friends get higher grades than he does, and he feels that this is because of a personality factor. He is always frightened and tense when he appears before a group. He feels that he exhibits excessive dependency upon the professors and that they look down upon him for this.

Two Special Follow-Up Interviews (sixteen months after conclusion of therapy). In these two interviews, one week apart, Mr. Dvorjak discussed his difficulties in his dating behavior. He had dated several girls during the past year. The relationship with one of them became mildly serious, although not deeply so. As it continued to develop, Mr. Dvorjak found that he and the girl were not very well adapted to each other. He has the feeling that as he exhibits his dependency needs, the girls become less interested in him. He feels that perhaps he is neurotically inclined to terminate any relationships with girls as soon as they seem to become serious. I commended him for the progress he has made in this area.

In other respects, Mr. Dvorjak feels that he is handling most of his life situations quite well, a fact which seems to be substantiated by several outside sources. He reported that his public masturbation continues, although less frequently than before. He hopes that eventual marriage will eliminate it.

LETTER WRITTEN BY RUDOLF DVORJAK 35 MONTHS AFTER THE END OF THERAPY.

Dear Dr. Snyder:

I'm writing to you to fill you in on some recent developments in my life. Also, I'm writing because I am proud and want to brag a little, and also because I want to express my deep gratitude. Another reason is that I often think that I should take the responsibility for a follow-up to contribute to the completeness of your case. There's a lot to tell, and I would much prefer to be able to sit and tell you about it so that I could enjoy the relative ease of communicating orally.

The general pattern of my life has changed noticeably in a favorable direction along lines developed over the period of years since we began working together in therapy. I have moved much closer to the efficient, productive, achievement-oriented behavior that, whether I like it or not, has emerged as a valuable way to behave in my thinking. Formerly I was obsessed and was anxiety-ridden about the tasks that confronted me. As the time pressures increased on the Ph.D., I slowly began working, and got to the point at which I wasted very little time; in the face of obstacles I would get fighting mad, rather than complaintive, despairing, and upset. Along with all of this I realized, in retrospect, that the movement that I had made in this direction previously included a great deal of sham, and that I had regressed in my productivity a great deal since termination of therapy. I also realized how great was the guilt that I felt for not meeting my academic responsibilities. As I became more productive in response to the pressure, the changed adjustment developed a momentum-- I have taken up bowling, and I play a competitive and improving game of golf; I have taken up bridge, I read more, I do more -- and it all makes me feel fine. I slip and slide back at times, but I fight to move forward again. Over the past months the movement has been sporadic but steady.

Now I am 29 years old. This spring I became truly emotionally involved with a girl, the first time that I have been really involved with anyone, and we have had a full range of sex, just short of intercourse. I have had some mild fears of impotence, but they have proved unfounded. The development of the relationship was agonizing -- she dangled me but I persisted. We have worked out some tentative commitments, but nothing definite about marriage yet. I insist on that. She is insecure, and it is hard for her not to want a total commitment right away. Anyway, she makes me feel powerful and masculine, and although the development of the relationship has slowed down my schoolwork, it does have real satisfactions. Needless to say, the particular sexual behavior that we discussed in therapy has subsided completely at present. I feel extremely confident that I will be able to eliminate it completely from here on in.

Let me simply express my deep gratitude for your generous help. Indeed, you have contributed to a positive reconstruction of my life. Although I realize that you are not likely to need any help from me, I want to say that if at any time I can be of some help to you or of some service to you, please feel free to request my cooperation.

ADDENDUM

Q. Did you formulate a specific diagnosis before you began psychotherapy, or was it made after psychotherapy was in progress?
Do such pre-therapeutic diagnoses inhibit or facilitate taking a
patient into treatment? Are your diagnoses subject to revision
as psychotherapy proceeds, and do they vary depending on the
way the patient responds to the treatment? Do you distinguish
between diagnosis as such and simple spontaneous diagnostic
reflections?

A. Since I had known Mr. Dvorjak as a student for about three years
prior to the beginning of therapy, and had supervised him in two
therapy courses, I had formulated my impressions of his psychodynamics long before therapy began, and they did not change much
during therapy. I had, of course, not known about the sexual
compulsion which he told me about in therapy. I believe that pre-
therapeutic diagnostic impressions (concerning psychodynamics,
not nosology) greatly facilitate therapy. In general, these
impressions are subject to change for me as therapy proceeds,
and they do vary as a result of a client's response. Good therapy
depends on an accurate picture of the client being available to the
therapist; the more the therapist knows about the client, the
better his therapy. This position, of course, assumes that
opinions of and decisions by the therapist influence the course
of therapy, which I certainly believe to be true. In general I
find a "diagnosis" in the stricter sense of the term not very
helpful, however. I am much more interested in dynamics.
Insofar as a diagnosis constitutes a fairly tenable and reliable
generalization about dynamics, it is useful.

Q. Did you approach your patient with a consistent and verbalizable
theory or set of hypotheses on personality structure and/or the
genesis of psychic illness? Was such theory used directly
(or indirectly) in selecting the patient for treatment? How was
it applied in the treatment and how effective was your theory in
reaching the goals of treatment? What do you see as the function
of such hypotheses or theories?

A. This client (I never use the word patient) was not selected for
therapy; he was accepted because he asked for it and I had an
opening in my schedule. However, in general, I would not accept
actively psychotic persons, mental defectives, nor seriously
disturbed character-disordered clients, for the reason that I
do not like to work with them. The consistently applied theory of
personality to which I subscribe is the theory of reinforcement
commonly labeled "learning theory." In this theory, psychic
illness is the result of improper conditioning, and "cure" is the
result of relearning or reconditioning according to the generally
accepted principles of reinforcement (punishment and reward).

This is the only theory of personality which I have found to be consistent with all that is known about the nature of behavior. Freud had some splendid insights into the nature of behavior, but his explanations for them were usually primitive and magical in character, and do not stand up under empirical testing. Every intervention which I made in therapy was subject to the question "How will this affect the client in terms of what we know about reward and punishment?" Of course, sometimes it is not yet possible to answer that question accurately, but an approximation of a correct answer can usually be made. As far as I can observe, the theory held up beautifully in this case. I would not want to conduct therapy without a guiding principle or theory; it would seem futile and meaningless to do so. It is the basic set for the principles which govern the direction of each action the therapist takes; otherwise he has no guidelines.

Q. What did you think of the prognosis of your case before you accepted the patient for treatment? What did you think during the first several interviews; and during the latter stages of treatment? Do you feel prognostic judgments about ultimate health or ultimate illness are useful? Can we dispense with a prognosis as a formal event in clinical treatment?

A. Since I considered Mr. Dvorjak a case of "immaturity" I considered the prognosis fairly good. People have a way of growing, even without help, but with therapy they grow considerably faster. Insofar as Mr. Dvorjak's condition represented misconditioning rather than nonconditioning, the prognosis was less favorable. In the first several interviews I was concerned about whether we were developing a good relationship. In the latter stages of therapy I was concerned that the therapeutic relationship had not been a sufficiently potent force to cause Mr. Dvorjak to move in the direction of establishing the heterosexual relationships which he seemed to wish at the more conscious levels of awareness. I don't think prognosis has very much value, except as a guide in deciding whether to spend the time with a particular client. As a formal aspect of therapy, I consider a prognosis of little value.

Q. What particular therapeutic techniques did you apply in this case? Which of them were most effective and which ineffective, and for what reasons? Did you attempt any technical innovations on an empirical basis? When did you feel that a "peak" experience or turning point occurred?

A. The principal therapeutic techniques were clarification of feeling, interpretation, labeling, asking "leading" questions, teaching discrimination, offering reassurance, providing information, and most importantly, building the relationship. This latter was effected somewhat by means of all of the previously mentioned techniques, and also by deliberate interpretations relating to the relationship, as well as by offering support and encouragement. I considered all of these techniques effective in accomplishing my goal. Perhaps the therapy reached a peak around the twenty-eighth interview and for some time thereafter, when the relationship was at a very strong and positive level. I did not make any technical innovations with this case. All of the procedures used have been described in my book, The Psychotherapy Relationship.

Q. Did you feel that Freud's formulation of transference and counter-transference were sufficient to account for the therapeutic encounter with your patient? How would you describe your encounter?

A. I use the terms transference and countertransference to refer to all positive and negative affect between the therapist and the client. I do not feel that Freud's formulation of these concepts is at all adequate; Freud himself was apparently frightened by countertransference, whereas I employ it therapeutically (as I define the term, that is). He considered it a mistake, and I consider it an absolute necessity in therapy. I have described the therapy encounter previously as an ego-oriented relationship therapy in which the therapist takes on the role of a benign parent surrogate.

Q. It has been said that psychotherapy is a white, middle-class, urban phenomenon which does not necessarily apply to other social stratifications or cultures. In what way did your patient's cultural background influence his illness and treatment? In what way did your own cultural background assist or deter the treatment?

A. To a very considerable extent I agree that therapy is a white, middle-class, urban phenomenon. Mr. Dvorjak's lower-class background made the therapy more difficult, but fortunately he was himself socially mobile and striving for the upper-middle-socioeconomic level. Thus, he could at least partially accept the upper-middle-class values held by the therapist, and could identify with them as a part of his goals. To some extent he wanted to become like the therapist, and I deliberately utilized this fact in weighting the valence of different rewards and rein-forcements. My own cultural background had a fairly beneficial effect on the therapy since it represented the socioeconomic stratum to which Mr. Dvorjak aspired.

Q. There is an increasing tendency for neo-analytic thinking to ascribe the genesis and treatment of psychic illness to the social psychology of the family. How did this apply in your case?

A. I think it is so true as to be axiomatic that all behavior is the
    result of the family and other social influences impinging on the
    client. All of Mr. Dvorjak's problems stemmed from his bad
    family "upbringing." Had he come from a different sort of
    family he would probably have had no problems. There are
    some constitutional aspects of behavior, but I believe they are
    incredibly minute in influencing behavior.

Q. If your treatment was concluded what criteria did you use for
    terminating it? If it is still in process, what guide points would
    you use to determine when your patient is sufficiently improved
    to discontinue treatment? Do you feel that a patient should be
    seen as long as he feels he needs it and is willing to pay the fees?

A. The treatment was concluded when it became apparent to me that
    we had reached a point of diminishing returns. I have observed
    that, with the sort of therapy I use, optimum results seem to
    occur in something between thirty and fifty interviews. After
    that the material becomes repetitious and not much further
    change takes place. I have, however, had some cases which
    profitably continued up to ninety interviews. Under twenty
    interviews, I think that in general very little of value has been
    accomplished. I would not be willing to continue with a client
    indefinitely just because he was willing to pay fees. If he has
    reached the optimum level of improvement for his particular
    problems and his prognosis and his therapeutic goals, the
    therapist has a moral obligation to stop the therapy at that point.
    Sometimes it is appropriate for a client to re-enter therapy at a
    later date after he has done some further reality testing or has
    experienced more of life's problems. For example, an unmarried
    client may go a certain distance in therapy, but only after he
    experiences marriage is he ready to work with certain of his
    problems in a constructive manner.

Q. Did you make any mistakes in this case -- in the sense of "if you
    had to do it over"?

A. If I had it to do over, I would have made even stronger efforts to
    demonstrate positive affect toward this client and to involve him
    more in feelings toward me. I have recently developed a
    technique of moving much closer to this kind of client physically
    during therapy, and I think such a technique would have been
    beneficial in the case of Mr. Dvorjak. Also, I believe that had
    the interviews been held twice a week, rather than only once
    each week, a better relationship would have been established
    and the therapy would have "gotten farther." At the time, it was
    a "logistics" problem for me; I simply couldn't afford the additional
    time required.

Q. In treating your case did you perhaps feel that the classical distinctions between psychoses and neuroses were breaking down? (This question may apply even if your case represents neither a psychotic or neurotic.)

A. I believe the traditional distinction between psychoses and neuroses has long ago outlived most of its usefulness. In Mr. Dvorjak's case, there was much about him that seemed "schizoid" at times, and the MMPI score supports this observation. I worked with him as a person who had certain needs and felt certain feelings. I really believe the differences between psychotic and neurotic behavior are quantitative and not qualitative. If the behavior is deviant enough, we call it psychotic. In therapy I feel we should work with attitudes and feelings, and it is not awfully important what we label the behavior which these feelings and attitudes sometimes produce.

Chapter VII

THE ECLECTIC METHOD IN PSYCHOTHERAPY

By Frederick C. Thorne

IDENTIFYING DATA

Marie referred herself for therapy at age nineteen, having just completed her second year at junior college. She comes from a middle-class Catholic family with an high matriarchal-feminist structure consisting of her father who is a moderately successful business man, her mother, and three female maternal relatives, all living together in a large old house belonging to the mother's family. The ideological background of her family is extremely conventional and proper. Marie was an only child, early recognized as precocious, intellectual, artistic, and with strong bohemian traits. Marie's personality is as different from those of her close relatives as day is from night. As a young girl, both at home and at school, she was always regarded as being different. Intellectually precocious and interested in music, literature, and the stage, she acted out the role of a bohemian esthete, rebelling against middle-class conventionality, grooming herself and dressing unconventionally, shocking adults with unconventional attitudes, intimidating age peers and particularly boys with ultrasophistication, and otherwise expressing herself individualistically in such a deviant manner that she was ostracized by the family and age groups with which she would normally be identified. She is a very individualistic, emotionally intense and sensitive, cognitively alert and imaginative, highly verbal, conatively dominant and stubborn young woman. In a sense, she is too highly bred and exotic a person to have been born into a pedestrian family and social group. She is like a swan born into a family of black ducks. Her middle-class Catholic background has conditioned her in attitudes of conventionality and even reactionism, and at the same time her temperament and bohemian tastes are in entirely opposite directions. She is essentially a house divided against itself, with neither component of her personality gaining controlling ascendancy. Her associates recognize the rare quality of her personality and try to get along with her, but they never really understand her and never get emotionally close to her. Her immediate family for some years has been frustrated and in despair concerning how to get along well with her.

THERAPY PHASE I: DEALING WITH PRESENTING SYMPTOMS

Therapeutic Process: Marie's (M) presenting complaint was, "I don't know if I am going crazy." When asked why she felt that way, she stated that all through college she had never felt completely in control of herself or of the situation. She described herself as being in a constant anxiety state manifested by nervousness, fears of losing control

of her mind, feelings of being out of contact with reality, and even of
having experienced several episodes of feeling "outside of myself, "
almost to the point of losing feelings of personal identity. The first
three interviews were largely taken up by discussions of such symptoms
and repeated demands to be told whether the therapist (T) thought she
was sane.

> Technical Comments: During the first two interviews, T
> handled M's recital of symptoms nondirectively. This made
> M quite anxious, to a point when she accused T of trying to
> hide something from her and demanding to be told the worst.
> She became very insistent on being told whether T thought
> she was psychotic.

> T recognized her need for heavy reassurance and gave it to
> her. Each symptom was interpreted as a manifestation of
> anxiety, and she was reassured that the symptoms would dis-
> appear if basic causes were dealt with.

> A tentative diagnosis of Anxiety State, Existential type, was
> made.

Therapeutic Process: It was obvious during early interviews that M
was testing out T and the limits of the therapeutic situation. She showed
a great need to be in close rapport with T and to be properly appreciated
by T. At this time she was entering a beatnik period manifested by
careless grooming, unconventional clothing, use of a beatnik vocabulary,
and talking of bohemian things.

> Technical Comments: It became immediately obvious that M
> was testing T to discover whether he would be temperamentally
> and intellectually compatible and able to understand her. T re-
> assured her on this point by using beatnik vocabulary and ideol-
> ogy to convince M that he understood her background and prob-
> lems. A friendly compatible rapport quickly developed on the
> basis of conversations concerning the beatnik bohemian life.

Therapeutic Process: M is extremely verbal and uninhibited. No topic
is sacred to her. She is well aware that she is a very fascinating and
complex personality, and expresses the full gamut of her feelings, thoughts
and appetites, describing her experiences and mental contents with
verve and gusto. In many ways she is very glamorous and exciting,
constantly saying genuinely witty things and commenting on life in a
blasé, sarcastic manner. She is thoroughly cosmopolitan and highly
verbal about all kinds of developments in the art and musical worlds.

> Technical Comments: T immediately recognizes that M is a
> very complicated and unusual person. She obviously considers
> herself to be one of the intelligensia and rightly so, if not a
> near genius.

Although her behavior has large exhibitionistic components, it is also authentically different and talented. She is really a person.

This constitutes a definite problem to the therapist who must be her equal as a person or he can never maintain her respect or hold on to control of the therapeutic situation.

Therapeutic Process: She delights in relating exotic experiences, unusual unconventional to the point of constantly shocking entrenched conservatives. She is full of wisecracks, snide comments, suggestive jokes, cynical reflections, and intriguing psychological insights about others.

Technical Comments: Fortunately, this therapist has dealt with such types before and knew how to handle her by challenging her intelligence and making her feel that here was a worthy opponent who could hold his own, win and hold her respect, and get her to do things for her own good which weaker persons had not been able to accomplish in the past.

Therapeutic Process: She delights in relating exotic experiences, unusual sensations, complex mental states, complicated symbolism, and flights of intellect, all of which she flashes before audiences like the efforts of a child prodigy striving to impress. M made many wisecracks and showed disappointment if T failed to match them.

Technical Comments: T frequently had the impression that M was trying to pull strings to manipulate him like a puppet. A definite clash of wills often occurred.

Therapeutic Process: During the fourth and fifth interviews, M admitted that she was practically incapacitated for everyday living by her neurotic symptoms. She was staying home, rarely seeing anyone outside the family, sleeping all day, and staying up all night reading, playing records, or practicing on the piano. She felt better living this way because it enabled her to avoid close contacts with those who did not understand her.

Technical Comments: Although such behavior contains an element of schizoid withdrawal, it was not one of pathological ruminations but rather into a rich inner life of her own which she enjoyed very much. However, it was causing her some anxiety because she recognized that others thought her abnormal; also, she was not actualizing her life, staying by herself away from others like herself for whose companionship she longed. T interpreted this to her as a typical teen-age adjustment problem of exceptionally superior young people.

Therapeutic Process: M had been a wide reader and was adept at using psychiatric and Freudian terminology. With her psychiatric pseudo --

and partly genuine -- sophistication, she was always talking in Freudian jargon, parading classic interpretations, and otherwise showing her need to be T's equal. M frequently expressed doubts as to whether this therapy would do her any good, and frequently compared it with some superficial counseling at college which apparently did not get to the roots of her problems.

> Technical Comments: T early learned to be very cautious about advancing any interpretations which did not have at least face validity. He accepted her critical attitudes and banterings with good temper, contenting himself with frequently asking M why, if she knew so much about psychology, she had not been able to solve her own problems. T and M did a lot of sophisticated joking about the dynamisms underlying her behavior.

THERAPY PHASE II: UNDERSTANDING ETIOLOGICAL MECHANISMS

Therapeutic Process: M quickly accepted the principle that the study of etiologic causes was more important that discussion of symptoms, and began talking about her family relations. She described her parents, grandmother, and aunts as hopeless "squares" with whom she was indescribably bored. She stated that she could never respect or get close to her father even though she recognized that others think he is a fine man. She likes her mother because of past kindnesses but doesn't get along well with her because "we are completely different, and she doesn't understand me at all." However, M admits to being somewhat intimidated by the mass force of her family's attitudes and expectations.

> Technical Comments: T delicately tried to probe M's relation with her father but elicited only expressions of hate and disrespect, and denials of any traumatic sex episodes. M repeatedly expressed desires to have the kind of a father more like herself so she could respect him. T made no further interpretation of this relationship, and it was never further clarified.

Therapeutic Process: M expressed feelings of hopelessness of ever gaining any close rapport with her parents. She states that her family is very critical of her because of her unconventionality and failure to get along independently on her own. She resents the fact that she is dependent upon them economically because she has not felt up to getting a job and keeping it. She complains that her family is constantly putting pressure on her to be more conventional and get out on her own. She resents it because they are suspicious of her bohemian ways and questioning her.

> Technical Comments: T encouraged M to give up her longings for complete rapport with her family and to accept and be contented with a more limited relation. T discussed causes of parent-child temperamental incompatibility and encouraged a live-and-let-live solution.

T repeatedly emphasized that M can hope to escape from unhappy dependence on her family only by getting herself integrated enough to become economically independent.

Therapeutic Process: T stimulated M to consider the mechanisms
whereby she had always related to her parents, namely by dominating
and disparaging them. Early in childhood, M had gotten "the jump"
on her parents because of her native shrewdness. M frankly admitted
that she had always gotten her own way by refusing to do anything else.
M described ways in which she constantly needled her parents, ridicul-
ing their way of life. M considered herself as so much smarter and
sophisticated than her parents that she constantly belittled them and
"went against them."

> **Technical Comments:** T deals with a life-style disorder by
> exploring the strategy and tactics which M is using to gain her
> ends and satisfy her power needs. T constantly pointed out
> self-defeating mechanisms and suggested alternative strategies.

T assigned M the task of relating to her parents in noncontro-
versial ways. M is to stop needling her parents, stop disparaging their efforts, and cease criticizing their mode of life.

Therapeutic Process: T encouraged M to relate to her family more
tolerantly and acceptingly. It was pointed out that this mode of interpersonal relating was frustrating and self-defeating since no one liked
it. The interpretation was made that M was trying to build up her own
ego by constantly deflating other egos.

> **Technical Comments:** M begins to get along better at home as
> she becomes less threatening to her parents. However, gains
> are only tentative. When extremely anxious, she tends to
> quarrel and heckle her parents for being "squares," not under-
> standing her, etc.

Therapeutic Process: M frankly stated that she had little respect for
all men because she had little respect for her father. However, she
hopes sometime to meet a man who can dominate her and win her
respect.

In the meantime, she was encouraged to stop "going against" her father
and to try to build a positive relationship based on other interpersonal
techniques.

> **Technical Comments:** M continues to experience great difficulty
> in relating to "squares." She feels she is not living unless she
> can be with bohemian people. T outlines some techniques where-
> by beatniks and squares can at least tolerate each other.

THERAPY PHASE III: HANDLING ACUTE REACTIVE DISTURBANCE

Therapeutic Process: As M began to ventilate her acute doubts and conflicts concerning her family more openly, she simultaneously began to have increased adjustment problems at home. She began to argue and quarrel with her parents, shouting accusations at them, remaining in states of emotional excitement and tension for hours, and otherwise keeping the whole household in a state of agitation.

> **Technical Comments:** In many cases, things become worse before they become better, particularly when the client comes to face conflicts consciously. These expressions of conflict were handled nondirectively with a minimum of interpretation as to their cause.

> M is learning to ventilate her frustrations more openly but is not yet able to control their expression in appropriate channels. She must learn not to confront her family with them but to reserve them for the therapeutic hour.

Therapeutic Process: At the same time, M became more consciously tortured with doubts about herself. She developed guilt over the question whether she herself might be a bad or a very sick person, and questioned whether anyone would ever like her or whether she could ever find a place in society.

> **Technical Comments:** Acute self-doubts faced openly for the first time threaten to incapacitate her. During this period, she cannot keep her anxieties to herself but is brutally lashing out at those she considers responsible.

Therapeutic Process: The situation became so acutely tense at home that M's parents were counseled not to argue with her or try to advise her about anything, but to try to find a place outside the family where M could stay for a while until things quieted down a little. M agreed to go for a vacation to a near-by youth camp. There she found some other beatnik types and felt more accepted again. T continued weekly interviews at the youth camp.

> **Technical Comments:** T decides that the family situation is becoming too tense and conflictual and that M should temporarily remove herself from it for the good of everyone. Her parents cannot stand up under much more of this anguish and hostile complaining.

Therapeutic Process: One advantage of being at the youth camp is that M associates with other young people having adjustment difficulties. At first she is threatened by close contact with neurosis and comes to doubt her own stability again. However, by talking it out and engaging in group psychotherapy, she rapidly became desensitized to instabilities

n herself and others. She no longer becomes panicky when conscious
)f instability in herself.

Technical Comments: M needed protective support during this
acute period of instability. At home she had been constantly
arguing and quarreling with her parents, who became distraught
at experiencing her instability. At the youth camp M related
with strangers, showed more self-control, and eventually came
to feel superior to less integrated campers.

Therapeutic Process: Early in her stay at the youth camp, M surrounded
aerself with the most unstable and rebellious elements among the
ther young people. She became involved in a number of escapades,
dentified with the rebels against authority, and succeeded in achieving
. dubious leadership by virtue of being the most beatnik female in the
,roup. T explored this situation with M, interpreting it as a miniscule
xample of her general adjustment difficulties. T interpreted this
attern as the only way M could in some degree actualize her needs.
he feels greater security in the company of less adequate people who
nake her feel relatively more superior than when with normal people.

Technical Comments: T follows his practice of waiting until
prototypical adjustment difficulties arise and then analyzing
them interpretively as the patient lives through them. T
encourages M to try to get a perspective on her own style of life
and adaptive mechanisms, pointing out inadequacies tolerantly
and suggesting more adaptive alternatives.

T repeatedly challenged M to face up to the challenge of relating to her natural peers rather than to other inadequates.

Therapeutic Process: During one productive interview in this period,
ae following exchange took place:

I: Sometimes I feel that I'm an awful kook.

: You and me both, pal!

I: Oh, no! Don't tell me that you are a kook too?

Technical Comments: M insists on using a beatnik vocabulary
at all times. T goes along, developing rapport by relating in
similar language.

: Of course. Everybody is somewhat kooky at times. Kookiness
is sometimes very near to the surface and can come out if you
are not looking.

Technical Comments: T reassures M that everyone has neurotic moments, and that it doesn't necessarily have bad implications.

M: I have felt particularly kooky recently. I have felt like saying all kinds of kooky things to shock people. I feel like shouting, "To hell with God." Sometimes in church I have an impulse to say the most awful things.

    Technical Comments: M tests out T for rejecting critical attitudes. T doesn't take the bait.

T: I know just what you mean. I used to feel the same way, and many times I did stick my foot in it by saying something I knew would not be well received. Most young people have impulses to make fun of organized authority. It gives you a big kick at the time, but in the long run you learn it doesn't pay.

    Technical Comments: T repeatedly utilized the technique of admitting to similar experiences, and pointing out possible solutions.

M: Who would think my favorite old headshrinker was once a kook himself. When I first met you I was afraid you would be just like my family, just a square. It was touch and go whether I would stay with you. I was just ready to fly at the first sign that you were a stuffed shirt.

    Technical Comments: M often stated that she could not work with any psychiatrist who was not of her "type."

T: It's really hard to find somebody in this world that one can really feel comfortable with and communicate easily with.

    Technical Comments: T offers a philosophical commentary on life.

M: Don't I know. I only feel comfortable among other kooks. One of my favorite kooks is a colored boy who is really on the beam. He really cuts it. He understands me better than anyone else. We just sit and talk by the hour.

T: You never can tell where you will find a kindred soul, can you?

    Technical Comments: T accepts M's right to grasp opportunity wherever she finds it.

THERAPY PHASE IV: GAINING INSIGHTS AND LEARNING TO APPLY THEM

Therapeutic Process: After about three months at the youth camp, M feels strong enough to return to community living. T persuades M to make a detailed plan for the future, taking into consideration new insights about herself.

I is gradually getting and accepting many insights into the nature of
er personality, the ways she is different from other people, and
ome techniques for getting along with other people. She is coming
ɔ accept T's principle that she cannot continue to strive for complete
ndividuality but must take into consideration the limitations imposed
y her life situation and environment.

Technical Comments: T encouraged M to go back in her life
and consider prototypical situations in which she had formerly
failed. T discussed with M alternative solutions for such problems when encountered in the future.

Concrete and detailed tutorial counseling was given on many
small details of adjustment, including grooming, dressing
more conventionally, handling other people more diplomatically,
keeping her own impulses under better control, etc. Such
details were brought up naturally by T in response to problems
or questions cited by M.

herapeutic Process: M and T work out the following decisions: (a)
[must try to leave home and town where there is little understanding
r future opportunity. (b) M is to try to compromise with environmental
emands and to be conventional enough to get and hold a job. (c) From
ne city, M is to try to maintain communication with her family and be
ɔ more dependent upon them than she has to. (d) M is to report back
▸ T to continue to work out developing problems.

Technical Comments: In our experience, detailed planning for
the future should not be left to chance. The client should be
encouraged to face future problems in great detail so as to
anticipage optimum solutions.

T recognizes that M feels very insecure about going to the city
and tries to coach her in how to face some standard situations
she will meet there. This allows M to ventilate her anxiety
about such situations.

herapeutic Process: During this period, T encouraged M to evaluate
ɔr self-concept and to contrast it with reality. For some years M
ɪs persisted in regarding herself as an undiscovered artistic genius
hom the world has refused to recognize. T encouraged M to bring
 some of her artistic productions and also to let him hear her per-
rm musically. Somewhat reluctantly, M brought in some paintings
nd also played the piano. In T's judgment, based on her past history
nd also on her actual artistic accomplishments, M is marginally
fted, having much natural talent but lacking the self-discipline to
hieve real distinction, and also falling short of commercially saleable
oductions. T encourages M to secure frank opinions from artistic
perts concerning the actual level of her talents. T made the inter-
etation that M was in reality aware of her shortcomings and rational-

izing lack of real achievement by blaming failure on external factors. She was admonished to "fish or cut bait," to make up her mind to discipline herself or give up the illusion of being a genius.

> Technical Comments: T kept emphasizing the disparity between M's ego ideals and her actual levels of performance. This was done gently, while at the same time providing her with considerable support in the form of affectionate friendship and reassurance that she would be no less accepted and liked in her deflated but more realistic status.
>
> At no point did T represent himself as an authority in assessing M's abilities, at all times encouraging her to seek the opinions of experts in evaluating her performance.
>
> At times, M seems happier since she no longer has to play the part of the artistic genius all the time. She can play the piano now primarily for her own enjoyment.

Therapeutic Process: M went through a period of resentment over being forced to face realities about herself. She quarreled with T concerning his pessimistic prognosis concerning her actual level of ability. However she gradually came to accept less inflated self-concepts.

> Technical Comments: T had built up friendly enough relations with M to preserve rapport even in the face of T's critical evaluations of some of M's abilities and performances.

Therapeutic Process: T encourages M to consider the effect which her flamboyant beatnik behavior has on peers whom M would like to get along with. T makes the interpretation that M obviously wants acceptance and high regard from others but her overcompensatory efforts are self-defeating. T encourages M to use her acknowledged talents a little less indiscriminately.

T encourages M to use her talents for her own enjoyment rather than exhibitionistically. She shows poor judgment by expressing her individuality and unconventionality in inappropriate ways. T indicates that he enjoys M's personality, but many others may not understand it.

> Technical Comments: T makes some diagnoses concerning the impact of M's personality upon others. Her more conventional peers and adults are definitely afraid of her and threatened by her radical attacks upon conservative values. Boys her own age cannot cope with her. She is too outspoken and uninhibited, to the degree that she antagonizes others. She is so high-geared and surgent herself that she tends to exhaust others. Her attempts to show off her precocious wares are threatening to others. M works so hard to relate to other people that she tires out everyone, including herself.

Therapeutic Process: M cannot understand why a person of her talents, intellectual power, and esthetic nature should not have been more successful in gaining recognition and success. T points out that high ability has to be channeled and disciplined before becoming harnessed to useful ends. M expresses the attitude that if squares do not appreciate her, then to hell with them.

Technical Comments: T considers M a promising case for intensive therapy because of her conscious dissatisfaction with herself and her obvious motivation to work hard in therapy.

THERAPY PHASE V: WORKING THROUGH THE DETAILS OF BETTER ADJUSTMENT

Therapeutic Process: M went to a large city and with the help of friends secured a job in an art store. She obtained an apartment in a bohemian section and furnished it with things sent down by her parents. Within three months she returned home in a state of mild anxiety for further therapy.

Technical Comments: T anticipated that M would experience many adjustment difficulties in the city and encouraged M to return for more therapy as needed.

Therapeutic Process: It seems that things developed faster than she had anticipated. Her apartment quickly became a beatnik center with a "pad," assorted white and black associates of both sexes who came and went, smoking marijuana, drinking, and engaging in sex interludes. M hung on to her job but recognized that she was not doing well. After hours she found herself surrounded with homosexual beatniks with whom she would make a nightly tour of the bars, dressed in a lavender evening gown with a donkey tail attached in the back and slung over her shoulder. She became known as the "queen of the queers." She was quite ambivalent about her new life, proud to have such acquaintances, and yet ashamed of them and of herself. However, the life was very exciting, and she couldn't stay away from it.

Technical Comments: T listened to M's recital nondirectively, not criticizing any details. After M had exhausted herself cathartically, T inquired whether she was pleased with her new life. M's reaction was to defend her friends while expressing doubts of herself because of her seeming inability to attract heterosexual males. The interpretation was made that she was afraid of a normal relationship with men and defended herself against it by going with homosexual males from whom she had nothing to fear.

Therapeutic Process: M again returned to the city, determined to make some kind of an heterosexual adjustment. Before going back, T discussed in detail M's previous relations with boys. M admitted that in school she had never had any boy friends because of mutual fear. M's only real attachment had been to a very neurotic young man who had no steady employment and a very dependent personality. M reported that she treated him dreadfully, accepting everything from him but giving back nothing. This man seemed to enjoy being insulted and humiliated, and returned for more. M professed to despise him, stating that some such pattern was prototypical of her relations with men. She always seems to attract weak men, treats them sadistically, and drives them away at the point where they begin to make demands upon her.

> Technical Comments: T recognized the deep feelings of lack of confidence and insecurity which M constantly shows in her relations with men. She is afraid of men and yet driven to prove her own adequacy with them. In the past she has evaded any direct commitments by surrounding herself with ineligibles.

> M consciously faces her need to "defeat" men rather than to relate to them in a complementary way.

Therapeutic Process: Six months later, M again returned from the city in a high state of anxiety. She has lost her job and been on relief for several months, with supplemental aid from her family. During this period she appears to have thrown herself into free affairs with men in a compensatory attempt to prove herself. She reports that she is three months pregnant, with no marriage prospects or even knowledge of who the father is.

> Technical Comments: T is not surprised with developments. It was evident that M was working into more intimate relations with heterosexual males. That she did so with poor judgment and timing was to be expected in one who has so much to make up in such a short time. T remained accepting and uncritical.

Therapeutic Process: M shows no embarrassment in relating the conditions of becoming pregnant. There had been a number of men hanging around her apartment, including her old neurotic suitor who follows her around, enduring her insults and trying to help her. During this period she had relations with several men (often with the neurotic suitor in the next room) and is not certain who the father of her child is.

> Technical Comments: It is obvious that M had thrown herself into promiscuous relations with men in an overcompensatory manner to try to make up for lost time and prove her own adequacy. Because of the beatnik atmosphere in which the pregnancy occurred, in which her beatnik peers seemed to accept such a development naturally, M showed little guilt over the circumstances of her pregnancy.

Therapeutic Process: It was her neurotic suitor who insisted that she return home at this point and seek further counseling. He wishes to marry her and assume paternity of the child but M will have nothing to do with him, saying that he is too weak for her and such a marriage would end only in unhappiness.

> **Technical Comments**: M shows considerable independence in not accepting the easy solution of marrying her suitor as her parents wished her to do. T concurred with her decision not to marry him, agreeing that a second error would only compound the first error.

Therapeutic Process: M and her suitor came together for an appointment, and the suitor tried to persuade T to intervene on his behalf to get M to marry him. When she heard this, M flew into a tantrum and berated the suitor in humiliating terms. T had a good opportunity to observe the dynamics of her relations with men.

> **Technical Comments**: M was devastating in her humiliating attack upon the suitor, who seemed to come back for more. T interpreted the sadomasochistic elements in the situation which M agreed was totally unhealthy. M states that she always related to men that way in the past. T suggests that there are more adaptive life styles.

Therapeutic Process: On returning for further counseling, M appears unabashed by developments. Expresses no regret, guilt, or penitent attitudes toward the situation. When asked by T how she expected to handle this situation, M said she was determined to return to the city and go on relief until the child is born. She has been living with another unmarried girl who has a child, and figures she could do the same thing. M is very unrealistic about financial support and thinks, "Of course my family will give me anything I need . . . I know my mother would take the baby and help me raise it."

> **Technical Comments**: Going on relief to have an illegitimate child is currently accepted practice in the beatnik element. T did not discourage this plan but simply encouraged M to consider future obligations of trying to raise the child alone.
>
> T also encouraged M to be more realistic about how much cooperation she could reasonably expect from her family.

Therapeutic Process: Her father and mother accepted the situation bravely, insisting that M return home where her health and nutrition could be watched more closely. Her mother told M that she definitely could not assume the care of the baby because she felt too old. M did not seem to care what people thought about her pregnancy and was rather careless about appearing in public in her home town.

Technical Comments: T talked these developments over with
M realistically, not insisting that she do any particular thing,
but simply repeating many pertinent questions such as, "Do
you think that you can care for the baby alone yourself?"
"Do you think it is right for the baby's future?" "Are you
mature enough and healthy enough to go through with it?"

Therapeutic Process: M was initially somewhat resentful when her
mother refused to cooperate in raising the child at home, and at first
insisted that she would do it alone. T raised the alternative of going
to a maternity home and later placing the baby out for adoption. M
first reacted violently against this proposal, insisting that she would
never give up a baby. T did not insist strongly but simply suggested
that M might at least visit a secluded maternity home and talk with
the personnel who knew how to handle such things. M again refused
to have anything to do with such a proposal. T mildly insisted that M
could at least keep it in mind.

Technical Comment: This was the first direct pressure which
T had ever exerted on M to accept advice and adopt a plan
which M initially rejected. T adopted a plan of watchful waiting, allowing the new idea to be assimilated, and gradually
applying gentle pressure. T had made the diagnosis that M
was not mature enough and had insufficient resources to attempt
to raise the child alone.

This was a very difficult period in therapy in which M repeatedl
threatened to break off the relation, charging T with being too
much like her father, and allowing herself to indulge in emotion
tantrums to which T did not react.

Therapeutic Process: After two interviews with no progress towards
any solution acceptable to all, T took the initiative of making an
appointment for M to visit the maternity home to look it over. M
somewhat ungraciously agreed to go down with her mother and look
it over. She still refused to have anything to do with it on her return
home. However, T bided his time and moving slowly brought increasing pressure upon M to accept this solution since she was now
five months and obviously pregnant. M went to the home on a "trial"
visit and was the first two weeks quite difficult to a point at which
the management was considering asking her to leave. Then she
quieted down and settled in.

Technical Comment: Here, T was recognizing M's own ambivalence towards the plan of raising the child herself, so T
deliberately reinforced the arguments on the side that it would
be wiser to give up the child.

Therapeutic Process: M maintains contact with T while at the maternity home by sending humorous commentaries on postcards. She is happier, having discovered that her piano-playing gives her status with the other girls. For the first time in many years she is not rebelling against authority and is accepting the rules of the maternity home. However, she is still encouraging visits from her weak dependent admirer who is not the father of the child but who masochistically persists in enduring her insults.

M still insists that she will not give up the child and is making plans to bring it home for her mother to take care of. For a few days after the birth of the child she is ecstatic over motherhood, hovering over her baby which she regards as the perfect epitome of herself. But she soon becomes less intrigued by the novelty of the situation and gives more realistic attention to how she might actually care for the child.

> Technical Comments: For the first time in many years, M feels reasonably secure in the relatively protected environment of the maternity home where no demands are placed upon her. After being threatened with expulsion if she did not cooperate with the rules, M came to accept them gracefully. This is a new and constructive experience for her.

> M returned to her former dominating life style as soon as she resumed active planning with her family for the future.

Therapeutic Process: M comes home to discuss the future with T. T merely questioned her emotional maturity and the advisability of accepting full responsibility for keeping the child. M has a plan for assuming a false married name and inventing a story about a missing husband. Her family is inclined to go along with this plan but T advises against it.

> Technical Comments: T never goes along with poorly-thought-out plans of clients, taking the attitude that a second mistake never corrects a first mistake. By fabricating a false story to cover up her unmarried status, M is simply creating further problems for herself, along with more anxiety and conflict, and fools no one.

Therapeutic Process: M finally decided to give up the child and let it be adopted. This was accomplished without too much conflict. M returns to live with her family. She still has much conflict over whether to settle down in her home town or return to her beatnik pad in the city. She paid several short visits to the city but each time returned voluntarily within a few days.

> Technical Comments: This is the second time in many years that M has deferred to the judgment of others on a major decision. She admits that she is not emotionally stable enough to be a responsible parent.

Therapeutic Process: T encouraged the parents to be more realistic in their financial support of M. Formerly they had handed out relativel large sums of money for her support without questioning her use of it. Or M would simply take on financial obligations and then send the bills home. It was agreed that the family would stop financing irresponsible plans. M accepts these decisions without too much protest.

> Technical Comments: M has largely given up the concept of her self as a bohemian beatnik. M is being less exploitative of her parents. Now she is more tolerant of them and is admitting that much of the problem resides within herself.

> T advises M's parents that the only way to stop her exploitation is to refuse to let it work, not sending her any more money whenever M demands it nor acceding to her unreasonable demands.

Therapeutic Process: M still unable to secure steady work. Her parents would like to see her working, but subtly discourage her from starting out at the bottom of the ladder by allowing her to use an expensive car, and otherwise maintain high social status by living on their resources. M is getting along better at home but accomplishing this by staying up all night and sleeping in the daytime. However, she is trying to reverse this pattern.

> Technical Comments: M is still unable to harness her exceptional personality to pedestrian living and the rough-and-ready tumble of everyday life. Unwilling to regard herself as being "average."

THERAPY PHASE VI: RESOLVING INCONSISTENCIES AND CONFLICTS CONCERNING THE SELF

Therapeutic Process: Throughout the treatment, M continued to express doubts and conflicts concerning her true nature, what she reall wanted to be, and whether she would be willing to pay the price. The horns of the dilemma, as repeatedly brought out in her longitudinal history, were whether to (a) express herself freely and be herself at all costs, or (b) conform to family and social conventions in order to be accepted and integrated into the social body.

> Technical Comments: For many years M has succeeded to a remarkable degree in having her own way. Rather than having too little freedom, T believes that she has suffered from too much freedom. As a little girl she was spoiled and allowed to develop a "pampered-taking" life style before she had the maturity or stability to utilize her freedom and power in healthy ways.

Therapeutic Process: In her early life M did only what she wanted to do, and persisted in expressing herself in individualistic ways which stimulated only ostracism from the environment. She found that she could insist on being herself but only at the price of estranging friends and relatives, being unable to get -- or losing -- jobs, and in general being "out of tune" with the environment. This status might have been bearable if she could have made some genuine artistic accomplishment, but unfortunately she never turned out to be anything better than a "near miss." Gradually, the cost of being a beatnik individualist became too high to pay.

Technical Comments: T repeatedly pointed out to M the cost which she was paying for her insistence on living the bohemian life. These costs are: (a) poor family relations, (b) no real friends except other beatniks, (c) no job or economic security, (d) no healthy heterosexual life, (e) no real actualization as an artist, and (f) continuing and progressive anguish, anxiety, and neurotic symptoms.

Therapeutic Process: In a bull-session-like atmosphere, T repeatedly discussed with M the two-way responsibilities of genuine maturity, i. e., giving as well as taking. T constantly implied that M was creating her own problems, even to the point of "screwing herself" (a point which M could appreciate very well and which needed to be put to her in just such language as she was constantly using herself).

Technical Comments: We feel that the therapist can never completely abrogate his responsibilities as the representative of health, sanity, responsibility, conformity, and other social values. In a friendly way which he can accept and not be too threatened by, we always try to confront the client with reality after he has shown enough resources to be able to face it.

Therapeutic Process: When M continually complained about people not treating her better in life, T always responded with, "What can you expect?" T repeatedly advised that "If you want to be loved, you've got to be lovable." The give-and-take nature of social adjustment was constantly reaffirmed in terms of "No tickee, no shirtee."

Technical Comments: Clients usually can accept the truth about themselves if it is presented in nonthreatening, objective manner.

Therapeutic Process: Much as M disliked to give up any of her selfish ways, she gradually came to see that she must pay something for everything she expects to get, and that she cannot expect to be on the receiving end indefinitely. T pointed out that while once she might have been a cute precocious little child, now she is being "a pain in the neck."

Technical Comments: T often sets clients tasks to practice as part of the retraining program. Here, M was encouraged to help her mother around the house, try to say something polite each day to her father, and otherwise rehabilitate personal relationships whether she felt like it or not.

Therapeutic Process: T continued to try to get her to face up to her existential and self-actualization problems. He pointed out that success is the only real antidote for existential anxiety, and that she could not expect to feel better or to really come to like herself until her success-failure ratio was at least 51 percent - 49 percent. T constantly encourag M to go out and tackle the things she is neurotically disinclined to do.

Technical Comments: Therapy is never complete until the client returns to everyday living and applies his newly won insights. Insight alone is recognized only as a precondition for cure.

T plans to apply continuing gentle pressures and tutoring to get M back into the active world.

Therapeutic Process: M shows definite demoralization reactions. Expresses fears and insecurity about getting into the huckster world and facing the challenges of life. She is consciously afraid of further failures and rejections.

Technical Comments: M requires continual prompting to get her to face life actively. She sticks her neck out once in a while but withdraws at the slightest intimation of defeat.

DIAGNOSTIC SUMMARY

Behavior inadaptability, self-actualization disorder, manifested by style of life difficulties, ambivalent self-concept and weak ego functioning, reactive existential anxieties, and demoralization reactions.

On phenomenal descriptive levels M shows continuing behavior inadaptability, manifested by continuing interpersonal difficulties with family and men, persisting inability to find and hold a job, continuing emotional instability and irregular life habits.

Although intellectually and esthetically gifted, M has never been able to actualize her potentialities. Early in life, in relation to the matriarchal family structure and a relatively ineffectual father, she developed a maladaptive life style manifested by attempts to dominate and intimidate parents and suitors into giving in to her. Pampered and spoiled, she never succeeded in developing her abilities and talents to the point where they became commercially valuable. There develope a marked inconsistency between the person she wanted to be and her actual achievement status. She developed a progressively ambivalent self-concept and weak ego functioning.

On a reactive level she developed progressive existential anxiety relating to her cumulative defeats in life and inability to actualize herself. Since leaving junior college she has shown a progressive demoralization reaction with inability to cope with everyday life, unwillingness to try to get a job, and progressive withdrawal into a protected world of her own in her family's home.

Although therapy has produced a marked amelioration of symptoms, better family relations, a more realistic understanding of herself and others, less guilt and greater ability to maintain integration in the face of such pressures as her illegitimate pregnancy, she still has failed to achieve any successes which would serve as an antidote to her existential anxieties. She is still very insecure, afraid of failure, and too demoralized to be able to get a job and support herself.

Although M has made little progress in getting a job, she has made some gains in relating to the opposite sex in a less sadistic and exploitative style. Even though not showing perfect judgment in her bohemian living experiences in the city, and even though becoming involved in an illegitimate pregnancy, she is at least showing more interest and confidence in meeting a marriageable young man. Her main hope for some actualization in life would appear to come from a good marriage. If she can find a strong older man who has had enough experience to understand and tolerate her vagaries, and who could command her respect, she would appear to have good prospects for marriage since she remains attractive, interesting, talented, and not basically damaged.

M still values her therapeutic relationship and personal friendship with T enough that she continues to come at irregular intervals to discuss further developments or to secure help with new problems. This is a hopeful prognostic indication for further progress.

It is always difficult to predict what might have happened if a client had not had psychotherapy. In this case the therapist believes that M would have become psychotic had not therapy been available when it was. In any event, she was brought face to face with some of her problems by psychotherapy. Even though her experiments with adaptive behavior did not turn out optimally, at least she was out in life trying to make something of herself. Therapy had little effect on M's bohemian temperament and constitutional precocities, but it has taught her to cope with herself and the environment more wisely. She continues to make active efforts to reach an adjustment.

ADDENDUM

Q. Did you formulate a specific diagnosis before you began psycho-therapy, or was it made after psychotherapy was in progress? Do such pre-therapeutic diagnoses inhibit or facilitate taking a patient into treatment? Are your diagnoses subject to revision as psychotherapy proceeds, and do they vary depending on the way the patient responds to the treatment? Do you distinguish between diagnosis as such and simple spontaneous diagnostic reflections?

A. A tentative diagnosis of a self-actualization disorder was made immediately after preliminary evaluation of this client. This pattern is well known to the therapist, who can predict the various associated problems and developments. However, the diagnostic process continued throughout case-handling as new developments provided deeper diagnostic insights into etiological factors, dynamic mechanisms, etc. Diagnoses are subject to continuous revision and modification. Diagnostic insights occur at all levels of confidence from slight intuitive impressions to well-thought-out rational formulations.

Q. Did you approach your patient with a consistent and verbalizable theory or set of hypotheses on personality structure and/or the genesis of psychic illness? Was such theory used directly (or indirectly) in selecting the patient for treatment? How was it applied in the treatment and how effective was your theory in reaching the goals of treatment? What do you see as the function of such hypotheses or theories?

A. Clinical experience has provided us with prototypical knowledge of standard patterns which tend to repeat each other in a series of cases of the same type of etiological determination. The ex-perienced therapist knows from his own empirical clinical back-ground what can be expected from certain types of cases. Theor-etical formulations help to provide hypothetical models to help clarify the therapist's thinking in terms of relating knowledge of psychopathology, statistical incidences of factors, etc., with the actual givens of the immediate case. We never approach any case with preconceived theories but instead proceed to weave a specific theory inductively to fit the individual case. This is the eclectic method.

Q. What did you think of the prognosis of your case before you accepted the patient for treatment? What did you think during the first several interviews; and during the latter stages of treatment? Do you feel prognostic judgments about ultimate health or ultimate illness are useful? Can we dispense with a prognosis as a formal event in clinical treatment?

A. These are notoriously difficult cases with which to deal. Dealing with late adolescents and teen-agers is always difficult unless the therapist can relate on their levels. Dealing with beatnik types is always even more difficult, since they tend to reject anyone who is "square." We usually reserve judgment concerning prognosis until we see how well the young person is able to establish rapport, develop some basis for communication, and to utilize what therapy has to offer. In general, prognosis looks hopeful when the client can come to grips with therapy and shows some motivation to "work" intensively with his problems.

Q. What particular therapeutic techniques did you apply in this case? Which of them were most effective and which ineffective, and for what reasons? Did you attempt any technical innovations on an empirical basis? When did you feel that a "peak" experience or turning point occurred?

A. The "Technical Comments" provided in this paper provide a running commentary of what the therapist diagnosed, was attempting to do therapeutically, and how he felt about the prognosis. A verbatim transcript of a long term case such as this would show the therapist to be utilizing his entire therapeutic armamentarium at one time or another in case handling. We believe that the competent eclectic will show a more flexible and wider repertoire of clinical methods than any other school of therapists. Our own approach is essentially empirical, trying one thing after another in order of probable priority, until progress is shown on some part of the therapeutic front.

The peak moments in this case were the moments at which therapist and client were in a sort of psychic communion, in which both understood each other within the client's framework of experience (which is the only one the client can appreciate), at which moments the client felt genuine understanding and communion with another person.

Q. Did you feel that Freud's formulation of transference and countertransference were sufficient to account for the therapeutic encounter with your patient? How would you describe your encounter?

A. Freudian formulations are inadequate to explain the level of rapport with this patient. Although transference and countertransference were undoubtedly operating continuously throughout case handling, the level of rapport went far beyond what is ordinarily understood by these conceptions. Over and above the neurotic implications of the therapist's being reacted to and reacting in the roles of father, authority, healer, love object, friend, admirer, critic, etc., many aspects of the relationship were rational, normal, and healthy in the sense that people can react to each other in modes other than neurotic. At many points our client expressed appreciation and relief over being able to react to someone in a healthy way almost for the first time in her life.

Q. It has been said that psychotherapy is a white, middle-class, urban phenomenon which does not necessarily apply to other social stratifications or cultures. In what way did your patient's cultural back ground influence his illness and treatment? In what way did your own cultural background assist or deter the treatment?

A. Certainly such cultural factors as level of education, level of sophistication, intelligence, verbal ability, economic ability to pay, and many other subtle factors were necessary preconditions for therapy of this type. The client's self-actualization disorder was primarily culturally determined, not only in its etiology but also in its later manifestations.

If the therapist has not had some direct personal experiences and cultural background, there would have been little possibility of ever getting the confidence of such a case.

Q. There is an increasing tendency for neo-analytic thinking to ascribe the genesis and treatment of psychic illness to the social psychology of the family. How did this apply in your case?

A. Undoubtedly the social psychology of the family contributed importantly to the origins and pattern of development of this syndrome These factors have been discussed in the case presentation.

Q. If your treatment was concluded what criteria did you use for terminating it? If it is still in process, what guide points would you use to determine when your patient is suffiently improved to discontinue treatment? Do you feel that a patient should be seen as long as he feels he needs it and is willing to pay the fees?

A. We never consider cases closed until such time as the client fails to return for some arbitrary period such as five or ten years. Clients are always encouraged to keep coming back as long as problems continue. We feel that this client should be seen as long as she wishes to come back and the therapist feels that he is still constructive in his case-handling.

Q. Did you make any mistakes in this case -- in the sense of "if you had to do it over"?

A. We do not consider things which do not turn out well in case-handling as "mistakes." We consider that all case-handling is frankly experimental, and represents a special case of game theory. There is rarely any completely satisfactory or one hundred percent correct move in case-handling. Every action has its assets and disadvantages; in other words, its costs. Where there are no positive indications on an absolute basis for taking concrete actions, case-handling must to some degree be on a trial and error basis, experimenting with different facets until some objectives are attained.

Q. In treating your case did you perhaps feel that the classical distinc-
    tions between psychoses and neuroses were breaking down? (This
    question may apply even if your case represents neither a psychotic
    or neurotic.)

A. We consider the arbitrary differentiation of cases as purely a logi-
    cal or statistical convenience. We are interested only in formulat-
    ing valid hypotheses concerning how a case got that way -- if neces-
    sary, inventing new classifications to describe the case accurately.

Chapter VIII

SEQUENCE AND CONTINUITY IN LONG-TERM THERAPY

by Jane Pearce

METHOD OF WORK-UP

In working up this case, I typed all of my therapy notes on the patient, Evelyn K. The data recorded in the notes emphasized dreams, memories, interactions with the present people in her life, and other major current events. The data thus tend to select for that aspect of the interaction between us which I perceived as shared at the time, i. e., either communications from her that I registered as important, or communications from me that it seemed to me she had understood.

The history was reconstructed from all of those memories that I noted as reported during the course of therapy, set into chronological order and correlated with other major events going on in the patient's life at the time. The accuracy of this reconstruction was checked and confirmed with the patient toward the end of therapy as part of the terminating process. It thus records the probable major interpersonal interactions during the various eras of her life, with an emphasis on particularly vivid memories recalled during the course of therapy. Such memories were usually evoked in association with current interactions or dreams, or were given as illustrative of historical interactions. The events remembered probably marked moments of insight at the time of their occurence into significant interpersonal interactions from the present or past. They also consistently seem to highlight the mood of the interaction referred to.

The data thus compiled have been reviewed in detail with a colleague. The purpose of this review was to identify blind spots of mine, or unconscious conspiracies of avoidance between me and the patient, to which I might still be selectively inattentive. Our focus in the review was to identify what had been therapeutic in the interaction and to define more accurately the styles and context of the resistance to the therapeutic process (either on Evelyn's part or on mine). Thus, the interpretations of interaction being presented here are based also on hindsight. Because of the method of note-taking, we have little record of interactions which were perceived by me at the time as wasteful or diversionary. On review, particular therapeutic maneuvers often turned out to have had implications which were not clearly in my focal awareness at the time. On the other hand, Evelyn, as we reviewed the course of therapy before termination, was able to identify certain bodies of data of which she had been clearly conscious during the early part of therapy but which she had been afraid to share with me. Other bodies of data she had become aware of as the result of the therapeutic process.

She was seen three times a week for eight years from September through June. During my summer vacations she was sometimes seen briefly by myself or a colleague for emergencies.

The style of presentation here is to present a brief summary of the central communication of selected sessions. Each such summary is followed by my present interpretation of the theoretical significance of this data in the continuum of the therapeutic process. Some periods of therapy are summarized briefly so that other periods can be presented with more continuity.

It is inevitable that at times the presentation will read disjointedly, and the conclusions will not seem to flow from the material presented. Because of leaving out most sessions and radically condensing the sessions presented, valuable material had to be omitted.

The choice I have made is to include the analytic formulations necessary for continuity, even when the particular data on which they are based cannot be included in the presentation.

I have tried to keep the use of specialized terminology to a minimum and to place it in a natural context in which the references will be obvious. The conceptual framework was first formulated by Harry Stack Sullivan and is available in his published works.[1] However, certain concepts referred to are reformulations and also new formulations in interpersonal theory, developed by Newton and me in a recent work.[2]

---

1. Sullivan, Harry Stack. Clinical Studies in Psychiatry. New York: W.W. Norton & Company, Inc., 1956; Schizophrenia as a Human Process. New York: W.W. Norton & Company, Inc., 1962; The Interpersonal Theory of Psychiatry. New York: W.W. Norton & Company, Inc., 1953.
2. Pearce, Jane, and Saul Newton. The Conditions of Human Growth. New York: The Citadel Press, 1963.

I chose to present Evelyn to illustrate the difference between social adaptation and genuine maturation. In terms of our theoretical elaboration, she would fall into the category of "Diagnosis Normal" at the time of beginning therapy.

She was a twenty-nine-year-old lawyer affiliated with a prominent law firm. She was "well-adjusted" in most major areas of her relationships with people. Her superiors and colleagues considered her competent -- and even brilliant -- in her work, friendly and cooperative in her relating to clients and colleagues, as "levelheaded, " reliable, and an "attractive personality." She had a fair circle of friends, among whom she had the reputation of being a good conversationalist and a gracious hostess; they generally thought of her as a considerate, even compassionate, "solid" person. The acquaintances who knew them best thought of her and her husband as happily married. She seemed to meet strangers well and to make acquaintances easily, both socially and professionally. She had an air of innocent earthy charm. She looked and was considered attractive as a woman.

There were no areas in which her anxiety forced her into grossly unconventional behavior. As the data emerged in therapy, this success was an overlay for a far from superior level of maturity or relatedness. Thus, the discrepancy between manifest performance and inner disorganization was particularly striking.

I have tried to highlight the therapeutic difficulties in clarifying issues and promoting genuine growth at an appropriate level in work with a patient in whom major resistance to growth is expressed by intense investment in appearing sane and socially successful.

SUMMARY OF LIFE HISTORY

FATHER

Evelyn's father was born in Indonesia, the son of a successful Danish businessman, one of several children. The family was devoted to the upper-class traditions of authority, propriety, and superiority. He came to this country as a young man and completed his undergraduate work at the University of Washington in Seattle. He attended medical school in Chicago and during his internship married Evelyn's mother, an American citizen seven years older than himself. He established general practice in Gary, Indiana, and Evelyn, their only child, was born there two years later. About six years later, when the father was thirty-six, the family spent a year in Europe,

mostly in Copenhagen, visiting his relatives. On return, he became
the associate of a prominent specialist in Evanston, Illinois,[3] and the
subsequent decade was the high point of his professional career. At
forty-eight, he was approached about taking over the directorship of
a theoretical research program in his specialty. However, rather
than respond to this intellectual challenge, he accepted the directorship of a hospital in New Jersey where his duties were more on the
administrative side. Subsequent to this shift, his health progressively
failed. An old gastric ulcer became reactivated, and its exacerbations
were manipulated by a steady increase in his previously quite moderate
addiction to alcohol. His death in 1947, at the age of sixty, was the
result of a combination of these two factors.

As the interpersonal data emerged during her analysis, it
became clear that Evelyn's father spent very little time with his family until after he was forty. During the year in Europe he and Evelyn's
mother were near divorce, and their relationship deteriorated steadily
thereafter.

During his middle forties he spent a certain amount of time
with Evelyn, who was then in her teens, involving her in his hobbies.
After the shift to New Jersey he became progressively more angry,
demanding, and envious of her success. He tried to make her feel
responsible for his physical survival and for his psychological isolation. This reproach became more intense after his wife died in 1945.
He manipulated his poor health and his isolation to maintain both at a
crisis level.

MOTHER

Evelyn's mother was born in 1880, one of the older children
of a large, poor family in a farming community in the North Carolina
hills. She was the only ambitious member of the family. At fifteen,
she went alone to the neighboring university town, lived with a "cul-
tured" family, and studied singing with a well-known coach. She had
ambitions to become an opera singer. In her early twenties she moved
to Chicago, and undertook more systematic training in music at a
good conservatory. There she also continued with a better-known
singing coach. By the age of thirty-five, she had developed considerable standing as a talented teacher in the field but never developed

3. Locales such as this, as well as other identifying information, have
    been systematically disguised.

enough poise and self-confidence to become a performer in opera herself. She was married at thirty-five, lived in Gary, and had her only child, Evelyn, but continued to work at the conservatory in Chicago. During the year in Europe, when she was forty-three, she continued to practice singing but was ineffectual about making professional contacts. After they moved to Evanston, when she was forty-four, she developed new teaching contacts there while maintaining her connections with the conservatory in Chicago. Again, when she moved to New Jersey, she established connections with the appropriate teaching center and continued her work.

Certain other data about her emerged during the course of therapy. In the early years she was said to have been popular with younger colleagues. As time progressed, her work tended to be focused on developing intense relationships with particular students. After her marriage she became progressively more angry, depressed, and paranoid about colleagues of equal status. Her almost unitary preoccupation came to be the consolidation of more prestige in the eyes of the "right people." In this pursuit she considered Evelyn a perpetual embarrassment to her and reviled her publicly and privately for Evelyn's failures. As the marriage increasingly deteriorated, she kept both husband and daughter constantly preoccupied with placating her intermittent rages. She also reproached Evelyn intensely, though usually silently, for Evelyn's failure to make up for her mother's lifelong loneliness.

In the spring of 1943, at age sixty-three, she had her first coronary occlusion. At this time she admitted to having been aware for some time of symptoms of severe hypertension for which she had not seen a physician. With resonable care, she continued active until February of 1945, at which time she had a second and much more severe heart attack. Subsequent to this her condition progressively declined, and she died of a final coronary attack in July of 1945 at the age of sixty-five.

During the last six months of her life she was somewhat less attacking and reproachful to the immediate family.

HISTORY OF PATIENT

Early infancy (zero to one). Evelyn was born in Gary, Indiana, in 1917. She was said to have been a healthy, well-developed baby. At about six months, her mother returned to work and from then until age four, she had a baby nurse, Teddy, of whom she had the fondest memories.

Late infancy (one to two and one-half). Both parents were working long hours, and she was probably almost entirely in the care of the baby nurse.

Childhood (two and one-half to four). She was probably almost entirely isolated with Teddy, with practically no contact with children for parallel play experiences. She was described by other adult relatives as having been an unhappy, neglected child at this time.

The mood of this period of her life may be illustrated by a few typical memories. These memories were between age two and one-half and age four and are placed in probable chronological sequence.

Earliest memory: Her terror and "a swampy yellow color" associated with her tonsillectomy, and her surprise at surviving it.

Memory 2: Lying in the crib, being punished (spanked) by both parents, an image of two angry faces. Possibly for having torn a book.

Memory 3: Being afraid to fall asleep at night after the nurse left. She remembers it as if she were alone in the house.

Memory 4: Lying in the crib on a sunny afternoon, being afraid of snakes and harmful animals which she imagined were crawling on the floor or climbing in the window.

In contrast to the mood of these memories, she also remembers being somewhat adventuresome in exploring the neighborhood and near-by vacant lots during the time when she had Teddy as her nurse.

Juvenile (four to eight). Teddy was fired when she was four, and Evelyn recalls sobbing disconsolately as Teddy left. She subsequently managed an occasional visit to Teddy's home in a different part of town. Although both parents continued to work long hours, there was no other regular provision for her care. She sometimes stayed with a neighbor after school and was sometimes helped across streets by a ten-year-old girl in the neighborhood. During the next two years she became a much more overtly timid and frightened child, afraid of exploring places in which she had played comfortably before the age of four. At the same time, there are certain specific memories and also home movies of doing daring and dangerous feats on the school slide. During the years from four to six she was put in two nursery schools, a kindergarten, a camp, and first grade, each remembered as frightening and uncomfortable. She did not relate well to teachers, children, or required activities. During this period she remembers playing pleasantly with the girl next door in spite of the angry disapproval of both sets of parents.

Her sixth year she spent in Europe with her parents. During part of the time she traveled alone with her mother who, from the descriptions, seems to have been in an angry depression of almost psychotic proportions. For some months Evelyn was also placed in a strict Lutheran kindergarten in Copenhagen, which she remembers with fear.

When Evelyn was seven, the family moved to Evanston into a "good"neighborhood. During the first year she was mostly the scapegoat of other neighborhood children, and occasionally the bully. That year she and both parents were hospitalized for potentially fatal illnesses. The parents were snobbish with the community, and this added to her social difficulties.

Preadolescence (eight to eleven). During this era she made friends with a girl who was slightly younger and whom she probably dominated to a considerable extent. The parents built a new house and when she was nine, the family moved into it. In the first months in the new house she was again seriously ill with a potentially fatal illness. Subsequently, the parents' social status improved and Evelyn slowly became more comfortable with the neighboring group, both boys and girls. Memories from this period include several severe "accidental" injuries. Each occurred when she was seeking to associate with the neighborhood children against her mother's orders. Her participation in competitive group games was considered "overenthusiastic."

Adolescence (eleven to fourteen). Her memory of the puberty change was that it took place (literally) during a cyclone while on a trip to the Southwest with mother. At about this time, mother had a hysterectomy following a severe hemorrhage. One of Evelyn's closer playmates, a boy, was killed by a truck. Severe accident proneness when seeking out peers continued. The other girls began to develop an interest in boys, but she did not. Shortly after puberty she had the first occurrence of a lifelong recurrent nightmare, to wit: "My father phones me from a faraway city. He is bleeding to death, alone, and there is nothing that I can do to save him."

Young Adulthood (fourteen to twenty-one). From the puberty change until she left home at eighteen, the mood was essentially grim.

She had no boy friends and her mother constantly attacked her two remaining girl friends. Because of her poor social adjustment, the school suggested that she take an evening job at a local settlement house where she could help with the children and make some contact with sympathetic adults. She maintained this contact against her parents' bitter opposition. At home she was responsible for the housework and cooking, she read voluminously, she studied hard and quarreled with both parents about science, politics, and her behaviour. At seventeen she had a brief positive experience at a co-ed camp in Wisconsin where she had a boy friend and was not rejected by the group of girls her own age. At eighteen, she went to a prestigious college near Philadelphia known for its high academic standards and good social contacts. During the first year she was socially isolated, and her grades deteriorated. She lost a part of the scholarship with which she had started. After she refused to follow up on a tenuous introduction to a prominent Philadelphia family, her mother became furious with her and withdrew financial support, and her father stopped speaking to her. That summer she took a job away from home, was unable to continue because of illness, and returned utterly defeated to her parents' home for the rest of the summer. Meantime, the family had moved to New Jersey. For the following three years of college the situation slowly improved. Her health got slowly better, she had one boy friend, and finally a second, and made friends with several girls, one of whom had a somewhat active social life to which Evelyn had access. After the first bad year, her schoolwork improved steadily.

Subsequent Adult History (twenty-one to twenty-nine). At age twenty-two, she was admitted to a law school as a full-time student. For the next several years she lived separately from her parents, sharing apartments with several women in succession who were in varying degrees older and more experienced than she. During this period, on a date with one of her college boy friends, she had sexual intercourse for the first time. She also dated fellow law students, but was not "in love." She graduated creditably from law school at age twenty-five having essentially worked her way through school with the help of some fellowships from the school. She then took an apprentice job with a prominent firm specializing in corporate law. Her closest personal relationship was with a more experienced woman, a member of the firm, who was both friend and mentor.

During the spring of the following year, when she was twenty-five, her mother had her first coronary. In the fall of that year, at twenty-six, she met her husband, Al, and arranged a vacation with him on brief acquaintance. Though she was not a virgin at the time, they did not have intercourse on this trip. By the following June, as she turned twenty-seven, they became engaged, and they were married in December of that year. Two months later her mother had a second coronary and died in July, just after Evelyn was twenty-eight. Subsequent to her mother's death, Evelyn suffered severe insomnia and intense depression. Meantime, her husband had established himself in a law firm specializing (on the side of labor) in labor relations. They were both doing well, and moved into a somewhat nicer apartment. After her mother's death, Evelyn's father refused to get a housekeeper and lived alone in his relatively isolated house in suburban New Jersey, demanding that she and Al move in with him. Even before her mother died, he had been subject to recurrent medical crises, for the management of which he had made Evelyn responsible. After her mother died, both his crises and his demands became more intense. Evelyn herself had several medical crises, each of which she expected to be fatal. She also had recurrent nightmares of herself and/or Al in dangerous situations. The dream about her father, bleeding to death, alone, was frequent during this eighteen months. Both father's illnesses and her nightmares were more intense when she took vacations with her husband against her father's opposition. By the fall of 1946 father's pressure on them to move in with him and take care of him was increasing. At this time, when she was twenty-nine, her husband reluctantly capitulated to this pressure. He had been in psychoanalytic therapy previously in order to get help with his difficulties in relating to colleagues, clients, and personal friends. She was referred to me by his analyst.

COURSE OF THERAPY

11/19/46[4] (Consultation): In the initial interview, Evelyn appeared relatively well-adjusted. She had been married for two years in an "appropriate" marriage to another promising young lawyer slightly better established. She described her husband as reliable, masculine, withdrawn, and difficult to talk to, but spoke of her marriage as good and stable. She focused the interview around her conflict about her plan to move her household in with her father in the near future, to which her husband had reluctantly consented. She also referred glancingly to "minor" difficul-

---

4. Material reporting the summary of the content of sessions will be presented in this way, whether or not it includes direct quotes from the patient.

ties with people at work and in the marriage. At the same
time, for all the manner of being in control, she projected
a sense of urgency and desperation about getting quickly
into therapy.

On review, it is clear that it was her husband's acquiescence
to moving in with her father that made therapy urgent at the time. She
later admitted her rage with him about it. At the time of the interview she used my brief inquiry into her reasons as a directive from
me not to make the move. A more urgent reason for getting into
analysis soon became clear. This was the obscured but nonetheless
intense and conscious pervasive expectation of her own imminent death.
This was vaguely connected with the notion that she would not survive
her father who, she felt, was dying.

The discrepancy between Evelyn's outward poise and the
intense despair of which she was aware continued to haunt the
therapeutic process. Her investment in the facade of adequate
social adaptation and prestigious social performance made it
inevitable that any major attempt on my part to clarify either her
distortions in perception or her difficulties with people would be
perceived as an attempt to destroy her. She experienced her style
of fairy tale role-playing as the only alternative to total social
ostracism. This subjective dilemma was, of course, intensified by
her inevitable perception of me as being literally as contemptuous
and destructively critical as her mother had been.

1/4/47:   On relatively mild inquiry from me, Evelyn gave an
extensive history of the story of her mother's life. When she
described her own interaction with mother, she emphasized
and glamorized all positive memories and understated the
negative ones. She referred cryptically to incidents of
mother's depression, mother's rage, Evelyn's own moves
toward independence, and difficulties in peer interaction.

The time sequence was so scrambled and the data was so fragmented that the sequential timing of these events could not be reconstructed.

Following the initial session in November, she and Al had
taken a month's vacation. In this first session of ongoing therapy
she presented a more central analytic problem, which was to disentangle her percept of herself from that of her mother and to avoid
becoming like mother. However, in her choice of emphasis she tried

to create the impression that positive experiences with her mother had been in the continuum. By obscuring negative data, she subtly retranslated her difficulty in escaping from mother's domination into a lifelong search for mother's love.

The fragmented way in which she presented the data turned out to be a major style of resistance. Throughout much of therapy she would tell one part of a dream or a memory in one session and remember the other half after she had hoped that I had forgotten the details of the first part. She could then retain the feeling that she had in fact told me everything important while making it very difficult for me to figure out what was the specific importance of the data. She thus impeded obvious reconstruction of cause and effect sequences.

1/11/47: She introduced the subject of father by remembering the most recent episode of the recurrent "bleeding" dream. Asked for her earliest memory of father, she answered, "Father's brother lived with us - I have no memory of him - he was like Father." She then described her father as "sensitive, quick to react, warm, generous, sympathetic, popular, a patient explainer."

As it turned out later in therapy, none of these adjectives applied to his interaction with her. Such glamorization was probably based on her necessity as a child to see him as a somewhat adequate buffer between her and the angry mother. The distant quality of the interaction suggested by the early memory turned out later to be more accurate. During the early years father was rarely home and did not relate to her when he was.

1/14/47: She stated that in her dreams, "I tell myself stories, and go on and on." She then went on to embellish the prettied-up version of her relationship with her father. She also reported a variety of current psychosomatic illnesses, including gastrointestinal and back trouble.

The illnesses lasted throughout the spring and seem in retrospect to have been related to the severe anxiety incumbent on the exposure involved in beginning analysis. She truly expected to be murdered, either by her living father, her mother's ghost, or me, for revealing the family skeletons. Telling herself stories seemed to relate to the awareness she had of the degree of distortion in the history as she was giving it.

1/18/47:   First dreams since beginning therapy. The first was a
nightmare about a fire which was out of control and in which
the telephone wires were snapping.

In the second dream, her mother returned from the hospital
during her terminal illness, "glaring, anxious, angry -
glad to see me. "

Later in the session she filled in some details on her mother's
terminal illness. She then spontaneously switched to a review
of her sexual history, starting with childhood sex play and
emphasizing the intensity of her difficulty with sex since
puberty.

On first inspection this would seem to be a message about the
explosiveness of sex in her psychic economy with the reference to her
mother as the major source of the prohibition. However, in view of
later analytic data, it is much more likely that the uncontrollable fire
which destroys lines of communication symbolized her fear that either
her rage or what she thought of as her insanity would get out of control.
These, too, would have involved her relationship with her mother as
a central determinant. On this interpretation, her focus on sex toward
the end of the session can be seen as an attempt to recover her poise,
to obscure the more frightening communication, and to lead me away
from it.

1/21/47:   Two central communications: The first was her surprise
and embarrassment at finding that conversation with me was
more reasonable than she had ever found it with her mother.
The second was an anecdote illustrating father's current
sabotage of her work, and her vulnerability to his maneuvers.

As she noticed that communication with me was possible, her
sense of urgency about clarifying her relationship with father while
he was still alive began to be expressed.

1/25/47:   She openly complained about her father's demands and his
apparent dependence on her.

In this session she thus expanded on the subject introduced in
the previous session.

1/28/47:   She reported a dream of enjoying riding horseback, alone, in frontier country (an activity which she had never enjoyed). She then spontaneously filled in some of her medical history.

The dream is her first positive statement that it might be possible to explore new frontiers or to reintegrate previously anxious activities with pleasure. It was probably made possible by the preceding session in which she stated the urgency of disentangling emotionally from her father. Her factual style of giving medical history obscured the fact, later apparent, that she had been in terror of dying in most of the medical crises mentioned. Thus, after the positive assertion, her thoughts went to the fear of death, but her message was cryptic.

2/1/47: I pushed for more data about mother, and most of her responses were evasive or obscure. However, she referred to two incidents of her mother's gross sadism, which were carefully not elaborated in context.

The message seems to have been that she was still too frightened of her mother and appalled by the emotional reality of their interaction to report even factual data honestly. She hoped that I would understand and not press further at this time.

2/4/47: She volunteered the history of the relationship with her first durably available boy friend. Her definition of "love" was, "He did not ridicule me when I got depressed." She then referred briefly to her difficulty in loving another person.

Her definition of love was a statement of her discouragement about affection. Since the relationship turned out to be a constructive one, it was also an example of her chronic fogginess in communication, a style probably elaborated to protect herself in unavoidable communications with mother. As she said at a different time, "I never told my mother anything that mattered to me." Her revelation to me, both of the positive experience and of one of her important central current handicaps, was probably made possible by the fact that she had sent me a "cryptogram" about mother's sadism in the previous interview. This was a small move toward perceiving me as less sadistic than mother.

2/7/47: She followed the previous session by describing the next relationship with a boy (she was not in love). She included a statement of her fear of being like her mother, particularly in relation to mother's coldness and exploitativeness with men.

This is the first frank statement of her strong identification with her mother.

2/14/47: Dream: Evelyn tried to get off an island (isolation) but was stopped by mother on the mainland with a shotgun. In the dream Evelyn was also armed. Her associations indicated that her mother's objections to her making friends with girls interfered with her relationship with me.

Mother would destroy her if she tried to relate to me or to a girl friend. She thought that her only hope for escape was to use mother's weapons. The dream was exceptionally vivid, and was often referred to later.

2/15/47: Evelyn described meeting Al, and included the statement that it was six months after her mother's first coronary. She also said that Al was in analysis and that she invited him to go on vacation with her soon after this first meeting.

She could conceive of getting married after she knew that mother would probably die, and she was in a great hurry to get there before mother did die. She needed someone who had learned something about emotional difficulties (hers).

2/16/47: She remembered the finish of the dream about the island: "Someone running down a hospital corridor, screaming-- it was fear, not pain--was it me or Mother?"

On the one hand, if she could not get "past mother" (that is, get herself disentangled from her mother's isolating perceptions of life), she couldn't relate to anyone else. On the other hand, the penalty for getting off the isolation would be hospitalizable psychosis.

2/24/47: On 2/20/47, Evelyn had a tooth pulled, during the course of which she had a severe hemorrhage which was very difficult to control, and she was in the hospital for two days. She discussed her terror before, during, and after the operation, and connected it with the despair implied in the dream discussed in the previous session.

Since the operation was scheduled in advance, the obliquely
uicidal dream (the insoluble dilemma) reported 2/14/47 was probably
preoperative warning, and an explanation to me of her fear of
uicide and its reasons. Further, the terror in the operative situa-
on may have lowered her resistance and contributed to the difficulty
1 controlling the hemorrhage. It was one of a number of times in
er life when her terror of minor operative procedures seemed to
ush her physiological reaction to a point of genuine danger.

/26/47: She associated her hemorrhage after the tooth extraction to
her recurrent nightmare about father's bleeding to death.
She then spent the session on her husband's difficulties with
his own mother.

Her mother-in-law's frank psychosis was parallel to her own
other's disguised one. A connection emerged between her mother's
most fatal hemorrhage and hysterectomy during menopause and her
/n feeling about the onset of her menses, and the onset of the "fatal
eeding" dream. The data suggest that the dissociated strand con-
:cting the three topics of this session was the fear of and identifica-
on with her mother. The systematic reconstruction of such associa-
/e systems from those "peaks of the iceberg" that appear on the sur-
ce in any particular session is the basic groundwork of the analytic
·ocess. The plausibility in the current situation of each preoccupa-
on--in this instance the difficult operation, the push-pull with father,
d the invasiveness of the mother-in-law--served to intensify the
fficulty of grasping each as the symbolic reflection of an inner con-
ellation of perceptions.

'28/47: Dream 1: "I was riding by myself through the woods ...
one beautiful scene after another - I felt good."

Dream 2: A woman taking advantage of her by using knowledge against her. She then referred to her distrust of confiding pleasurable experiences to her mother.

In this image of me as her mother, I lead her down the garden
th in order to get damaging information. She omitted at this time
e fact that her mother had a seductive style of eliciting confidences
d then attacking Evelyn on the information she got from them. I
ggested that her relatively "good" functioning at this time in her
e was purely adaptive to people whom she perceived as dangerous,
:luding me.

2/29/47: After an initial reference to father, she reported a dream
in which she was the prisoner of a rageful male criminal.
The woman in the story fell in love with the criminal and
betrayed Evelyn to him. The night before she had the
thought that she would become too dependent on me and that
she ought to quit analysis.

She was in a rage with me after the last session because of my
attempt to identify the quality of her relationships with people. She
was becoming more aware of the extent to which she had incorporated
the chronic rage of the family. The fear of dependence was actually
a fear of exposure. She also reminded herself in the dream that any
woman will sell you out.

3/14/47: A dream, which she associated to the group interaction on
the job, in which "I am the one that got the greenest peach. "

She still felt discriminated against in therapy. She also felt
that moving to a genuine group integration might involve a loss of
status because she might turn out to be the least prepared.

3/17/47: Dream: "I was telling Father he could not live with us. "

Her life was not his life.

4/12/47: After the insight about the necessity of disentangling from
father, she described mother as follows: "Cold, domineering, didn't care, not affectionate - possessive, manipulative, dishonest. Little pretense--fond of me. "

This was the first frank description of her mother, although
there is a mild attempt to undo it at the end. It was probably made
possible by the preceding move to disentangle from her father.

5/4/47: Dream: "I am in an exposed position, being shot at. I want
to climb off. "

During this period, I had been clarifying her hostility in her
current relationships with people, and she felt attacked. She also
was afraid that somehow, in the process of clarification, other people
might see through her gracious facade. Her position was too exposed.

5/8/47: Dream: "A childhood girl friend of mine is ill--dazed and
confused-- the symptom is mild--the condition is serious.

Why did her parents have her on the street? The doctor was deciding what to do with her." Association: The girl was a person who was "brilliant, shy, reticent, and only associates with very immature people."

She considered herself incurably insane with a secret, tragic illness. Neither the parents nor the doctor understood it, but in view of the seriousness of it, what she had accomplished was a miracle. One might say that she thought she was there for supportive therapy or an incurable disease. At the same time Evelyn, for the first time, communicated clearly that she felt her troubles were serious even though she could cover them well.

/16/47: An elaborate dream in which she is first deserted by mother and then attacked by her because she, Evelyn, has her leg in a cast. In the rest of the session her concern was with her father's current rage with her. At the end she referred briefly to her growing need for "tenderness."

The urgent need of this period was to share with me the severity of the damage to her thought processes as she experienced it. At the same time, she assumed that such sharing would result in my contempt and desertion. My attempt to clarify her difficulty was experienced as the seduction which was equivalent to the sadism of softening her up for the kill. In her perceptual framework she could not distinguish between me and mother.

/26/47: Dream: A twelve-year-old boy with a slow-growing brain tumor who was generally stunted and misshapen. He had a devoted mother. He was in terminal condition. Her associations to the dream led to the year that she went away to college and the parents cut off contact with her.

The symbolic communication is that her illness is fatal, that I am unaware of it, and that I could not cure it anyway. The memory evoked is a direct reference to my forthcoming vacation. She was perceiving me as angry. In addition, she was accusing me, probably correctly, of not being clearly aware of how much panic she was in. She could not let me know directly for fear I would be destructive. She thus makes another appeal for a continuum of supportive therapy.

/5/47: Dream: On a very long, difficult, tiring hike with an elderly lady of eighty-six. Evelyn woke intensely depressed.

A dream of me as inadequate to the difficult task of treating her.

6/6/47:   Evelyn stated that her anxieties would be intolerable for anyone to share.

In stating her conviction that I could not tolerate her anxieties, she also asks me if I could.

6/7/47:   Patient had a "half-dream" of big cockroaches coming at her. She then talked about each parent's wish to be the most important person in her life. She afterward elaborated on her need for tenderness.

What she needed was for me to understand her dilemma. Later in therapy it became clear that she associated her reaction to large cockroaches with frank insanity. In retrospect, she felt that if she acted on her need to share with me her level of confusion, this sharing would put her in danger of an open psychotic break.

6/13/47: (Last session of 1946-1947) "If I'm sick and someone is very nice to me, I figure that I'm sicker than I knew. In illness--you have to carry yourself. "

At the end of the session she noted two neurotic security operations, possessiveness and domineeringness, presumably designed to overcome her lifelong isolation, and mentioned that they did not get her very far.

She presented a complete system for cutting off help within those two statements. If someone tries to be helpful, it proves that she is hopeless. If they do not try to cut through the barrier, they have proved their total uninterest.

* * *

In the first six months of therapy she had referred to many of her major problems. She had also indicated her difficulty in communicating frankly with me about them and some of the reasons for this difficulty.

* * *

The summer went better than she had anticipated, and she
.evoted her energies to a survey of the social structure of the group
f lawyers with whom she later affiliated.

;EPTEMBER, 1947, TO SEPTEMBER, 1948

/25/47: Dream: "I was out in a garden, on a walk, collecting a lot
of little things in my blue handbag--it was an aquarium or
a terrarium. The next morning I put my hand in the bag -
a handful of dead worms, turtles--clammy--I had a tremendous feeling of revulsion. "

This was the first dream that did not involve the mechanism
f projection. She saw the problem as within herself rather than
eeing herself as a victimized child in a destructive adult world. It
^as a clear statement of her self-revulsion--of her real feelings
bout herself. That is, she makes a pretty first impression but the
inside" is "slimy, " and there is a great deal that needs to be cleaned
p about herself in her relations to people. This was partly a
)llow-up on the initial move, at the end of June, toward clarifying
cr own unfortunate operations with people. It was probably made more
ossible by the fact that her actual relationship with people had been
etter over the summer than for some years previous.

)/2/47: Dream: "I was on one side of the fence - there was a
thread through a hole in it--I couldn't see the other side --
a little boy was on the other side--we were seesawing the
thread back and forth. "

This was a poetic statement of her difficulty in communicating
ith a peer.

* * *

As the year progressed, the level of communication with me
^adually improved and, concomitant with this improvement,
^velyn's fear of being understood was somewhat lessened. She
^came more aware of her fear of death and less victimized by it.
er father died on November 15. Her memory of the weekend follow-
^g the funeral was very foggy. However, the friends with whom she
^ayed reported that for a few days afterward she looked absolutely
^owing.

About a week after the funeral she discovered that her parents had saved a very considerable amount of money and could easily have afforded to help her through college and professional training. She was furious at both of them, both for their exploitativeness and their secrecy.

In December of 1947 Evelyn and Al drove through the Appalachian Mountains. While she was driving she was suddenly seized with a fantasy of the car hurtling down the cliff with both of them screaming. After this she let him drive. This was one of many symbolizations of the "suicide pact" aspect of her relationship with her parents; that is, if she could not keep them alive, physically or psychologically, it was her fate to go down with them.

During the course of the year her interest gradually shifted from corporation law to work involving the personal defense of individuals in trouble with society. She sought out a group of young, more progressive lawyers interested in anti-discrimination cases, civil rights, and medicolegal work. She worked with the Legal Aid Society and specialized in defending rights of patients suffering from or accused of suffering from mental illness.

During the winter and spring Evelyn consolidated her social position in the new professional group. While apparently being quite enthusiastic and unconflicted about this at the time, she later recalled that during this period she had been in great conflict about whether or not the group had adequate prestige, and was deeply concerned with their getting more. However, this derogation was kept private or subtly blamed on her husband. Such doubts were not available to therapy until much later.

In the spring she and Al rented a summer cottage at a resort on the Connecticut coast where many of this group spent the summer. They also found a better apartment. She sold her parents' house, had a phobic reaction to the furniture in it, and gave it away immediately.

* * *

She and her husband spent the summer in the country. As she moved solidly into being accepted by the group, she saw the leadership in it more and more literally as if in the structure of her nuclear family -- that is, some of the senior partners were perceived in the parental role, and she focused her preoccupation on her standing with them. In August some of the younger lawyers left; the others became immersed in work. She was thrown alone more with her husband. As a military alliance against the invasiveness of their respective parents, this relationship had served its purpose and was no longer needed. Also in August she developed a severe viral infection and was in bed for almost two months.

* * *

It seems to have been the year of decision, between analyzing the inner schizophrenic process and selling out for the facade of the adaptive pattern of living. The decision was anything but manifest at the time. The conscious goal was still to find a pattern of living that would obscure the horror rather than clarify it. The fantasy was still to find a better set of rules to beat mother at her own game.

SEPTEMBER, 1948, TO MAY, 1949

I returned to work late because I was finishing some research on therapeutic procedures. Making the theories underlying my work explicit may have subtly changed my style of work. If so, I was not aware of it at the time.

10/3/48: Evelyn told me that she had thought of me as "angry" and had felt "hurt and resentful" about my delay in returning to work. At the same time she was aware that both her perception and her emotional response were inappropriate to the factual reality. She told me that during the summer she had arranged an affiliation with a law firm specializing in antidiscrimination work. She chose to work particularly with and under a talented older woman in this firm, and this woman became her sponsor. She also, at their suggestion, registered for both social science and specialized law courses at a university in the city.

The feeling of anger and rejection toward me was reinforced by her anger with the work group "because everyone else was busy." She had also been distressed at having to notice her peripheral social position with the members of the new firm. She had been frightened in anticipation of the work requirements in the new job, of the content of the new courses, and of the relatively informal and penetrating quality of the anticipated group relationships at work in the fall. These fears probably had contributed to the prolonged convalescence from the virus.

10/10/48: Dream: She was afraid that her cat will beat up my cat. She decided that her cat wouldn't.

This dream was one in a series of dreams that indicated her preoccupation with the control of her own anger to avoid disrupting not only her analysis but also her educational, social, and work relationships.

10/17/48: Dream: A family situation, with adult offspring and bitter, cold, contemptuous older parents. She focused on the stiffness and distance of the older woman. Her associations indicated that the woman was the analyst.

She saw both my moves toward clarification and my interest in her work as a sophisticated, manipulative form of status-seeking on my part.

10/19/48: She took a Rorschach.

10/29/48: A deeply felt "cops and robbers" nightmare: Her husband saved her from a "screaming Chinese mob" - they were "angry and deprived" - their "primary intent was to kill" - "They were not reasoning" - She and Al hid in a big sewer with dead bodies and rats - "no place was safe."

She had been frankly upset by what she had seen in the Rorschach and by what she anticipated the report would contain. The gist of the dream is "Let's get out of here." That is, either I or her colleagues at work or the department at school would "get her." Both the fear of death and the fear of disorganization are intensely evoked by the possibility of clarifying the degree of distortion of her perceptions of herself and of her associates.

10/30/48: An elaborate and somewhat obscure dream in which the central figure was a very unpleasant lady with a "huge need." Evelyn became furious at the unfair demand beamed at her by the woman.

The dream illustrated a recurrent feeling of this period. As she moved toward more intimate contact, at work and in analysis, she experienced a general paranoid confusion in which the woman image had several references. It was at the same time her mother, angry at and envious of her material moves; herself with a reference to her fear of becoming like her mother; her sponsor in the firm; and her analyst. She was preoccupied with the fear that the analyst and the sponsor would emerge to be as demanding, envious, rageful, contemptuous, and reproachful as her mother had been.

For the rest of the year she was intensely preocupied with the "meaning" of any "friendly" moves on my part. She saw them in a variety of paranoid constructions, interpreting such moves as attempts to manipulate her sadistically, as a habitual refusal to tell the truth, as an insatiable need for tenderness, as my denial of my need for tenderness. At times she saw me as a professional psychiatric nurse. As psychiatric nurse I might be seen as either well-meaning or hostile, and as either competent or ineffectual in implementing my intentions. Only in rare moments she thought of me as a peer with a different education. The disentangling of these percepts was the project for the year.

11/1/48: Dream 1: "A gym apparatus - I was beating the hell out of it - with satisfaction - I was also glad that it couldn't hurt anyone."

Dream 2: A "Noah's ark" dream of animals in pairs - she had an intense desire to get out. She woke with the phrase "being beaten."

The first dream is a diffuse statement of the dilemma of what to do with her rage without doing anyone any harm. The second dream is her first statement that there was considerable mutual anger in her marriage, i. e., she saw it as a hostile integration.

11/12/48: Two Dreams: One of a woman, the other of a man, middle-aged, both acting younger and more alive than she had anticipated. In both she was "upset." In her associations she identified the woman as her sponsor, and the man as the senior partner in the firm.

She had now structured the work situation in the literal terms of the nuclear family. Her implied goal was first to compete with the leaders of the group, and subsequently to replace them. She was upset that they seemed to be active, effective, and would be around for a long time.

11/26/48: Dream: An older woman was living with her grown daughter. The mother would not allow the daughter to have friends, male or female.

One of her fears of developing a less guarded analytic relationship was that I, like her mother, would ultimately move to limit her relationships with friends. Her sharing of this suspicion was a move to clarify her perceptions of me.

12/8/48:   She reported a mild back pain.
Dream: In the process of diagnosing the possibility of an essentially sterile cyst from a previous diagnostic procedure, the stupid doctors have removed the lower end of her spinal cord. In this diagnostic process they prove that there had been no sterile inflammation, but leave her permanently crippled.

The analyst, in her "irresponsible enthusiasm" for exploring and exposing the real problems, would cause permanent damage much greater than the limited damage of the possible previous disability. There may be a specifically sexual reference here, or the diagnostic procedure may have referred to the Rorschach report, which would have been due at about this time.

1/14/49:   Dream: She was on a sand cliff -- there was a water moccasin at her feet -- she was ready to jump into the water -- she thought, "It is probably full of water moccasins" -- she saw a copperhead near the edge of the water. In the rest of the session she reported bitter quarreling with Al over the holidays.

The dream seems to have incorporated her regretful decision to break up the marriage with the bitter thought that all men are poisonous snakes; and if she "jumps into the water," there will only be more, equally poisonous. It was of interest that on later review she associated both species of snakes with specific experiences with mother. On this basis, a secondary reference was that her difficulty in making friendly relationships with men derived from her past interactions with mother.

1/25/49:   Dream 1: She was a Christian martyr thrown to the lions.

Dream 2 (two days later): She was with a friendly family, but they did not trust her to be responsible for their children because of her "suicide drive." She mentioned that she had been recently criticized by her employers about her attitude toward clients.

This pair of dreams could be a complex statement of her feeling about her work. On the one hand, she felt inadequate to the responsibility. She also accurately perceives her sabotage of her relationships with clients as self-destructive. On the other hand, she felt martyred and betrayed for having been accepted by the firm and then criticized for being herself. They should have known better.

2/11/49: Fragment of a dream: "A body and no head" - "Bits and pieces." Her immediate association was to a very angry friend who was driving dangerously.

In the context of other data from the session, the statement seemed to be that she could not do her work well or relate to her clients constructively because of the intensity and continuity of her rage, which interfered with thinking, talking, listening, or learning. This was a follow-up on the previous session about work, and it emphasized the fragmentation of her thought processes.

2/18/49: Dream: She is unable to nurse a baby because she is "sterile." She offers tenderness to a friend, but it does no good.

This dream states her feeling that the shortcomings in her relationships with clients, for which she had recently been criticized, were the result of her inability to give and not her unwillingness to try.

3/4/49: Dream 1: She was attending a class taught by her immediate sponsor in the firm (in this dream, young, feminine, and effective). Evelyn had nothing to contribute.

Dream 2: Evelyn saw a male friend at a restaurant - she walked away "depressed and dejected" - she wandered across the golf course which was "mined" - there were periodic explosions. From a sense of unbearable isolation, she went back to her friend and his other friends and walked off with them. To her surprise, no one was angry at her.

As she got clear that she had problems in giving, that she was a beginner in the work, and that she lived with the problem of explosive anger, she could cut down her fantasies of "special status" and be with people. She noticed that they would tolerate her anger, and this was preferable to her previous social isolation.

3/7/49:   I summarized some of her irrational demands on her husband, including her demand that he should see her the way
she wanted to be seen and the demand that he should seek
his fulfillment in saving her by nurturing her.

Subsequently, during that month, she worked out a separation
and moved to a hotel, alone.

4/10/49:   While in bed with a male friend she woke up with a hallucination of her father's face.

She also had a hypnogogue of "a painting of Dali's" to which
her thought was "craziness with complete reality."

She reported a dream: "You (the analyst) were lying
beside me in bed. Then I realized it had something to
to do with warmth to another woman."

The danger of relating to a man was that he would turn out to
be like her father. The hypnogogue suggested an image of herself, at
least in relation to men, as superficially plausible, but, in context,
thoroughly irrational. In the third dream she is enjoying the company
of a woman. She also, in the sequence of the dreams, made the statement that she would have to straighten out her relationships with
women before she could relate in a friendly way to men.

5/3/49:   Dream: About her making friends with a previous school-
mate, Jo, who like herself had been domineering in elemen-
tary school, but was different from herself when she got to
high school and "let the boys get fresh."

Since the divorce she had been looking for models to validate
her right to explore her sexual role and needs.

5/4/49:   Two dreams about "exposure": including doors that
wouldn't close and people wandering past the windows while
she lies with no clothes on. In both, she felt mildly embarrassed but not frightened.

A third dream referred cryptically to two couples of her
acquaintance, both unhappily married, but with different
styles of quarreling.

Being unmarried, unprotected, and exposed is not so bad. One might pursue this experience and at least postpone another restrictive partnership organized for defensive purposes.

5/8/49:   Dream: A recapitulation of a tender moment with her first boy friend when she got away from her parents and sent to camp at seventeen. She referred to "wishing and wanting." Later in the session she talked about a current incident in which she became paranoid with a salesman and gave him a hard time while getting something she wanted very much. "Wanting something feels both good and angry."

She referred to her relationship with men and her need to pick up on her adolescent experience. However, the more profound reference was to her repudiation of desire and her need to reintegrate the experience of desire. This thought made her feel good and also made her angry. Since the repudiation of desire would, of necessity, be the central target of both the fear of death and the fear of disorganization which had pervaded the record so far, the ambivalence toward it would be inevitable.

5/15/49:   Dream: A woman takes her shopping and, to Evelyn's astonishment, does not force her to buy clothes in the woman's own image.

The dream was one of the clearer statements of her attempts to disentangle the therapist from the image of her mother.

*   *   *

During this year she began to identify who I was as a person and no longer literally identified me with her mother. This shift in her perceptions was naturally focused on my attitude toward her real needs, such as her need for friends and her need for productivity.

Her feelings of inadequacy were, of course, in many dimensions paralleled by genuine incompetence. She had avoided certain crucial life experiences in deference to the parents' percept of her.

*   *   *

MAY, 1949, TO JULY, 1950

This block of time seems to constitute a unitary phase of therapy. By May of 1949 she was committed to her new work and accepted in it. Both she and her colleagues had come to see her as somewhat disadvantaged by her lack of previous personal and professional experience. Communication in therapy was vastly better.

She had given up the protective coloration of the very possessive marriage and the role of gracious social matron and had set out on the sea of life to try to find friends and friendly acquaintances. She was having massive difficulty with this. She found herself to be contemptuous, angry, demanding, manipulative, and in her defensiveness accusatory. Her perception of the other person was foggy and distorted by her preoccupation with the other's attitude toward her from moment to moment. She covered these massive gaps in perception by confabulation.

I had received the Rorschach report some months before, but could not get a clear picture of the relationship between the report and her interactions with people as I knew her. Also, perhaps I felt that the time of working out her divorce was not the time for an intense comprehensive summary. In the middle of May I reviewed the report and protocol in detail with the psychologist, identifying, as best we could, her perceptions of herself and the world and her styles of distortion of perception or defense against insight. We correlated these with the history of her relationship with her parents, the history of her relationships with people, and her present patterns of interaction with people. The protocol had been taken in October of 1948, at which time she had been in analysis for almost two years. This was also the period of adjustment to her new line of work. A protocol taken at the beginning of therapy might have been much flatter, more evasive, and better controlled. On this one, the preoccupation with devouring or being devoured, killing or being killed, murder or flight, was open and dramatic. Her perceptions often showed confabulation, contamination, and poor form. Preoccupation with and confusion about both body image and sexual function was prominent.

The inner quality of the relationships between people was seen in terms of a fight to the death. In this fight the the medium of power was the capacity to terrorize the other. A primary counter in this game was relative social prestige, and this led to an intense preoccupation with saving face. Survival in the fight was contingent on appearing normal and well-adjusted. Symptoms, as they emerged, had to be suppressed, denied, or otherwise accounted for. Both the preoccupation with destructiveness and the preoccupation with the illusion of social superiority led to drastic isolation from the human community. This discrepancy between inner perceptions and manifest behavior added to her intense despair. All these factors contributed to recurrent suicidal fantasies and occasional inadvertent self-destructive actions.

As I now saw it, her only basis for human contact as a child had been to participate in the fight for position, in which the capacity to appear better socialized than the other (at his expense) was the major ploy. Without some skill at this she would have been entirely crushed. She took this style of gamesmanship along with her when she got away from home. It did not work too badly at a distance, as long as she avoided intimate situations that would have exposed her frantic competitiveness.

As she moved into a social group which was somewhat humanistically oriented, her self-aggrandizement at the expense of the other's self-esteem was both more obvious and less socially acceptable. She was recognized as a beginner, both in work and in life. Her demand to be seen otherwise was met with puzzlement. They knew she was often angry, but since her friends and colleagues were not particularly intimidated by her anger, this did not result in social isolation.

5/19/49: I read the Rorschach report to her and went over as much of the relationship between her perceptions and her observed behavior as I could explain to her. During the session she became angry and defensive and felt injured and misunderstood. She tried to account for the test results in terms of the timing and circumstances of taking the protocol.

5/22/49: A nightmare: "It was in an old house or an institution - I was with a man in a white jacket and he was my height. We were going up to see a patient. It was gloomy, dark, and gray. He was leery of the patient. The patient was seven feet tall, sexless, grotesque. He had a pudgy body. His clothes were hanging. He had very little hair. There was a woman, just sitting there. She was a nurse, or a caretaker, sitting and knitting. The patient ignored everybody, he was playing with toys and things. He was standing behind the table, completely oblivious. There was a tremendous violence. It was nothing that he did. I talked to the resident. The patient moved across the room to get something. I jumped back, terrified."

Evelyn then added: "I don't know who it was! No hair. He was mean. It was me!"

"There was nothing of the child - he was just crazy!"

This dream is the most dramatic statement of the most terrifying aspects of her self-image that she produced during therapy. If she saw herself as a dangerous, psychotic, murderous, violent, overgrown monster with the mentality of an infant, this would offer an explanatory and organizing principle for a mass of paranoid and security-directed behavior which had otherwise been hard to interpret, including her withdrawals and her maneuvers designed to make other people withdraw from her. It was somewhat easier to discuss these with her, since after the divorce many of her socially successful adaptive, obsessive, security maneuvers had gotten swept away and had left her desperately clutching the more primitive and hysterical ones. She was currently more in conscious touch with the depths of her depression. From this point on in therapy it was possible to discuss openly with her how she organized her interpersonal field in such a way as either to choose contemptuous and sadistic people, or to provoke the others into treating her as she expected to be treated in terms of this image.

Since it is a point of theory that a positive growth experience is what triggers and brings to the surface a clear statement of the inner paranoid feelings, one would have to assume that such a clear and dramatic nightmare was precipitated by a growth experience. In this case it could have been the feeling of finally being understood after the summary of 5/19/49, together with noting that she had not been thrown out of analysis.

5/28/49: Dream: "I was with Elizabeth (an acquaintance). I was accusing her - not just of her conventionality - but of the murderous impulses underneath. She represented a part of myself. I woke up with a furious back pain. "

The woman referred to was considered to be exceptionally angry, especially in her handling of her own children.

With Evelyn the parallel was more likely to be a broader statement of her own capacity for nurturing, with friends and with clients as well as with children. That is, her rage incapacitated her for the role of helping the other to satisfy his needs.

6/2/49: Evelyn reported that she had been looking for an apartment.

Dream: A "haunted house" ... this one was dangerously in decay. It was being renovated, but there was a question of whether it was being built on shaky foundations. Many people were involved, in one role or another, some helpful, some not. She woke once in the middle, feeling as if she had been screaming, fell back to sleep, and woke later with the sun pouring in the bedroom.

This is one of a series of "haunted house" dreams. In this one, the house represents her character structure, which was being reorganized with help from others.

For all of the uneasiness and terror (the screaming suggests to me the thought of "surgery without anesthesia"), the thought on waking incorporates a hopeful possibility. If she has enough to build on and the plan is good, the change could lead to openness and sunniness in her life and the opportunity to learn to make friends. The new apartment was her first adequate social base in town since the divorce, and this move also contributed to the need for clarification of who she was.

6/11/49: I had all of the dreams typed up that she had presented for 1948-1949 so far. I gave her a copy, and we went over them and over my summary of them.

The recurrent patterns were of violence and flight, terror and self-revulsion, isolation and explosive rage. In several, she took consolation in fantasy ambition to avoid feelings of gross inadequacy.

In my review of the dreams I managed to get in an oblique warning of the possible danger of suicide, without bringing it into central focus just before my vacation.

The summary of dreams served as a reinforcement and validation of the Rorschach report. There was very little in the summary that was news at this point. In the interview she had a hard time seeing that the self-revulsion formulated the chronic fantasy ambition to dominate, and was played out in the compulsive preoccupation with status -- even though intellectually she had no respect for this maneuver, either in herself or in others.

6/22/49: Dream: "A man, or several, walking between office and corridor." She was not frightened and dozed off again.

In her associations she felt that the setting could only be in a mental hospital.

At this point she was simply relieved by getting her insanity into the open between us and noticing that there was nothing unmanageable about it. She was in the right place, and therapy was proceeding according to schedule.

6/24/49: Fragments from a long nightmare. Fragment 1: "I had a scalp disease - my hair was falling out - illness and ugliness."

Fragment 2: "I was on roller skates - there was a placard around my neck - I was feeling isolated - there were people around - I got frightened."

After the initial acknowledgment of how reassured she felt to be understood and in communication with me, she returned to a repetitive theme, that therapy was destroying her tenuous contact with people. The persistence of this theme is understandable. Her security operations, however unfortunate, had constituted her only contact with her parents and the great majority of her experience to date with others. The notion of major renovations in her styles of behavior aroused fears not only of loss of continuity with the parents but also of public exposure of the inner feelings developed with them. She was afraid that she would fail to find any new and less destructive modes of contact. Since this was the last session before my vacation, her feeling was undoubtedly intensified by her anxiety about two months out of therapy.

* * *

During that summer she returned to the same resort, met some new people, and spent a good deal of time with them. She remembered the summer as intensely uncomfortable. She handled her panic by swinging back into the previous social manipulative role, going to parties and staying as much as possible out of touch with what she had learned in June. The compensatory maneuvers worked most of the time but were interrupted by episodes of intense depression. During the depressions, she reported some unsafe driving with her car. One obsessive focus of rage was with her ex-husband for having found a new girl and having made some constructive use of his freedom to explore other social relationships.

* * *

1949 - 1950

In September, 1949, she was given more responsibility in dealing with clients of the firm. She also undertook some work in Family Court, defending the rights of children. She spent most of the fall with a new girl friend, Emma, whom she had met during the summer.

10/14/49: Nightmare: She was about to be smothered by a tall woman. Her association - "clearly Mother." She felt it was a repetition of an experience from early childhood.

Dream 2: "There was a panting animal - it was on four legs - there was something sitting in the middle of its back."

Dream 3: The story line emphasized her fear of being abandoned by a woman. In her associations, she talked about her fear of living alone, and about the interaction with mother which she referred to as "dependency." She said, "I was always fighting to get Mother's hands off of me. At the same time, I coundn't stand by myself."

The first dream was probably the communication of an infantile fear originally reflective of mother's unconscious preoccupation with doing the baby in. In dream 2, a four-legged animal for a self-image is a crawling baby. It describes a baby at the transition from early to late infancy. In reference to the third dream, much of this push-pull was, of course, projected onto me as analyst. She was afraid of being dependent on me, paranoid about being influenced by me, and afraid that I would desert her. The symbol of the woman in the dream was the current girl friend, Emma. The significance is primarily in the restatement of early interactions with mother as she had experienced them.

10/30/49: Two dreams about pleasant interactions with girl friends, one in the past, and one current. In the former, both sets of parents were disapproving. In the latter, with Emma, she was uncomfortable at being observed.

She expected contemporary observers to disapprove of her making a friend as much as her parents had.

11/20/49: Snatches of a series of dreams:

Dream 1: "I was in a room - there were things on the floor - it was a kid's playroom - the things were animals and insects - maybe I was frightened of them."

Dream 2: "I was walking in the park - it was very green - I heard something - I found a woman screaming - she was obviously crazy - it has been a recent repetitive dream."

Dream 3: "There was a sandwich on a plate - under it I found a big, fat, threatening, ugly spider."

Dream 4: "I saw you - sideways. There was grief on your face - I had hurt you - I started to cry."

In this session she remembered that when she was three or four years old, she would lie in the crib and imagine dangerous animals on the floor. She also reminded me that her mother frequently slapped her when she was between fifteen and seventeen years of age.

This dramatic statement of Evelyn's paranoid perceptions followed the anniversary of her father's death. About the same time there was a period of two days during which she "disappeared" and wandered around the area near her parents' New Jersey home. This was presumable a foggy attempt to relive or reconstruct what life with them had been like.

The four dreams explore and formulate the archaic structure of her paralysis - her paranoid dilemmas. The two principal parts of her experience with mother were her chaos and her sadism.

The first dream expresses the early pervasive squeamishness and terror that became associated with any spontaneous movement. The second, third, and fourth sort out major aspects of the emotional environment that enforced the terror. In the second, if she tries to

explore any direction of growth, she will re-experience the abandonment by the chaotic mother; i.e., the penalty will be the terror of
isolation. In the third, if she reaches for more love, her mother will
strike, enmesh, and paralyze her.

The fourth may refer to father. With him she was on the hook
of his seductiveness, the attraction to him, and the longing for him.
From there, the experience of feeling for another person could only
result in feeling profoundly accused of being responsible for the other's
despair.

The main quality of the transference expressed in the dreams
and the line of resistance was her fear that in the analytic clarification I would discover that she was crazy, I would be devastated, and
would then abandon her or punish her or demand her servitude as the
price for tolerating her.

There may also have been something of a time sequence in the
dreams -- a review of her life or of the course of her analysis --
from the victimized terror of early childhood, to the undifferentiated
identification with her crazy mother, to the perception of herself as
treacherous, and finally to a current request for understanding from
the therapist. Her weak attempt in the first dream to deny the terror
with the phrase, "Maybe I was frightened, " was soon swept away in
the vividness of the imagery.

Early in December, I went on vacation for a month.

1/17/50: Evelyn reported that a few days after I stopped work in
December, she found herself again in a state of confusion,
wandering the streets for hours in a snowstorm. She happened to run into a friend who, by coincidence, was equally
distraught. She was subsequently very distressed to realize
that she had not noticed how upset he was. Characteristically, she heard later that she had equally deflected him
from noticing her condition by muttering cheerily something
about being on an errand.

This was probably not a unique experience in Evelyn's life and
illustrates a basic dynamism. In her preoccupation with covering up
her own level of distress, she became not only unable to reach out for
help but also incapable of perceiving the other's distress.

1/19/50: She reported that subsequent to this episode of confusion in
early December she had two dreams. The first was a derogatory dream, clearly referring to me, in which she accused
me of being hypocritical.

The second dream: She was with a girl friend whom she
saw as beautiful and welcoming. They exchanged a hug, and
Evelyn went off with a guy.

Her anger in the first dream was apparently the result of my having taken a vacation. The second expressed a repetitive theme: she needed to get comfortable with people of the same sex before she could genuinely relate to people of the opposite sex. It is of interest to note that the person that she had so grossly misunderstood in the previous incident in the snowstorm was a man with whom she had some interest in spending time. She really could not pay attention to the man because her focus of attention was currently on improving her relationships with women.

1/21/50: Early in January she and Emma went on a two weeks' trip to the Virgin Islands. On this vacation the relationship between them was quite stormy. Evelyn was confronted with the fact that Emma's contempt for men was even more intense that her own. Toward the end of the trip Evelyn had the following dream: "I was in bed with a guy - he was heavy - we had sex. It was normal for the tip of the penis to come off. This didn't bother him or me. Then the shaft also came off - it was in my hand - it dissolved. I was left with white material - cheesy. I felt I had committed a terrible crime - I felt it even more that he did."

Her association was to the dream in May of the seven-foot infant. She added, in an association to the previous dream, that the woman knitting in the dream in May was "contemptuous, smug, horrible - it was my mother."

In dramatic symbolism, Evelyn clarified her fear that if she tried to relate to men she would be doomed to be as castrating as her mother had been. The despair was not only about her relationship to men--the relationship with the girl friend had also gone badly -- but the symbol of castration had a more general reference to the danger of her becoming destructive in any intimate interaction.

1/30/50: Dream: Part 1: She was bleeding to death. Part 2: She was dying of heart failure.

Having stated her powerful pull to take over her mother's psychotic war on men, she then experienced intense despair and went back to an old preoccupation with the choice of methods to commit suicide. At this time she still thought of the "bleeding" dream as referring to her father. In retrospect, it seems more likely that both dreams referred to her identification with her mother, who had almost died from a uterine hemorrhage and subsequently died of heart failure.

During the winter Evelyn began to handle some clients on her own. She had great difficulty in establishing contact. Her competitiveness and personal preoccupations repeatedly interfered with her work. She had several conferences with her employers about this difficulty. By the middle of spring her work was considerably better.

2/5/50:   She reported three dreams. In the first, she told a friend
with some embarrassment that she had once had intercourse
with her father. The friend was "slightly shocked but not
too much."

In the second, she dreamed that she had killed a plant by
overfeeding it. (She had been warned that overfeeding
would kill the plant.) In reality when she woke the next
morning and looked at the plant, it was still healthy.

The third dream involved an intricate structural collage
that obviously gave the effect of something human. "It had
a head - some kind of decorations were used for eyes and
nose. They were strung on wire. The wire was intermeshed
to give the effect of something round. It was suggestive
of heads of statues from an antique or ancient civilization."

Her associations included a review of small pieces of
friendly interaction with several of her male friends, past
and present.

The first dream seemed to be a positive statement, probably
mostly relating to her experiences at work. She was finding, in discussing her work with colleagues, that it was possible to share something embarrassing.

In the second, she expressed the beginning of awareness that
it was not inevitable that she carry out her deep expectation that she
would destroy whatever she related to.

The third dream meant that if she pulled together all of the positive experiences in her life, she might be able to construct an image
of a human being. The dream and the session left an ambiguity --
whether she meant a real person or the facade. Perhaps this dream
stated Evelyn's discouraged notion that creating a somewhat convincing facsimile of a human being was the best for which she could hope.
On the other hand, one part of growth in the adult years is the reorganization of awareness so that positive experiences are remembered
in continuity and can serve as a base for expansion into genuine human
potentials. This may have been what she meant.

Also, she used her relationship with clients as a laboratory in
which to clarify and improve her capacity for relating in her personal
life. In these dreams the alternate reference is about herself as a
woman with men:

Dream 1: Will her past contaminate the present?

Dream 2: Will her possessiveness (overprotectiveness)
smother the man?

Dream 3: Has she sufficient good experience to draw on?

2/10/50: Dream: The symbols used were green pears and ripe egg-
plant. The rest of the session she discussed her rage about
how her clients reacted to her.

The dream was again a reference to her capacity for being
helpful, probably still mostly in reference to clients. The alternate
reference is again partly sexual (based on similarity in shape of the
fruit to the uterus) -- is her femininity preadolescent or mature? The
question here would be partly about fertility.

2/24/50: She reported a nightmare about a chase. This was followed
by memories of her first move into nursery school at two
and one-half, her terror about it, and her subsequent difficulty in visual perception. As she put it, "I stopped seeing."

She both relived and recalled the terror associated with moving
toward peers. She stated her difficulty in understanding the other
person in the symbol of visual perception.

3/2/50: A contemptuous dream about advice from a very inadequate
superior. Association: Evelyn's last discussion with her
superior in the firm had been very helpful to Evelyn in identifying her difficulty in listening, her tendency to give technical advice without adequate knowledge, and her secret
competitiveness with clients.

This double perception of "constructive criticism" as both
destructive and indispensable was a repetitive theme.

3/10/50: Evelyn had heard that an old friend, with whom she thought
she was on good terms, had described her to a third person
as "very destructive." She felt both unjustly accused and
very despairing when she heard about it.

That week she also had read The Golem. She spent the rest
of the session on her reaction to the play. "The first time
I've ever deliberately exposed myself to monsters."

In her synopsis of the play, "The oppressed people create a
ruthless powerful monster suffused with anger with which to
defeat the tyrant. The monster succeeds in defeating the
tyrant, but his anger knows no bounds, and he goes on to
destroy the people that created him." As was clarified during the session, she identified with The Golem.

Evelyn implied that she could not distinguish between murderous
rage and self-assertion. If, in disentangling herself from her parents

and their values, she released the rage that she felt was involved, she would become the mindless monster of her earlier nightmare and would move on to destroy all of the current relationships with people who were helpful and friendly to her.

3/17/50: A somewhat complex dream referring to her difficulty in looking at scars from previous damage – her own or another's She subsequently reported, more clearly than usual, some of her own problems with personal friends. The scar in the dream was a burn.

She was saying that it was perhaps about time she took some responsibility for looking at her own problems. The burn also referred to a previous parallel between herself and her cousin Geraldine, who was severely burned as a child and whose mother "never forgave her for it."

4/16/50: In a dream she recapitulated a power fight with a client, in which the client felt "defeated" when she took Evelyn's advice. At the same time, the client had a "sly smile and a sense of relief."

In addition to sharing with me her problems of competitiveness and the fight for power in her work, she was also sharing with me one of her styles of resistance and her relief when I pushed through an obvious insight.

4/23/50: Evelyn had been assigned three new clients. She also noted a confusion in her thought processes: when she had reached to put her lipstick on, her thought was "put on ice cream." The rest of the session was spent on her intense reaction to seeing a movie about a little boy who killed himself in the desperate attempt to save his parents from themselves. "A frantic effort to win mother's love." Speaking of herself, she said, "I was a wistful child -- afraid to move."

She felt pressured by outside circumstances to take on her role as an adult in the world. This would involve relinquishing some of the fantasies of satisfaction at the late infancy level (ice cream). More centrally, it would involve relinquishing the hopeless and fatal project of the frantic effort to win her mother's love.

5/4/50: Dream: Reference to three pairs of close friends. In each partnership one dominates and one is dominated.

This was her picture of the quality of mutual interaction between partners.

5/7/50: A dream about a date with the friend with whom she had had the accidental meeting early in December. In the dream she was more aware of his mood and less frightened by it. She woke from the dream with a nosebleed. The rest of the interview included two references to the fear of going crazy and several references to profuse nosebleeds as a symbol and expression of the fear of death, all associated with her mother's rage with her.

She noted that terror could be shared with another who had had extensive experience with it. She then reminded herself that such sharing would be dangerous.

5/13/50: Dream 1: "A little girl sitting all by herself."

Dream 2: She was watching a play in which a young girl murders a mother-figure. Subsequently, the audience was concerned that although this murder was necessary, the young girl might go on to kill others.

A repetition of the Golem theme. Again, assertion was seen as leading to murder. She felt that the hazard of fighting her way to freedom was that she would "get a taste for blood." Perhaps isolation was preferable.

5/15/50: For the past week Evelyn had been in a state of fear and rage with nausea, colitis, and violent migraine.

Dream 1: She reported from one night a repetitive dream in different forms, all related to the possibility of "leaving home." A friendly girl kept saying, "It's all right."

Dream 2: Another three-dimensional collage, this time incorporating various symbols for feminity.

Dream 3: The setting was in the law firm, with many people taking diverse roles. The central figure was a man who was both the umbrella fixer and ran the knife-sharpening machine.

Dream 4: An underground tractor knocked over a pair of elms and partially uprooted another pair without permanently damaging them.

In this sequence she tried to hypothesize a possible pathway, sequence, and result of leaving home, i.e., of relinquishing her parents' values without catastrophe.

Dream 1 stated the problem.

Dream 2 repeated an earlier symbol of the reintegration of bits and pieces of her life into a collage, this time to become a woman.

Dream 3 underlined the importance to her of the senior partner of the law firm, whom she saw as handling protective devices against the storm and also as an expert on how to prepare weapons for self-defense.

In dream 4 she modified the outcome of the Golem nightmare, i.e., if she makes an underground constructive move, it might be possible to dispose of the influence of her parents and only damage but not destroy the people on whom she currently relied.

5/24/50:   Dream: Two cars, one black, heavy, and old-fashioned. The other, new, grey, and pretty. They were hitched together sideways. The geography of the dream resembled that of a trip in her teens with the parents, on which mother was a particularly poor model for womanhood. A young girl was driving the new car, a woman driving the old one. Evelyn was supposed to go somewhere with the woman in the black car. The driver was clumsily backing into something. Evelyn was apprehensive.

She still felt tied to and directed by mother with a current reference to me. The dream states that if she was doomed to follow the leadership of a woman, she would have to be preoccupied with the other's competence as a driver.

The prosaic terms of the symbol as compared with the previous dreams of her mother's power indicated some lessening of intensity of the paranoid perceptions following their symbolization in the extreme form and analytic interpretation.

5/26/50:   Dream: "I found the missing screw, and the machine worked." Actually, she considered herself inept at mechanical things.

Whether the symbol referred to sex or or sanity, it incorporated a somewhat hopeful statement that she might be able to learn to do things at which she had previously been inept.

6/22/50:   Dream: The story line incorporated an alternation of mood between frantic rushing and, when she slowed down, total paralysis. At the end of the session she reminded me that this day was her thirty-third birthday.

She here described a lifetime security operation of hers of frantic activity alternating with deep depression. The opposing feelings of "no time to waste" and fearful paralysis were intensified by noticing her age. In various sessions she had been concerned particularly with her age and with the pressure to have children, more than one, before the menopause.

6/27/50:   "Thursday, I met Ed and was immediately attracted to him. Friday, I had a dream - I was lying in bed - I was chained - I couldn't move - I was fighting to get up."

The dream formulated Evelyn's perception of the possible course of events if she and Ed were to become involved. As subsequent events showed, her fears were highly justified. She had made her bed and would be chained to it for some time.

* * *

During the summer Evelyn and Ed were engaged, and at the end of the summer they were married.

He was a successful customers' man with a good brokerage firm. He had charm and an elegant air, and shared her parents' valuing of prestige and social position. In his personal relationships he was both stormy like her mother and demanding like her father.

8/15/50:   Dream (reported in October): She was at the North Pole in a situation in which a landslide was threatening. She had some of the essentials for survival but not all. The others were to be brought in by the analyst. She and the analyst cooperated in entombing her mother's corpse in ice. The dream was in brilliant "cheerful" colors. There were other people present.

The dream sets the tone for the next three years. The bright colors typified a kind of prettying-up and "color projection" that continued during this period. Situations perceived as grim but inevitable were stated in icily realistic terms, though with an overlay of brilliant coloring. She relied on the analyst to provide the warmth which her relationship with Ed could not provide. In this project she felt that incautious movement could result in catastrophe for herself and her associates. She had not resolved the problem with mother but had set it aside for the duration, with the possibility that she might always thaw mother out and go back to the alliance with her if the venture did not work.

1950 TO 1953

This seems to be a relatively unitary period. In this period she got pregnant, had a son Paul, and got a separation before the baby was two years old. In analysis she spoke rather romantically of her relationship with Ed, but her dreams revealed a grim and bitter insight. In fact, they quarreled bitterly and frequently about people, politics, money, friends, possessiveness, baby care, education, and each other's personal idiosyncracies. Each quarrel was contaminated with the illusion of "finally getting the issue clear" -- and very few of the quarrels resulted in any change of behavior in either.

The relationship between them was something of a caricature of her relationship with her father. Although this crucial aspect of the relationship was rarely discussed fully between us, she often used her dream life to relive and work through particularly difficult aspects of her relationship with father.

She also had a series of dreams in which she tried to work out her potential for mothering the baby and to disentangle herself in this context from her identification with her mother's deadly destructiveness. Beginning during the pregnancy and particularly after the baby was born, she cautiously developed a friendship with Helen, a woman rather like herself. The interaction between them was more common-sense and cooperative than her usual previous friendships with women. After Paul was a few months old, Evelyn also used her dream life to work on her difficulties in relating to peers.

The write-up of these years has been condensed drastically to save space. I here illustrate the dominant trends of this period through the use of her dream symbolism, but the interpretations, in addition, are based on current interactions with others and associated memories from her childhood.

I have divided the write-up into four periods: before she got pregnant (September, 1950, to February, 1951), during the pregnancy (February, 1951, to November, 1951), the first three months postpartum (November, 1951, to February, 1952), and then the eighteen months between then and the separation (February, 1952, to August, 1953).

* * *

SEPTEMBER, 1950, TO FEBRUARY, 1951

In the context of her relationship with Ed, Evelyn dreamed of herself as "living at the North Pole," isolated on a barren rock in the North Sea," and "freezing naked in the snow." She felt inadequate, helpless, isolated. She also dreamed of herself as a hurricane (with associations to her mother's rage with men and destructiveness to plants), and as a partner in a murder team. The two latter images referred to her doubts about her capacity for nurturing growing things.

Ed was seen as both saving her from her parents and isolating her from her friends. She dreamed of him as "a smiling corpse" from whom "I must get a divorce." When they "swim into the mouth of the whale together," she has "a bloody time getting out."

The security operations she described or illustrated included denial, contamination of perceptions, depersonalization, dissociation, manipulated fear, and manipulated rage.

After the "entombment" scene of the North Pole dream, Evelyn's mother appeared less frequently than usual in her dreams. She was referred to in Evelyn's associations to the dream about the hurricane and appeared once as a "ghost, " haunting the interaction with Ed and vanquished by him.

Obvious transference dreams were also not prominent. I appeared as distantly helpful, with limited leverage, and "probable" good intentions.

She hoped that her friends would "bear with her for the duration, " expected them to disapprove of or be envious of her marriage, and felt that the marriage would isolate her from them anyway.

FEBRUARY, 1951, TO NOVEMBER, 1951

During her pregnancy the dreams clearly referring to herself were, in sequence: she lost her identity, she would become as depressed as mother, she was easily disorganized. In relation to Ed, they were "partners in murder" and joint owners of a "small shark. " He also helped her escape from a "mental hospital" by way of the "pediatric building. " By June she was "living in a concentration camp" and "about to be devoured by a male lion. " In the fall she and he were "cornered rats" for whom she had the repulsive responsibility.

She referred to her mother's depression and battle with men, but during this period, at least, considered the male the deadlier of the species.

She still saw me as friendly and well intentioned, but hard to get to. She had no dreams relating directly to other friends.

In relation to the baby, she started with frank terror of childbirth and horror of what she would produce as a child (a small shark?). There was an interim period of despair about her capacity to keep the baby alive. By fall she was evaluating her handicaps and moving toward overcoming them, and felt "she had what she wanted. "

Paul was born on November 11. She had expected a girl. The delivery was uneventful.

NOVEMBER, 1951, TO FEBRUARY, 1952

In the immediate postpartum period Evelyn had both some suicidal fantasies and a positive dream about baby care. Subsequently, she clarified her perception of Ed as irresponsible, stated the necessity for her to take the responsibility, and formulated the danger to the baby of the quality of the relationship between her and Ed.

FEBRUARY, 1952, TO AUGUST, 1953

During the first year of her son's life her dreams were focused on evaluating her potential as a mother. Was she responsive? damaging? a child and terrified? adult and barren (nothing to give)? or just destructive?

After her son's first birthday she dreamed of herself as moving toward making friends, but she felt awkward. She dreamed that she had survived a long winter under the snow. She then evaluated briefly whether she should risk the rest of her life in the project of "saving Ed."

In the next two months she evaluated her fear of his rage at the separation, decided she would survive it, and that any practical action was up to her. Her final statement was that they made "a weird, very unrelated couple."

As the partner in these interactions, she dreamed of Ed as isolating her or terrifying her. She saw him as "going nowhere" and the image of "empty elegance." Later she represented him as irresponsibly self-destructive, murderous, incompetent, and finally, just unrelated to her.

In her dreams relating to Paul, Ed was conspicuously absent.

The prominent security operations of this period were her denial of facts about the marriage which were obviously known to both of us, and her anger at my attempts to put these data into words.

She dreamed of Paul first as damaged by her incompetence. She later saw herself walking up a long hill alone with him. By spring there was a joyful dream of growing things and their expansive impact, clearly referring to him.

In the early dreams about her capacity for nurturing Paul there was always some oblique reference to her identification with her mother. However, the strongest analytic reference to her mother was in her many memories of the latter's interference in Evelyn's attempts to make friends.

Her only unambiguous dream image of me was in February of 1952. She was "starting a new phase of treatment" (expanding her life) and was regretting the inevitable dependence on me inherent in this project.

The new element of this period was her concern with relating to people. In sequence, she had these dreams:

2/24/52: Ed isolated her from people.

4/4/52:   If he did not, she would have to deal with her fear of people.

11/21/52: Are people constructive or destructive? The transition to
            them would be lonely but she would make it.

12/1/52:   She expressed some squeamishness about making closer
            relationships with women.

4/3/53:   She expressed her amazement that others seemed to be able
            to overcome interpersonal barriers and wondered if she
            could too.

During the summer of 1953, Ed moved out at her insistence.
They got a divorce rather quickly.

* * *

During the last year of therapy she reported relatively few
dreams. This may have been because she was "closing up shop."
On the other hand, verbal communication between us was much freer
and more open, and therefore communication by dream symbol may
have been less urgent.

One of the most important relationships of this year was the
evolving intimacy with Helen whom she had met at work and grown to
know over the previous year. They progressively shared work and
personal problems, including difficulties in handling their respective
children.

After Ed left, she was free to use her own judgment in her
handling of Paul. She undertook as the major project of the year to
undo some of the damage done to him as the result of the anger
between her and Ed.

She also undertook to be sure that his interactions with other
young children would go more smoothly than hers had gone.

With the elaborate protection and camouflage of the marriage
removed, she also found herself on more friendly, related, and communicative terms with many of her previous friends. She could talk fairly
openly about her life or theirs, and she often did.

Her concern for the other person was fairly appropriate to the
quality of the relationship, though often inept in execution. Although
the old styles of evasion, distance, control, or glittering illusion
were sometimes evoked under stress, they were the exception rather
than the rule and could be cut through more easily.

12/3/53:   She reported a date with a particular man whom she had
            always considered exceptionally interesting. The date

worked out gloriously. Two nights later she had had her first dream of the year. In the dream "my date was driving the car, which was filled with several people. He was in such animated conversation and so spontaneous that he forgot to watch where he was going. The road turned, but he went straight into the woods. I put my head down but woke before the car crashed.

It is of interest that what is fatal in the dream is spontaneity, particularly in respect to communication.

For a week or so after this she was quite preoccupied with the hazards of getting "deeply involved" in a situation where she could by no means be sure that he would be interested in an intense or continuous relationship.

12/12/53:   Dream: "Would I be able to make out with putting on an appearance of competence? -- then I thought 'not quite.'"

In telling the dream, she was appalled with the fact that at this point the psychopathic maneuver could still seem a possibility to her.

Her work was quite good by now, and this dream, with the double-take on waking, may have been her way of validating with me that the old style had truly been outgrown.

Late in December she complained of a general feeling of depression about the functions of desire and enthusiasm. During January she reported several dreams of being pregnant and enjoying it.

Later on, in reviewing these shifts of mood, she said, "I started dating a lot. I was very optimistic for several months. Then I suddenly got depressed and withdrawn and started putting on weight." This description suggests that though she was much freer in associating with friends of both sexes, she was least comfortable with experiencing herself as a woman in a positive context with a man who was attracted to her.

She did, in fact, gain some weight and withdraw somewhat from the "flirtatious" role with men. However, she was moving ahead in many areas and seemed to be much less depressed than previously. Even with the men she found interesting, she was improving her level of communication. This would be a necessary base before more open and genuinely affectionate relationships could develop.

Starting in November Evelyn had become active in a large piece of work that was to involve collaboration with colleagues over an extended period. During this project she related to her field with great seriousness. Because of the increased competence she demonstrated, she was given increased responsibility, and felt both frightened

nd gratified. Her collaboration with others was still somewhat clumsy.
he would often do the right thing but manage to interject a discordant
ote so that less intimacy would result from work with others than one
1ight have hoped.

In the spring she raised the question of terminating therapy.
'his was put partly in terms of the financial pressures of supporting
er household alone. She also felt that she had a good grasp of her
revious impediments to growth and wanted to see if she could move
head in developing her capacity for intimacy on her own. We both
1ought of the termination as tentative with the possibility that a period
f consolidation of what she had learned in therapy might later be fol-
wed by further analytic work.

During May and June we jointly reviewed her interpersonal
istory and the course of our work together. She added some new
1emories of the circumstances surrounding her puberty change and
arly adolescent years. She was busy trying to understand her con-
nuing unsureness about femininity.

In May she repeated the Rorschach, and in June we reviewed
1e comparison of the two protocols. We used this as a base for clari-
ing what had been consolidated, and what she still had difficulty with.

This comparison highlights some of the changes in her percep-
ons over the period of her analysis.

The immediate impact of Evelyn's 1948 Rorschach was of her
nderlying feeling of pervasive, undefined, and overpowering terror
at ran through the entire record. She literally seemed to be terrified
everything, and apparently managed to function as a going concern
 a combination of evasive, escapist tactics, and by a massive dis-
ciation and/or denial of her fears. Beneath a tenuous facade there
as the impression of a person who had inwardly consigned herself
isolation in a dark room filled with unseen and unknown malevolences.
e seemed to feel that she would fall apart at any sudden stress.
1plied in the imagery were intense feelings of anger, depression,
spair, and loneliness, all of which she made frantic attempts to
retty up" by romanticizing.

No real attempts toward contact with people were apparent in
e 1948 Rorschach. Rather, it seemed that any attempt at genuine
iendship was then totally out of the question under the impact of so
uch undifferentiated fear of her parents. For one thing, she was
able to discriminate between them and the rest of humanity. They
d also apparently made specific inroads on her attempts to form
er relationships and had made her feel unlovable. Her self-revul-
on was prominent.

The dynamics of her early interpersonal milieu were only sketchily apparent in the early record and were submerged under the overlay of fear, confusion, and evasion.

As Evelyn perceived life at the time of the first Rorschach record, there was little conflict. Life was a matter of surviving daily terror with the alternate thought of suicide as a simpler way out.

In 1954 there was less over-all terror in the record. She had more accurate perceptions of herself and her parents, and the specificity of the parents' neurotic patterns. The dynamics of the early interpersonal milieu were spelled out, and she had become aware of the particular direction and intensity of some of her parents' prohibitions against the satisfaction of her needs. Although she was still frightened of her parents, the fact that she could formulate clearly who they were indicated that this fear was greatly reduced.

In the second record Evelyn had come to accept and to express explicitly her feelings of anger, depression, despair, and loneliness. She had also identified some of the sources of these feelings, both current and historical. This had made it possible for her to formulate in the six-year interval, some perceptions of real people and real situations and some of her own real needs. She was then confronted with the choices, dilemmas, and the problems of satisfaction and human interaction arising from these insights.

Evelyn had become much better at organizing her perceptions of the world into meaningful, communicable, and useful symbols. Her perceptions tended to be more accurate and to encompass broader fields. She was more consistently intelligent because her thought processes were much less fragmented by terror. The confabulation which was conspicuous in the earlier record was minimal in the secon The earlier contamination of percepts evolved into a sophisticated style of communicating either her conflict about alternate interpretations of a complex situation or her perception of alternate facets of it. However, the image of herself as mediocre in conceptualization persisted, and she still pressed to convince herself and others that she was intelligent, against the long-standing delusion that she was not.

As the level of her fear and despair diminished, she expressed a greater sense of inner energy which was reflected in the quality and number of her movement responses as contrasted with those in 1948. She had become aware of the possibility of tenderness in the world, but the recognition and expression of her tender feelings remained tentative and subject to inner constraint and prohibition. Her genuine interaction with peers was, in 1954, in parallel play situations and in the beginning establishment of juvenile alliances. In this connection, her general debunking of the omnipotence of the parents in the second

ecord, and her specific definition of their personalities as different
·om those of other adults, implied some experience with juvenile
iteractions. Evelyn's moves toward people were appropriate and
ere open to further development. Under stress, however, she still
·nded to romanticize and play-act her capacity for feeling for the
·her person.

In 1954 she made the timidly hopeful statement that she could
·nceive of life within her after all, however contained and subdued
appeared to her, and however it had to be concealed from others.
·e had thus begun to abandon her lifelong sense of desolation and
·vastation. She still thought of herself as a stiff, graceless, "not
·male" person. This was partly the reflection of her parents' ori-
nal perception of her. It was reinforced by her perception of her
·other's destructiveness with her father.

This conflict about adult sexuality was the most conspicuous
·oblem stated in the second record. She felt relatively free to
plore relationships appropriate to the normal development of the
·pacity for intimacy before puberty, including body contact, coopera-
·n, and ultimately compassion. She also was not phobic about
cepting responsibility as an adult if the "feminine" role was not
·volved. She was still subject to the mystique that to function as a
ature woman with a friendly man would, mysteriously, transform
·r into her mother. She would be compelled to take on her mother's
·ttle with men.

Although in the later record her parents were seen as determin-
·g her image of herself as unfeminine, previously she had thought
·at her survival itself was in their hands.

* * *

Over the next two years she gradually moved her work to
·shington. In the spring of 1957 she phoned me for a referral to
·analyst there, to help her work on her relationship with a man whom
·e had met in that city, the director of a government research branch.
·nderstand that she was in therapy with this therapist for about a year.

ADDENDUM

Q. Did you formulate a specific diagnosis before you began psychotherapy, or was it made after psychotherapy was in progress?
Do such pre-therapeutic diagnoses inhibit or facilitate taking a
patient into treatment? Are your diagnoses subject to revision
as psychotherapy proceeds, and do they vary depending on the
way the patient responds to the treatment? Do you distinguish
between diagnosis as such and simple spontaneous diagnostic reflections?

A. I do not formulate a specific diagnosis in the conventional sense,
either before, during, or after psychotherapy. I try to evaluate
whether or not the patient is serious about undertaking change and
whether I feel we will be able to establish communication. It is
indispensable for the therapist to evaluate the patient's central
problems and the layering of his defenses, and this understanding
is progressive throughout therapy. During the course of intensive
psychotherapy every patient exhibits some characteristics attri-
butable to all of the conventional diagnostic categories, neurotic
and psychotic. Each such trend must be analyzed in terms of the
specific character structure of the patient, and each person's
character structure is unique. As therapy progresses, the pat-
patterning of such defenses will shift from time to time. The pre
dominant patterning of symptoms at a particular time may or may
not be the significant organizing principle in understanding that
person at that time.

Q. Did you approach your patient with a consistent and verbalizable
theory or set of hypotheses on personality structure and/or the
genesis of psychic illness? Was such theory used directly (or
indirectly) in selecting the patient for treatment? How was it
applied in the treatment and how effective was your theory in
reaching the goals of treatment? What do you see as the function
of such hypotheses or theories?

A. Every therapist inevitably works within a consistent theoretical
framework, consciously or unconsciously. This framework affec
his judgment about a patient's capacity to change, determines the
design of the course of treatment, both in terms of origins of difficulties and in therapeutic maneuvers, and defines the goal of
treatment. I work from the point of view of Harry Stack Sullivan'
theory of interpersonal psychiatry as expanded in a recent book
by Saul Newton and me, The Conditions of Human Growth.

The method of application of such basic theoretical concepts as
the capacity for interpersonal intimacy, the central paranoia,
dissociation, and parataxic distortion is illustrated in the review
of the sessions. With this particular patient the results of treatment were rewarding.

Theory is indispensable in organizing the therapeutic process. Without an explicit theory of individual human development, of the genesis of psychological difficulties and of the ameliorative processes indicated, "intuitive" therapy tends to founder on the power of the resistance to change (in both therapist and patient) and tends to settle for illusory gains.

2. What did you think of the prognosis of your case before you accepted the patient for treatment? What did you think during the first several interviews; and during the latter stages of treatment? Do you feel prognostic judgments about ultimate health or ultimate illness are useful? Can we dispense with a prognosis as a formal event in clinical treatment?

.. I approach any patient with an open mind concerning prognosis during the course of therapy. Neither the patient nor the therapist can possibly anticipate the reality of the strength or weakness of the patient's wish to change and of his hidden resources, nor how much the particular therapist will be able to contribute to the project. Prognostic judgments are more likely to have reference (perhaps accurately) to the particular therapist's availability.

During the last year of therapy with this patient her use of the previous work became sufficiently clear that I would hazard the estimate that she was probably committed to continuing growth whether or not therapy was continued.

In general, I consider prognosis as a formal event in clinical treatment to be an impediment.

. What particular therapeutic techniques did you apply in this case? Which of them were most effective and which ineffective, and for what reasons? Did you attempt any technical innovations on an empirical basis? When did you feel that a "peak" experience or turning point occurred?

. In this case I particularly emphasized the technique of repeated, incisive, organized summaries to the patient of my impressions of the over-all picture of her past and present status and character structure as of that time. Summaries were organized to include the particular growth experience toward which she was moving and the particular style of resistance with which she was impeding it. I also used the basic psychoanalytic techniques of establishing communication, interpreting transference perceptions, re-evaluating perceptions of interpersonal interaction, reintegrating memories and ruminative associations with dream symbols and current events.

Since the work with each patient is a creative process, new techniques for communication and interpretation have to be invented
in order for anything effective to take place. In this case one
important turning point followed the presentation of the Rorschach
and comprehensive summary in May and June of 1949. The subsequent three years events could be considered her style of "work
ing through" the insights first consensually validated during that
six weeks' period. Another significant turning point was at the
beginning of the last year of therapy when she implemented the
insights worked through during the previous three years into
actual practical, durable patterns of living.

Q. Did you feel that Freud's formulation of transference and counter
transference were sufficient to account for the therapeutic encoun
with your patient? How would you describe your encounter?

A. The patient's tendency to project onto me her perceptions of eithe
parent was massive, and it was indispensable to analyze these
projections. I also emphasized the importance of her perceiving
me as a particular person with genuine assets and limitations,
and a genuine concern that she should find her life more rewardir
The transference problem was, then, the gradual disentangling o:
her perception of me as either mother or father from the confron
tation of who I was as a person.

Q. It has been said that psychotherapy is a white, middle-class, urb
phenomenon which does not necessarily apply to other social stra
tifications or cultures. In what way did your patient's cultural
background influence his illness and treatment? In what way did
your own cultural background assist or deter the treatment?

A. The patient's white, middle-class, urban, social background was
a major impediment to the progress of treatment. The fact that
I came from a rather similar background and had put considerab
work into getting some perspective on the implied social values
was in some ways helpful. To the extent that I had not freed myself from either the values or the mannerisms of this backgroun
this was a handicap in treatment. The general cultural approval
of the prestigious operations, so massively structured into her
resistance against genuine growth, created constant static. My
goal was to disentangle the socially successful values of money,
power, and prestige from her real needs for tenderness, intima
and creativity. In general, any patient's social origins tend to
reinforce certain security operations as approved, and to streng
the patient's investment in maintaining these particular defenses

Q. There is an increasing tendency for neo-analytic thinking to ascr
the genesis and treatment of psychic illness to the social psychol
ogy of the family. How did this apply in your case?

A. The quality of the interpersonal relationship between the patient and the immediate members of his family during the first few years of life is the single most important determinant in the patterning of his resistance to growth later in life. Dueing subsequent developmental eras, the parents' attitude toward his relationship to children of his own age is also a critical factor. The explicit social values of the family tend to determine more the form of the resistance than the content of individual capacities. With Evelyn, her parents' cruelty during her infancy, their opposition to her need for friends during the later developing years, and their frank exploitation of her from puberty on were massive handicaps in the development of her capacity for intimacy. Their lip service to her pursuit of professional status and "social success," against this background, was an additional massive handicap to her subsequent attempts to divest herself of their hypocrisy and find a new approach to people.

The psychotherapist can only make an indirect, but perhaps very important contribution to the treatment of the milieu, by contributing to the clarification of human needs and the nature of the growth process.

Q. If your treatment was concluded what criteria did you use for terminating it? If it is still in process, what guide points would you use to determine when your patient is sufficiently improved to discontinue treatment? Do you feel that a patient should be seen as long as he feels he needs it and is willing to pay the fees?

A. The choice of a terminating point in therapy is partly a practical decision in terms of time and money. When Evelyn terminated, she was still making productive use of therapy and she still had problems, the solution of which could have been facilitated by continuing therapy. On the other hand, she had consolidated many genuine gains, she had identified the next important project, and she had thoroughly reviewed the sources of her anticipated anxiety about working out her relationships with men. I felt that the decision to terminate at this time was up to her, and I did not raise any major protest about her discontinuing therapy. I considered that the experience of functioning at the new level on her own would reassure her that the strength was within herself, not simply a reflection of the integration with the therapist.

If I had felt that she was discontinuing therapy for the purpose of avoiding an impending insight, I would have protested at the time. I would discontinue work with any patient who was not making productive use of the time, since continuing would only contribute to his discouragement about further therapy at a more propitious time.

Q. Did you make any mistakes in this case -- in the sense of "if you had to do it over"?

A. In my review of the material for the work-up, I was struck by the "anticipatory" nature of communication. In both her dreams and her choice of what data to present in particular sessions, there were cryptic messages to me about decisions and perceptions which it was not possible for us to share verbally at the time. If I had been able to follow this underlying dynamic sequence of motion, I might have expedited the process and saved time without startling her with confrontation for which I had not laid the ground work.

Also, if I had spent more time organizing data already collected, put more energy into understanding the meaning of particular sessions, I might have achieved the same results with less total analytic time.

Q. In treating your case did you perhaps feel that the classical distinctions between psychoses and neuroses were breaking down? (This question may apply even if your case represents neither a psychotic or neurotic.)

A. I have never felt that there was any useful distinction between psychosis and neurosis, and my previous conviction about this was not affected by the data in this particular case.

The universal mental illness in our culture is massive damage to the development of the capacity for intimacy. The universal security operation for maintaining this immaturity is the dissociat of data relevant to growth moves. This resistance is universally implemented in the organization of paranoid perceptions and patterns of interpersonal relationships designed to actively obstruct the development of the capacity for intimacy.

In serious moves toward more intimacy, temporary disorganization of the ongoing character structure, resulting in "schizophreni phenomena is also universal. Each of us has unlimited access to both the "neurotic" and the "psychotic" dynamisms for the suppres sion, containment, or expression of anxiety under "stress" situations. Such moves toward more satisfaction and interpersonal validation may result in either growth, "stasis," or ultimate deter ioration with retreat from the pursuit of need-satisfaction.

Chapter IX

ANALYTIC INSIGHTFULNESS AND NEW EXPERIENCE

By Helm Stierlin

THE FLIGHT OF MINERVA'S OWL

Hegel writes, "When thought appears, painting life grey on grey, one of life's forms has grown old. Painted grey on grey life cannot be made young again. It can merely be understood: The Owl of Minerva starts her flight only at rising twilight."[1]

Insight implies distance from action and agitation. Id turning into ego, primary process becoming secondary process, rational thinking replacing wishful emoting: all these processes, so central in analytic thinking, denote a gaining of greater psychic order and structure. But, also, they indicate the "growing-old" of one of life's forms.

Many patients of Freud's earliest analytic period -- diagnosed as hysterics and characterized by great psychic immaturity -- appeared to leave no doubt that for them such growing-older, along with the psychic ordering and structuring it entailed, was imperative. For them Minerva's twilight could come none too soon. But when more obsessional patients appeared, such structuring and growing-older seemed no longer enough. In these patients, Minerva's Owl, it seemed, had no difficulty flying. But nothing came of her flights. For them there was only growing-older, but no growing wiser: the bird of wisdom made only the empty motions of gaining wisdom -- yet wisdom itself remained elusive. What seemed like insight for these patients had turned into a device for preventing and perverting it.

Inevitably, analytic thinking had to face the question, What makes insight true insight? And that, in turn, meant: How is the gaining of insight tied to the gaining of new life experience? This question has many angles. In order that insight may not become wasted and stereotyped, there must exist -- this became evident -- a kind of "creative dialectic" between a person's conscious thinking and his largely unconscious affective life. Kris, in developing his concept of "regression in the service of the ego," Rapaport, and many others have subsequently tried to throw light on the nature of this creative dialectic.

---

1. Vorrede zur Rechtsphilosophie, Vol. VIII, p. 20.

But the question -- what converts insight into true insight -- had, moreover, to deal with the question of new life experience itself. How, one must ask, can life be newly experienced so that new insight will be derived from this experience? Thus formulated, the arena of life experience becomes the focus of inquiry.

Apparently the analytic situation itself is such an arena. To the degree that the analytic relationship becomes meaningful, the patient's most central life experience becomes condensed into the analytic hours. The gaining of insight then seems immediately tied to this unique experience, and this insight is in many respects unique. "The psychoanalytic insight which initiates therapeutic changes," writes Hanna Segal, "is different from insight in any other situation. It is different, for example, from the insight possessed by the artist or the ordinary, well-integrated, intuitive person. It involves a conscious knowledge of archaic processes, normally inaccessible to the most intuitive person, through reliving in the transference the very processes that structured one's internal world and conditioned one's perception. It is thus always dynamically altering. For instance, the moment the patient realizes how he has split himself, he is already beginning to integrate himself. When sufficiently worked through and integrated, the structural changes remain stable."

Yet the analytic situation, crucial as it is, is not the only are for new life experiences. There is also the life outside the analytic hours. It is bound to have its impact on what goes on in the analysis, and vice versa.

And just as we can conceive of a "creative dialectic," constantly occurring between our conscious thinking and our unconscious, affective inner life, there exists, on a somewhat different level, a similar dialectical cross-fertilization between what goes on inside and what goes on outside the analytic hour.

It is in the light of this dialectic that I want to present here some aspects of the analysis of a young man. I want to try to illuminate some of the complex and intricate cross-influencing that goes on between intra-analytic and extra-analytic factors and situations. Often it seems arbitrary to separate the two groups. Instead, analytic insightfulness and new life experience can often be seen as intermeshing circles -- as two moments, hardly

---

2. Segal, H. The curative factors in psychoanalysis. Int. J. Psycho: 1962, p. 217.

separable, in <u>one</u> process, constantly begetting each other anew, constantly widening the experiential horizon of the personality.[3]

At the same time I want to describe, in presenting aspects of this case, how Minerva's Owl also flew for me, the analyst. I want to try to convey my own growing insight into some of my patient's problems. This, in retrospect, appears much more an open-ended endeavor, proceeding in leaps and jumps (and not seldom leading to dead ends), than the following presentation might indicate.

THE PATIENT'S PROBLEM

Max Lattimer was twenty-eight years old when I saw him the first time. He came from a small town in the Midwest. His parents and his two sisters, ten and twelve years his seniors in age, resided there. Up to a few days ago, he had lived in the home of his parents. Then he had driven east in his car in order to seek treatment at the psychiatric sanatorium with which I was affiliated. He had admitted himself voluntarily the day before I saw him.

Mr. Lattimer seemed eager to work with me. A rather tall man, well-dressed, and not bad looking, he talked in a soft, serious manner. Most noteworthy seemed a strong subservience. He frequently would say, "Yes, Sir." I noticed some formality and stiffness, yet not to the degree that he appeared awkward. He asked me for instructions as to how to proceed in therapy. I told him I would see him four hours a week. He then asked to lie down on the couch, to which I agreed. He was apparently familiar with the analytic procedure. He at once began to talk about what troubled him.

His troubles, he told me, were his "symptoms." He was handicapped and tormented by a number of obsessions, and for one thing, he could not avoid dismantling or hiding any scissors and forks he saw. He was afraid somebody might be hurt by them. Since he often could not discard these objects safely, he had to secrete them in special hideaways. Also, he was afraid to cut his meat for fear the knife would slip out of his hands and hurt somebody. He had spent many hours checking his bathroom for fear of having mislaid a razor blade. When he stroked the cheek of his girl friend he was seized with

---

3. This focus of my presentation, it may be added, is different from many accounts of psychotherapies. For my focus is not primarily on the dynamics of relatedness, but is on the evolving vicissitudes of resistance, transference, and countertransference. A focusing on these dynamics would have, by necessity, brought out of focus the interplay of intra-analytic and extra-analytic factors as mentioned above. Therefore, the following study must be seen as complementing the more immediate dynamics of relatedness which in this presentation are touched upon but not systematically outlined.

the idea that she might take poison and die. He was haunted by the thought that he might have left the brakes off on his car, thereby unwittingly contributing to an accident. While driving, he had to combat sudden impulsive wishes to hit other cars or run over pedestrians.

These symptoms, I learned, had been present in a mild form throughout much of his adult life. It was during the last nine months, however, that they had become more severe and paralyzing. Six months ago he had started visiting a psychiatrist, seeing him in two-weekly sessions. This psychiatrist, dissatisfied with his therapeutic progress as well as with his living situation, had finally advised him to seek analysis in a hospital setting. Thus it was that he came to see me.

He had graduated from an Ivy League college, and afterward he had served with the Marine Corps. Here he had volunteered for a number of dangerous missions and had carried them out well. Still, he was dissatisfied with himself for having acted and felt like a coward on several occasions. At the time of his discharge from the Armed Forces he was a first lieutenant. He subsequently entered the car business headed by his father, and shortly thereafter he began having disagreements with his father about his job. He doubted whether the car business was right for him and wondered whether an artistic career might not be his true vocation. He quit his father's firm and for a while worked for another car dealer. Finally -- and this coincided with a "worsening" of his symptoms -- he gave up working altogether. He managed, however, to appear in a near-by city in a few night club performances, singing and playing the guitar. Apart from this, he appeared to do little which seemed constructive. He was drinking a lot, and for lack of anything better to do, he would play the guitar and listen to records.

He left his parents' house less and less frequently. One day he decided to have his room repainted in white squares. This, among his friends, added to his reputation of being a somewhat bizarre, though interesting, fellow. In this room he would often see his girl friend -- the one whom he feared dooming to death while caressing her. But these meetings were unpleasant, not only because of his tormenting doubts and obsessions, but because she clung to him like a leech. And, last but not least, they were made unpleasant because of his mother's frequent interference with his encounters. Jealously and inquisitively excited, his mother would try to find out how far their sexual relations had gone. At the slightest suspicion she would unleash a flood of stringent accusations at both of them. In addition, his general aimlessness and idleness became the targets for her many sarcastic comments. In these, she was not infrequently joined by the patient's father. In a sense, therefore, it was a relief when he could pack and drive east.

This being said, the first hour had come to an end.

THERAPEUTIC REFLECTIONS I

Mr. Lattimer's behavior as well as history suggested an obsessional neurosis, for his struggles with his hostility seemed the central theme. Against a fearsome eruption of this hostility characteristic obsessive defenses were employed. On the character level these were mainly obsequiousness, reactively developed, and intellectualization (isolation of thought from feeling). On the symptom level, typically ritualistic obsessive defenses were merging into more phobic patterns: they also reflected his predominant fear of, and concern with, hostility.

Two other questions, less clear after one hour, yet nonetheless of great interest remained:

First: the amount of intact ego -- the question, How "sick" was the patient?

Second: the dynamic constellation out of which his obsessive neurosis arose -- the question, What was the central conflict?

In trying to answer these questions, I reflected as follows:

(a.) The amount of intact ego.

The patient had become unable to function, and in view of the ongoing deterioration, his prognosis might seem not too bright. On the other side, I felt encouraged by his separating himself from his parents and his home situation. In seeking therapy he had displayed initiative. He had managed to make the trip to the sanatorium. He was intelligent. He evidenced a penchant for introspection, though, at present, rather sidetracked into intellectualizations. He did not strike me as an "obsessive" obsessive, inaccessibly entrenched in his obsessive armor. His guitar-playing, singing, and attraction to the stage pointed to possible areas of richer self-expression. He had been successful in the Marine Corps, indicating a sense of responsibility and perseverance.

(b.) The dynamic constellation out of which his neurosis arose.

As regards this question, I felt I could so far deal with only a few problematical signposts. I was struck with mainly two aspects of his situation: first, his -- up to now mostly futile -- attempts at finding a clear-cut masculine identity and career. In seeking his career he appeared to vacillate between choices that embodied conventional virility (Marine Corps and the "clean-cut executive") and others which pointed to more passive and, in the light of his background, more unconventional artistic longings and tendencies. Establishing a professional identity appeared interwoven with having to find a factual modus vivendi with his father: there was the unsolved

dilemma of either working under or completely apart from him. Unable
to decide himself in either way, he seemed bogged down in an obsessive
stew of indecisive drifting and halfhearted rebelliousness as, for
example, acting out in his drinking and flouting his father's career view
The themes of his problematical relationship to authority (cf. , his
servility) and of his not being able to accept and thereby better integrate
his passive and "homosexual side and concern" (this being only touched
upon in this first hour) seemed, partly at least, related to this conflict
with father.

Hardly separable from his father problem, his tie to his
mother appeared, at best, no less problematical. What he had told me
seemed to indicate, on mother's part, a closely binding, possessive
attitude toward the patient. Along with this, she seemed to have
considerable sexual interest in him, hinting at a partially acted-out --
and thus unsolved -- Oedipal conflict. Further, this Oedipal
constellation seemed intertwined with his problens about "clinging"
women and "homosexuality" as already mentioned.

At this early point I could not clearly see which layers of his
personality and relatedness were principally implicated. Particularly
I asked myself, Had his problems and central anxieties a more Oedipal
or pre-Oedipal dimension? This question in turn pointed back to the
first one mentioned: the amount of intact ego. His analysis and life
during the months to come were to provide further answers to these
questions. First, therefore, some comments about the conduct of his
life as I observed it.

HOSPITAL ADJUSTMENT

Mr. Lattimer's adjustment to the hospital was nearly perfect.
He was eager not to break any rules. He caused hardly any of the
"troubles" with which life in a psychotherapeutic hospital is normally
replete. He would have been the delight of any boardinghouse landlady.
That he was hospitalized at all seemed to be a matter of relative
insignificance. Within five months he smoothly made the transition
from inpatient to outpatient. In another six months he severed all
connections with the hospital and became a private patient of mine.

Outwardly, the course of his analysis during this first period
appeared similarly unremarkable. Its most outstanding aspect, in a
sense, was the fading from the center of his interest of his more
flamboyant obsessive symptoms. The forks, I learned almost
incidentally, had for the time being ceased to concern him. Also,
his remaining obsessive preoccupations or concerns either disappeared
or became more cryptic and unobtrusive. He appeared to match his
good "boardinghouse" behavior with "good" conduct during the analytic
hours -- he was usually more than punctual, eager to talk, and in
general, ready to do what he felt was expected from him.

Thus, his initial behavior inside and outside the hours gave evidence of more adaptability and "intact ego" than might have been expected from the first impression and history. At the same time, this initial behavior appears to throw some light on the question with which this study is primarily concerned -- the intricate interplay of new life experience and insightfulness.

SEPARATION FROM HOME

The patient's initial conduct, as sketched above, seemed immediately tied to a lessening of conflict-born anxiety. And this lessening of anxiety, in turn, appeared related to his separation from home.

His whole life situation at home -- this became clearer -- had been grinding him ever more deeply into his conflicts and, consequently, into anxieties bound to produce a neurotic symptomatology. He appeared caught in a web -- a relentlessly operating vicious circle leading to increasing incapacitating anxiety -- and only a rigorous tearing asunder of the web could, it seemed, bring to a halt the vicious circle. Analytic insightfulness, in other words, in order to have a real chance to grow, required a decisive move on the part of the patient. And this move he had made by packing his things and driving east.

Surely, being neurotic and having internalized his conflicts, he was bound to recreate a choking web anew for himself wherever he went. He was bound to re-establish the old neurotic constellation with any persons with whom he would get into more meaningful contact, but with this difference: he had managed to create a better starting position for the development of growth and change. He had given analysis a fair chance to propel and maintain him in a positive circle of expanding, insight-fed life mastery, as compared to the vicious circle in which he appeared to have got stuck. How, then, did he make use of this chance? With this question in mind, I shall now turn to what Mr. Lattimer talked about in the period following the first hour. Somewhat arbitrarily, I will consider this period the first month of treatment -- this month ending shortly before Easter, the time when the patient made a first visit home.

FIRST ANALYTIC MONTH

Following the first hour, he talked about his wish to be liked by everybody. He would like a profession in which he could most strongly move and influence people. He thought principally of three choices: becoming an Army commander, a singer, or an actor. He tried to say complimentary things about me, such as, "You seem to know your stuff," etc. From the fourth hour on, he talked more about his relationship to girls. They had been many, but fleeting. The relationship would usually start with a dash of excitement and promise, sometimes lead to a single intercourse, and then, as a rule, fade out. His last relationship, though, was an exception in that it lasted longer and did not lead to intercourse. Yet this relationship, as already mentioned, was made extremely unpleasant because of his fears that he might cause the girl's death, and also because of many obsessive worries that she might be unfaithful to him. She had to be pure and angelic in order that he might be able to love her. At the same time, in elaborating this line of thinking, he admitted that loose, disreputable women had a special attraction for him. He was entranced by acting and talking obscenely with a woman -- "to immerse himself in an orgy of dirty sex." Dark female underwear and big bosoms could exert a spell over him.

He reported his first dream in the twelfth hour. It dealt with his relationship to his girl friend:

> I am trying to have intercourse with Mary -- she seems ready and has her skirt up. But for some reason this does not materialize. I notice another girl lying beside her on the table. All of a sudden I realize my penis is broken and that part of it is stuck in the other girl's vagina. I am then finding myself holding the other part of the penis in my hand.

There were no associations to this dream. In the next hour, his thirteenth, he related how tense he usually felt about sex. He mentioned having sought and had fellatio with a number of girls, this also being the thrill of the "dark and dirty." This hour, occuring two days before Easter, ended the first month of treatment. The patient went home for a week.

THERAPEUTIC REFLECTIONS II

What had come out of this first month? In trying to review the situation for myself, I noticed the unfolding -- at least on a descriptive level -- of some aspects of the Oedipal drama. In particular, he evidenced a splitting of the love object -- the pure, angelic versus the dark seductive woman -- as described by Freud. In this attitude he reflected an isolation of the aggressive, lustful drive components from the tender adoring ones (their integration being normally a prerequisite for a successful and non-neurotic heterosexual adjustment). At the same time, this isolation of attitudes and subsequent splitting of love objects appeared to point to a relatedness to his mother in which these two drive components were strongly activated but also feared. A stronger reactivation of these two aspects of his relatedness to mother -- e.g., in a transference situation -- was then bound to mobilize the deeper castration fears and threats as manifested in his first dream. The isolation of these drive components and their being acted out in different contexts with different persons, therefore, had to be seen as a defense (and therewith avoidance of insightful acceptance) against his fear of castration and a destructive engulfment by mother.

At the same time, while tentatively reaching these conclusions, I was aware of the meager insight value for the patient of probably all which so far had been said. The modest insight value of his elaborations seemed reflected in the dry, unemotional, completely intellectualizing quality of his talk. Also, his first dream -- though seemingly highly meaningful in its content -- was given in a most detached, intellectual manner. It seemed unprofitable, for the moment, to encourage or await associations which would be equally cold, detached, and intellectual.

Genuine insightfulness, therefore, had to await the (at least partial) re-experiencing and thereby "working through" of his conflict in its affective depth in the analytic situation, that is, in a characteristic transference constellation. What then could I, on my part, contribute to foster the development toward a greater genuine insightfulness?

Perhaps not too much at this early stage. Yet essentially I felt I could be helpful in three ways: first, by simply displaying an understanding, nonmoralizing attentiveness which could possibly lessen some of his super-ego pressures. In particular, I tried to encourage him to amplify on the description of feelings and experiences of a more unconventional nature, especially when these had a lustful and homosexual flavor. In other words, I tried to encourage him to give the "feeling tone" of an experience instead of immediately tying this experience to conventional cliches most of them in bad repute.

Example:

> Patient: I recently met the pop singer A. in a plane. There was something homosexual about him. I at once got homosexual feelings myself and got panicky.

> Therap.: You mention homosexual feelings. Can you describe what you saw and felt?

> Patient: I think the fellow just looked queer to me. And then I got a tingling sensation in my lower body and --- uh --- I think in my penis also ... (Silence.)

> Therap.: Let's hear more!

Now the patient talks in an increasingly obsessional and intellectual manner about his "homosexuality."

There was, as this example shows, a subtle and quick merging of what might be called a flicker of expressed feeling into straight obsessionalizing. This obsessionalizing, to a degree, appeared as a counterphobic maneuver: by anticipating (visualizing, uttering, doing) that which was feared, some sort of magic control of the anxiety was attempted. Instead of "feeling out" his anxiety, he took the intellectualizing short circuit. That this had happened was conveyed to me, as a rule, less by the content of his talk -- that often seemed to have classical analytic relevance -- than by its tedious and boring quality.

Secondly, in order to be helpful, I could try to let him come to better terms with his hostility. The problem consisted, not so much in "encouraging the expression of his hostility, " as in increasing his awareness for more subtle, varied, and unconventional feelings. And this, thirdly, particularly implied a growing awareness of the interactional aspects of our relationship. In other words, this relationship could hopefully turn into a place where, among other feelings and attitudes, his hostility could be more safely experienced and expressed. He begins, for example, the eighth session by stating: "What can I do to make these hours useful?" This leads to his talking, though still very politely and mildly, about his dissatisfaction with having to make all the contributions himself. He complains about not getting more advice from me. He felt, he tells me, some irritation at my non-helping attitude. This leads to his (though again still rather mild) doubting of certain professional qualifications of mine. This and other trends then set the stage for what appeared as the central concern of the next phase -- namely, violence.

SECOND ANALYTIC PHASE

Several dreams during this period reflect some of the nature of this concern. The following dreams are representative of others which are not reported.

In the 33rd hour he reported this dream:

> I am riding on a motor scooter. A rabid dog is said to be running around loose. A few girls -- among them a nurse -- are with me, but they get lost somehow. I try to get into a tavern in which some rough boys are sitting. Yet they do not allow me to come in. I, in a somewhat forceful movement, break a window and thus enter the room. I learn later the rabid dog has killed many people.

The following two dreams were reported in the 38th hour:

> (1) I feel like dying. My head has been smashed, and the brain tissue and blood is spurting out.

(2) My nephew (the oldest son of his eldest sister, twelve years old) and I are breaking each other's arms. We get our arms broken about the same time. When I see his arm is broken, I feel I should take better care of him and I am embarrassed when the doctor comes.

The following dream was reported in the 42nd hour:

Six planes are crashing together in the air. I am watching the collision from the ground. Then I get concerned as to whether the parachutes are going to open. Also, I am beginning to worry that my nephew (the one mentioned in the last dream) might have convulsions. At the same time I feel rather strangely detached from all this.

The next dream, reported in the 44th session, shows how his concern with violence is, among other things, rooted in his relatedness to his father:

I was with my parents in the house of a couple, friends of the family. My father gets active in the conversation and starts bragging to the other man. A tiger approaches my father. I am scared but do not dare to shoot the tiger. Finally somebody else shoots the beast.

Five sessions later, in the 49th, he dreams of belonging to a team of bank robbers. In another dream he is getting instruction in the use of hand grenades and explosives.

His attitude toward these dreams is still detached. He talks about them seemingly unmoved. A feeling of anger is hardly noticeable: his violence appears still de-virulized by compartmentalization and isolation. This he himself expresses when he reports six crashing air planes and comments: "I feel rather strangely detached from all this."

His concern with violence appears, on this level, very much a matter of fearing its unforseeable but, as he believes, disastrous consequences: Are the parachutes going to open? Will I destroy a weaker person such as my nephew -- something I would have to feel ashamed about? Will my brain -- my intelligence, my defenses, my functioning self -- go to pieces? Where will it all lead to once I let loose?

The more such consequences are feared, the greater the need for isolating defenses with consequently more fear of explosive break-throughs. It seemed up to the analytic situation to provide the experiential proof that matters had not to be quite that way: that the feared break-throughs of feelings of anger and violence need not be catastrophic. In other words: that somewhat different ego- and superego-attitudes could be developed vis-à-vis these feelings, making them less fearsome as well as more controllable.

The strategy, I felt, had to be along the lines mentioned earlier: increasing his awareness for unconventional and uncliched impulses and, also, letting him feel it was not dangerous to express and enlarge these. I encouraged him to talk about "fringe feelings and fringe thoughts" -- feelings and thoughts which were on the fringe of his awareness -- and which possibly were having an unpleasant tinge to them.

Thus, in the 35th hour he reported the feeling that he could hit someone. When asked to enlarge on this feeling, he tied it to a comment I had made during the preceding session. I had impressed him as "soft and literate." With a fleeting sense of panic the thought had struck him: Dr. S. is a homosexual! He became obsessed with wanting to ask me whether I ever had had a homosexual affair. In obsessively worrying about this question he figured out that no answer from me could possibly satisfy him. Nothing could really remove his doubts. The theme of my "homosexuality," thus ignited, was -- while coming in waves -- to stay with us throughout the next two years. It served first as a peg on which he could hang hostile and distrustful feelings toward me. Secondly, it became a launching pad for his defensively cherished "virile toughness," his main stronghold against exposing himself to passive, "soft," dependent strivings and feelings which for him were often sexualized.

In the 50th hour I heard thoughts such as, "There is this German doctor who has been in the Hitler Youth and who is now screwing me up." In another hour, the 58th, he obsessively had to think "Shit on Dr. S. !"

Along with such verbal productions I noticed him becoming less servile in his attitudes, during the sessions as well as in his life outside the hours. At one session in this period he presented himself dirty, unshaven, and late -- all this being in strong contrast to his usual meticulousness and punctuality. Before coming to this hour he had been drinking. Drinking, I learned from him, would normally bring out his rebellious and nasty side.

In his life outside the analytic sessions he showed more initiative. He became rather active in various group activities. At that time he took the lead in a play performed by patients.

Also, he looked for a job. He soon found one as a tennis instructor -- tennis having been the one sport he had actively and ambitiously practiced in his youth -- and he began a relationship with a girl. He found himself an apartment outside the hospital, although administratively he continued to be an outpatient of the sanatorium.

All in all, the patient seemed ready for tackling his problems on a deeper level of insightfulness. This level, it turned out, implied greater focusing on the ties he had formed with his mother, manifesting themselves in problems concerning his dependency, passivity, and incestuous bind with her.

THIRD ANALYTIC PHASE

This phase, again, is delineated somewhat arbitrarily. I let it end with the day he became a private patient of mine.

Two dreams, one in the 69th and the other in the 72nd session, appear to reflect dominant themes of this phase.

(1) I meet a boy on the street. He looks soft. A Greek boy, good-looking, is with him. I enter a house with the soft-looking boy, and we begin listening to records. The records sound strange. There is also a picture of a cross. I then draw very close to the boy. I get my hands under his pants - there is no underwear! I wonder whether I will find male or female genitals. Finally I end up holding a penis in my hand. I enjoy this, but feel at the same time that I have become completely defenseless. In waking up I think: "Now, after all, has happened what I always feared!"

(2) I am close to my mother. She is pulling my head down toward her breast. Then she is putting a knife into my chest, and with a pair of scissors she is cutting my heart out.

He adds, similarly to the first "violence" dream: "I feel distant toward this dream. It was as though I were taking an inventory, knowing that I was dreaming." And just as was the case then, he produced no further comments or associations to the dream.

The second dream appears to point to the central duality in his tie to his mother: he lets her pull his head down to her breast, but in letting this happen runs the danger of being killed by such closeness -- mother, in offering the nourishing breast also draws the killing knife.

The first dream, among other things, again reveals his concern about his masculinity: Am I going to find, in opening myself up to analysis, male or female genitals and therewith a male or female identity?

Sexual preoccupations in one form or the other pervade much of the analytic work of this period. But it is sex with a strong oral tinge. Again and again he mentions being fascinated by big breasts. "Big bosoms," he says, "simply knock me out." Along with this fascination, passive homosexual strivings are more openly revealed.

A dream reported in the 48th hour finds him sucking the penis of a nude man. He talks about his wanting to suck my own penis. His greed, passively experienced and sexualized, sometimes seems to have the quality of an unbearable craving: he appears trapped in a vicious circle wherein insatiability and frustration only lead to more excitement with no chance of release.

While these preoccupations and experiences are revealed, he increasingly reports details about the seductive bind which his mother had constellated with him. Up to the age of ten and beyond, his mother would display a strong interest in his bodily and genital functions. She would often watch him urinate. He remembered her frequently giving him enemas and enjoying whipping him. At a time when he could easily have done this himself, she would wipe his behind following his bowel movements. She would reveal herself to him seminude, in girdle or nightgown, distinctly showing her full breasts. Long into his adolescence she would manifest a possessive, anxious overconcern about his heart and physical fitness. As a result, the patient developed a hypochondriacal and narcissistic investment in his body as well as his physical appearance. His body image, in fact, could be considered precariously fragile and immature.

LIFE EXPERIENCES IN THIRD PHASE

During this phase he continued to show initiative in working at his new-found job.

As the above themes were developed in our sessions, his relationship to his girl friend was greatly intensified. In a way, this girl had to bear the brunt of his sexual obsessions. He insisted on having intercourse with her three or four times a night and still felt frustrated and greedily craving in the morning. He developed an interest in watching his girl friend urinate. Subjectively he could experience his girl friend in two images which seemed polar opposite. He either saw her as very soft, childlike, and seductively exciting, or he experienced her as empty, small-breasted, abused, and stripped of all vitality. At the same time he became intensely jealous and possessive of her. This went so far that he distorted reality in a flagrantly paranoid manner. His girl friend, for example, had received the visit of a handsome athlete. For days after this visit he had to count the condoms in his drawer and got into obsessive doubting whether or not one was missing. He was convinced that he had seen a smear of lipstick on the face of the athlete after the latter had left his girl friend. His jealous possessiveness drove him to exclusively monopolize the evenings of the girl. However, this overcloseness, born out of anxiety, soon became intolerable to both of them. Violent quarrels and dramatic separations resulted. The separations soon became intolerable so that the partners were pulled together again. This then led to new separations, and so on. It was this interpersonal climate of dramatic separations and reunions which seemed to further foster the patient's sexual excitement as described above.

While all this happened, some of his old obsessions flared up anew. For example, he once more felt strongly driven and tempted to hit other cars while driving. He also again began collecting forks.

His girl friend, under the stresses of this situation, decided to enter psychotherapy herself.

THERAPEUTIC REFLECTIONS III

How -- and with this question I once more focus on the subject of this presentation -- was this relationship to his girl friend to be evaluated in the light of the analytic process? In reflecting on this question four aspects, all complexly related to each other, emerged:

(1.) This relationship re-enacted many elements that were characteristic of his earlier relationship to mother. Both relationships are marked by strong separation and castration anxiety with the concomitant mobilization of much greed and sexual excitement. In both relationships his ego controls appear subjected to maximal stresses, sometimes making precarious his adjustment to reality.

(2.) To the degree that this partial re-enactment of his relationship to mother amounted to a defensive avoidance of experiencing these elements in the analytic situation -- that is, in the transference -- the patient's behavior, as reflected in his relationship to his girl friend, had to be seen as "acting out." It is, however, questionable whether -- and if so, how far -- this acting out was avoidable at the present stage of his analysis. In order to answer this question, several other considerations have to be taken into account:

(3.) His relationship to his girl friend, as sketched above, was not merely re-enactment of his earlier relationship to his mother. His girl friend, though in many aspects like his mother, was different in others. This in itself constellated a somewhat different relationship. Furthermore, sufficient analytic ground had been laid by now to influence his relationship to the girl through what had transpired in the analysis. Meaningful analytic material had already accumulated. The patient increasingly could begin to draw parallels between what happened in his relationship to mother, what happened in his relationship to me, and what happened in his relationship to his girl friend. From the analytic situation he could begin to draw the ammunition of insightfulness in order to make transparent important repetitive and neurotic patterns in his over-all life.

(4.) And this seems important in order to see in final perspective the question raised above -- the intensified "acting out" of his separation anxiety in the relationship with his girl friend must, I believe, also be seen in the light of the greater expansion and initiative displayed by the patient outside the hours, and mentioned earlier. Though the patient was bound to experience these moves as liberating and as establishing trust in his masculine assertiveness, nonetheless they entailed a certain loss in closeness and protection as offered by the analytic relationship. Mother's stab in the back, in the eyes of the unconscious, was thus repeated by me. At the moment, however, the relationship to his girl friend might have been a safer area in which to give vent to his separation anxiety than the analytic relationship itself. The latter, in a sense, was still too much needed as base for a certain intimate, though passively tinged closeness, to be risked for the exposure of too much anxiety.

However -- this follows from the above -- things could not stay this way. Sooner or later the analysis had to absorb into itself more of those aspects of the patient's behavior which were re-enacted and acted out in his relationship to his girl friend. In order to be worked through and outgrown his dependency and separation anxiety would have to enter the analytic transference arena with greater emotional impact.

This "working through," along with other factors, could then help to de-neuroticize the relationship to his girl friend -- he could be expected to outgrow, in this relationship, more infantile and neurotic elements in his behavior. Hopefully, there could then develop a mutuality in which he increasingly recognized the real personality and needs of his partner.

What, then, could happen in the analysis to possibly facilitate this development? With this question in mind I shall turn to the fourth -- and by far longest -- analytic phase, lasting from the 166th to the 450th hour.

I let this phase begin with Mr. Lattimer's becoming a private ambulatory patient. It ends with a significant event in his life: his marriage to the girl friend mentioned above.

FOURTH ANALYTIC PHASE

This phase, necessarily greatly condensed, continued to show an increasing emotional "defrosting" of the patient. His report of his dreams lost much of its wooden, distant quality. He more frequently volunteered associations which revealed feeling. He became more direct and open in commenting about me. In particular, his passive wishes and homosexually tinged strivings were more freely related to traits or comments of mine.

However, this trend toward a greater emotional freedom seemed strangely counterbalanced by another trend: a tendency to "paint life grey on grey." The most central feeling to emerge in the first part of this phase appeared to be one of general dullness and depression. Sometimes with considerable irritation or with an apathetic resignation he stated that he found the hours unproductive and useless. I myself was seen as unsympathetic, ungiving, and distant. He believed nothing of value was coming out of our work any more. He wanted to reduce the number of weekly sessions from four to three and talked about stopping analysis altogether. The following dream reported during the earlier part of this phase reflects the basic mood and attitude pervading many of our sessions:

> I am riding on a horse over a prairie. I finally meet a woman with a voluptuous figure. She is clad in a bikini that brings into strong contours her huge buttocks. I try to touch the buttocks. But when I stretch out my hands, the buttocks collapse -- they crack up like an old walnut which is empty.

A short time later, while again talking about his "emptiness and depression," he developed the following fantasy:

> I feel like I am in a dark whirlpool. Somebody is sticking his dick (penis) into my mouth, and I am trying to hold on to that -- somewhat like a circus artist dangling in the air by biting a rope. But it's no use: I am going down deeper and deeper. Then I get a feeling as if I wanted to go back into the womb again. Yet the womb turns into a bubble. Nothing remains. Then I am beginning to feel like a child who is curling up under a blanket.

Still a little later he has the fantasy of sucking on a huge breast, "but the nipple tastes like rubber." He is struck by the terrible thought of being tied throughout his life to a flat-chested woman (his girl friend is, in fact, rather flat-chested).

The theme of his "disillusionment" with the big breast continued to stay with us throughout this period and, in waves, also up to the end of the analytic work.

However, another theme became gradually more central, particularly from the middle of the fourth phase on. This theme clearly reflected the growing importance of his relationship to his father, and along with this, the father's relationship to his mother (viz., the triangular aspect of the Oedipal situation).

I again began to hear more comments, many of them sharply hostile, about my "effeminate, intellectual manner." At the same time I began to learn more of the details of his father's personality and life, and the relationship the patient had with him.

In these accounts the father emerged as a basically weak and insecure man who managed, because of his ambition and shrewdness, to become reasonably successful as a businessman. He was emotionally impoverished and self-absorbed, an unquestioned slave to the clichés of the Midwestern culture in which he grew up. One of the greatest blows in his life was not being elected to membership in the country club despite the fact that he was financially successful. His relationship to women in general, and to his wife in particular, was, on the surface, characterized by much chivalry, but underneath, he had fear of, and contempt for, them. He met his future wife -- the patient's mother -- when the latter asked him, pantingly and excitedly, to pose as her friend so that she could frustrate a suitor who was pursuing her. At this very meeting he offered the girl a "bigger ring" than her suitor could possibly give her. She accepted, and thus they came to be engaged. The father throughout the marriage had fleeting and clandestine affairs with secretaries, etc., while outwardly posing as a most gentlemanly spouse and the defender of the honor and purity of women.

While this and related material was being dealt with in our sessions, he reported the following dream:

> I am at a party with a woman. The woman is about thirty-four years of age, not pretty, but well-built. She is wealthy, and that attracts me to her. I am going to put the make on the woman but feel the husband is standing in the background and watching me. Then I feel, also, that you are in the house and that you are disapproving of what I am doing. Her husband turns out to be one of the superiors in my office. He is successful in causing her to undress. I am reaching out for my guitar and begin to play. But I am not heard, and I am fading into the background.

In this dream, as well as in others, the father and, along with him, the triangular aspect of the Oedipal situation became more important. In a number of successive dreams he appeared more successful in combating and even eliminating father than the above dream suggests.

LIFE EXPERIENCES IN FOURTH PHASE

We have first of all to turn to his relationship to his girl friend. There was in this relationship a distinct development toward "de-neuroticization." Certainly, crises and upheavals flared up again and again -- this was the case up to the very end of the analysis and beyond -- yet through all these crises the partners appeared to grow closer while learning to appraise each other more realistically. Gradually the thought of marrying the girl took hold of the patient. As time went on, he showed increasing initiative and firmness in his wish to marry. I myself continued to have doubts regarding the wisdom of this decision. Some aspects of his choice of partner, I felt, had not yet been fully understood and worked through in the light of his neurotic needs and conflicts. Yet taking into account all factors, including the fact that the girl herself was in analytic therapy, and after reviewing my doubts and objections openly with the patient, I finally consented. I decided, since I could see no overwhelmingly destructive factor in the situation, to respect the patient's decision.

In the second place, I had to deal with the development of the patient's professional life. This development seemed hardly less important than that which marked his relationship to his girl friend. For the first time in his life he had made a reasonably realistic and straightforward appraisal of what he wanted to do. Based on this appraisal he decided to change jobs. He enlisted in a training program that promised to make use of his organizational interests and skills and also gratify his artistic propensities. Within a period of not quite three years -- and herewith I am somewhat anticipating future developments -- he managed to obtain a rather responsible position in the organization with which he had become affiliated. This course of his professional life confronted him with many stresses, problems, and challenges. His relationship to authority again and again seemed to pose the most difficult problems of all. This was true for the trainee period as well as the time he himself became increasingly a wielder of authority and responsibility.

THERAPEUTIC REFLECTIONS IV

I shall now try to tie together some of the developments inside and outside the hours as these have been sketched above.

In accordance with what could be expected from my earlier speculations, we notice a reshifting of the arena on which his central dependency problem is experienced. It is now above all in the analytic situation where he experiences the drying-up of the maternal breast, the coming to naught of his nipple kingdom. Along with this, some steam seems to have been taken out of the separation anxiety experienced in the relationship to his girl friend. In this relationship, we have seen, there was a trend toward increasing de-neuroticization.

At the same time the depression and futility manifested in the analytic situation must be seen as being interdependent with the initiative and success he displayed in the work arena. This initiative reflected as well as fostered a growth of his self-worth. This helped him to find a more secure position in relation to his girl friend. But, and more important in this context, it made it possible for him to face more freely and to admit what he feared and what he had missed in life. Being visibly confirmed in his masculine competency and assertiveness as displayed and measured in the professional arena helped him to reveal further in the analysis what he had learned to consider his weak, soft, dependent, and contemptible sides. It also increased the security base from which he could afford to more openly feel and express his annoyance, futility, and disillusionment with me. In the light of increased hope and knowledge of his abilities he could feelingly face and analyze his underlying depression and deficiencies.

But further -- and herewith I turn to the developments which fell mainly into the second part of the fourth phase -- the greater prominence of Oedipal problems in this phase of the analysis has to be seen in connection with his professional life. In a sense, his new professional situation was bound to reconstellate important aspects of the Oedipal drama: in entering the competitive professional field more earnestly, he again was forced to solve the problem of finding a maturer modus vivendi with masculine authority figures. In particular, he had to develop and integrate the abilities both to compete and cooperate. But this precisely had been the arena on which he had floundered previously. His earlier relationship to his father, intensified by the patient's living with and working under his father, had resulted only in a paralyzing neurotic conflict. In some respects the patient thus appeared over-identified with the father -- the patient, for example, was strongly motivated to become a conventional, "tough," obsessive business hero. But such goals were also bitterly despised and hated -- in himself as well as in newly found father substitutes. Such conflictful strivings and identities vis-à-vis father had, so far, merely gone underground and were not solved.

When, therefore, his present job situation brought him into emotionally significant contacts with authority figures there began to smoulder in him, behind the facade of outer obedience and affability, a tendency to attack, undermine, and belittle the other person's authority. All this was experienced with much anxiety. And this anxiety was heightened by the interdependence of his authority problems, thus activated, with his Oedipal conflict: the hated father figure (with whom he was nonetheless over-identified in some respects) tended to be experienced as a sexual rival also. This fact was most dramatically impressed upon me when the patient got entangled in a brief sexual affair with the wife of one of his immediate superiors. It was exactly this man whom the patient hated most because of this person's seeming arrogance and ruthless ambition, though outwardly the patient acted quite obsequiously toward him. This affair stopped at once despite continuing encouragement from this superior's wife as soon as its self-destructive elements and, in particular, its repetitive Oedipal aspects had been discussed in our sessions.

FINAL PHASE

This period lasted thirteen months. In a sense, it appears to bring no new developments but a ripening of old ones. The themes which were taken up in previous periods are continued, revealing new aspects and interconnections. The flower of insightfulness, after having learned to grow in the analytic soil, can now bear fruit. Deeper levels of emotional meaningfulness are reached as many aspects of his past and present life and his behavior and productions during the sessions are integrated. Thus, his central conflicts and problems appear in even stronger outline.

I shall first turn to his relationship to his mother. Increasingly, this relationship, marked by a binding and infantilizing intimacy, was experienced as lacking trust. He said: "I never dared to trust Mother in a feeling sort of way. Mother's feelings never seemed to correspond to her actual state of being. I think most of the time she was depressed behind an outer facade of gaiety. Not knowing what was real -- the depression or the gaiety -- I tried to keep emotionally distant." And, he adds, after a pause: "Now I am sure that the depression was more real." He also comments frequently on mother's unpredictability resulting from the lack of genuineness in her demonstrated feelings.

As these things were talked about, I heard more comments about my own -- his therapist's -- lack of trustworthiness. "Why do you see me, after all? It must be in your own interests which have nothing to do with me. You are distant and uninvolved like a cold fish!"

Yet along with such and similar comments I heard statements indicating an almost opposite concern: that I might become drawn too close to him. In this concern his fear of boundary loss is clearly evidenced. He speaks of the "pit of intimacy" into which he fears falling together with me. At another time he compares his being drawn closer to me to the "wobbly interpenetration of two egg yolks -- one mixed-up mess!" His hostility -- feared, impulsively eruptive, and coloring so much of his behavior and symptomatology during the earlier phase of the analysis -- was to a considerable degree an outgrowth of his need for reinstating boundaries as these were threatened by his strivings for over-closeness, over-identification with and overdependence on others.

As he developed a greater awareness of his dependency needs and as his relative autonomy grew, there was, accordingly, a fading away of much of this violent demeanor (manifested mainly by the reaction formation of obsequiousness) and of his at times super-virile assertiveness.

On a somewhat different level, however, this reactive toughness and tendency to become violent appeared directly related to his Oedipal dilemma, and along with this, to his hate of his father and competitiveness with him. His fear of castration was the central theme in a number of dreams. Yet these dreams also seemed to reflect a sense of increasing strength and masculine wholeness on his part. In the 620th hour, for example, the following two dreams were reported:

(1.) I am in an armored car and direct artillery fire against an enemy. I get scared as the enemy, despite my fire, is drawing closer. At the end, however, a reconciliation takes place: I become friends with the enemy. A huge Negro woman is serving hamburgers to all of us.

(2.) I am in a little blockhouse. A woman is with me. (This woman, in his later associations, reminds him of his mother.) A tough-looking man enters the blockhouse and draws a gun. At first I feel paralyzed and inefficient, but finally I draw a gun myself and fire. I realize with horror that my leg is shot off. The stump is bleeding profusely. But then I see it growing again, and I am overjoyed. Everything on the leg grows to size again, except for one toenail which is missing.

During the first months of this last period I heard his perhaps most biting comments about my being an "effeminate, soft, intellectual weakling," etc. There occurred impulsive lines of thought such as, "Dr. S. looks so tired again. With whom -- which one of his boy friends -- has that hairy cocksucker made out last night?"

In tying such feelings and attitudes to his past relationship to his father, his father emerged as a weakling. His greatest weakness of course was his inability to establish a more mature relationship to his wife in order to prevent the latter from overinvesting herself so destructively in the patient.

His relationship to his father -- distant, hateful, contemptuous, and failing to provide him with the base for a successful masculine identification[4] -- was experienced as having exacted a heavy toll from him. This toll was paid in terms of his crippled emotional development, and in particular, his inadequate capacity for friendship. His youth, it was revealed with increasing clarity, had been essentially friendless. There were many accounts of his trying to find a friend or buddy, and this failed each time. He felt stranded as a lonely outsider. His decision to join the Marine Corps, apart from its evident counterphobic aspects, thus appeared strongly motivated by his wish to finally find a group of comrades. But this was essentially in vain. Since the capacity to feel freely, to enjoy a relaxed self-expression, and in a wider sense, to have creative relatedness to life depends on the feedback from and through actual relationships to actual people, his deficient and conflictful relationship to father was seen as accounting for what, at this stage of his life and analysis, emerged as one of his most central problems: his own relative

---

4. This statement is not totally correct as there was also a partial identification with father.

emotional impoverishment, his deficiencies in the art and skills of living, loving, creating.

He became more able to face these deficiencies. The lost and missed opportunities of his life, he realized, could not be undone. He felt sad. But while reviewing his past in the light of these losses, the past did not look totally blank. There emerged a person who had once served as a model for a positive masculine identification. Later this identification had been greatly demolished and made ineffective for the conduct of his life. But now, after a good deal of analytic work had been done, the remnants of this identification could serve as a basis for gaining new attitudes and experiences. This person had been an uncle, a brother of the patient's mother. He was a lawyer, lived in the close vicinity of the patient's family, and showed some paternal interest in the patient when the latter was eight to ten years old. The patient, expressing warmth and admiration, recalled the joyful walks he had with this uncle. He remembered sitting in his uncle's studio and listening, his fantasy richly stimulated, to accounts of this uncle's activities and travels. When the uncle died -- the patient was then about eleven years old -- he left a sizable amount of money expressly earmarked for the patient's education.

During the first months of this last period, as I have mentioned earlier, the patient used to attack me sharply because of my "effeminate, intellectual manner." These attacks now subsided. Instead of hearing derogatory comments, I began to notice a note of admiration and friendship. He found similarities between me and his uncle. Along with this, he appeared to be more relaxed a number of times. He simply noticed more and found more things he could enjoy. For example, he developed an interest in foreign movies which previously he had shunned as being "fairy stuff and bloodless." Also, sometimes I noticed a delightful sense of self-irony and humor.

I began to reflect more about this uncle's role in the patient's life. The uncle probably had much to do with keeping his homosexuality latent. Bieber[5] and associates, in the majority of their analyzed cases, found a rather typical family constellation in which the developing male homosexual occurred. This was an over-intimate, binding mother, and a father who was weak and, for mother, despicable. The prognosis for the eventual analytic correction of the homosexual problem, Bieber found, improved to the degree that the father was at least partially respected by mother, and thus allowed to have, particularly during the Oedipal phase, some qualities with which the patient could positively identify. The prognosis also became better when a more positive father-figure was at least temporarily available. These were probably the two reasons that prevented Mr. Lattimer from becoming more intrenched in a homosexual way of life.

---

5. Bieber, I. et al. Homosexuality. New York: Basic Books, 1962.

TERMINATION

Gradually the patient had become more "real" to me. Toward the end of analysis he sat vis-à-vis myself in a chair. Along with such elements of "realness," the forthcoming separation was bound to be experienced as a real loss. "The task for me," he stated on one occasion a short time before ending his analytic work, "will now consist in finding through other relationships -- foremost in those I have with my wife and my friends -- what I found here. Most of all I will miss being freely myself with another person as I could be with you." In addition, he expressed other feelings about my leaving and the approaching end of our work. Among these feelings were relief, satisfaction about having "stuck it out," resentment about being abandoned, and anxiety as to whether he was "going to make it"--all these feelings corresponded to different transference constellations and levels of awareness.

His life during this last phase continued in the direction outlined earlier. In his relationship to his wife -- brought about also through the latter's own therapy -- one more serious crisis developed. At one point it seemed doubtful whether the marriage would continue. The crisis was resolved when, after a separation of ten days, the partners found themselves together again. Thereafter they managed to live with each other more successfully. Their sex life, having been rather barren for some time, became, upon the solution of this crisis, more enriching and satisfying to both of them. Once more a crisis helped to bring into clearer focus the central problems arising from his relationship to his mother.

He continued to advance in his career. Along with such advancement he was once more confronted with choosing between activities typical of the "organization man" and activities of a more artistic and, in a sense, more creative nature. Once more this choice, pressed upon him by his professional advancement, highlighted for him the problem of being partly identified with as well as being hatefully rebellious against his father. Also, it contributed to his having to face with great acuity the factors and events, outlined earlier, which had prevented him from developing in himself a more richly emotional and creatively expressive dimension.

This implied, of course, a re-facing of the dilemma which, before the start of his analysis almost four years ago, had led to his neurotic capitulation vis-à-vis the difficulties encountered. Now, however, he appeared in a position to tackle this dilemma more successfully. In his personal development as well as in his whole life situation he had reached a more secure and promising base for facing and solving it. By now, it appeared, analytic insightfulness and new life experience had joined in a positive movement permitting the prospect of further movements despite the actual termination of the analysis.

ADDENDUM

. Did you formulate a specific diagnosis before you began psychotherapy, or was it made after psychotherapy was in progress?
Do such pre-therapeutic diagnoses inhibit or facilitate taking a
patient into treatment? Are your diagnoses subject to revision
as psychotherapy proceeds, and do they vary depending on the
way the patient responds to the treatment? Do you distinguish
between diagnosis as such and simple spontaneous diagnostic
reflections?

. My case presentation has partly answered these questions. In
general, I tried to assess the patient in terms of his assets and
liabilities, but less so in classic diagnostic terms. Since I
consider therapy an ongoing process of understanding-
participation, my evaluation of the patient is bound to change
and deepen to the degree that this process gets under way.
Spontaneous diagnostic reflections are part of this process.
However, too strong a preoccupation with questions of diagnosis
should make me suspicious about some unsolved countertransference problem of mine.

. Did you approach your patient with a consistent and verbalizable
theory or set of hypotheses on personality structure and/or the
genesis of psychic illness? Was such theory used directly
(or indirectly) in selecting the patient for treatment? How was
it applied in the treatment and how effective was your theory in
reaching the goals of treatment? What do you see as the function
of such hypotheses or theories?

. Any theory is like a telescope, bringing into focus certain aspects
of reality while blurring or excluding others. In this sense, I
approached the patient with a theory which was, I believe,
essentially psychoanalytic. How far I have been able to thus
grasp and appropriately react to the patient's difficulties, I do
not know. An acceptable therapeutic outcome seems to me to
offer no proof for the correctness of any theory about personality
structure and/or genesis of mental illness. Therefore, I think
any theory, at best, can serve as a guideline for our therapeutic
attitude, which must be open to revision in the light of new and
contrary evidence.

What did you think of the prognosis of your case before you
accepted the patient for treatment? What did you think during
the first several interviews; and during the latter stages of
treatment? Do you feel prognostic judgments about ultimate
health or ultimate illness are useful? Can we dispense with a
prognosis as a formal event in clinical treatment?

A. I have dealt with this question in my case presentation. I see the problem of prognosis in a similar light as that of diagnosis. A certain trust in the patient's recuperative powers -- which will convey itself to the patient -- seems to me more important than a formal prognosis.

Q. What particular therapeutic techniques did you apply in this case? Which of them were most effective and which ineffective, and for what reasons? Did you attempt any technical innovations on an empirical basis? When did you feel that a "peak" experience or turning point occurred?

A. In general, I feel that I was rather attentive and passive with my patient. I was confirmed in this more classical analytical attitude in view of the intrusiveness of the patient's mother, that is, her tendency to overpower, seduce, and dominate the patient. By greatly adhering to the classical analytic position, I, in other words, tried to present a certain counterposition to the patient. After about two years of therapy the feeling climate became livelier, and in a sense I then felt more engaged. But in contrast to a number of other therapeutic experiences, I feel unable to pinpoint in this case a distinct "turning point."

Q. Did you feel that Freud's formulation of transference and counter transference were sufficient to account for the therapeutic encounter with your patient? How would you describe your encounter?

A. Without Freud's formulation of transference and countertrans-ference this therapy would not have been possible. Both the characteristic structuring and investigation of the relationship between doctor and patient presuppose these two concepts. Certainly there is also much to this relationship which transcends the concepts transference and countertransference, but at the moment we are less able to grasp and describe this aspect of the relationship than the dynamics of transference and counter-transference.

Q. It has been said that psychotherapy is a white, middle-class, urban phenomenon which does not necessarily apply to other social stratifications or cultures. In what way did your patient's cultural background influence his illness and treatment? In what way did your own cultural background assist or deter the treatment?

A. This case -- at first sight -- seems to confirm the assumption that psychotherapy is a white, middle-class, urban phenomenon. I believe it is evident from my presentation that the problems of the present-day American middle class reflect themselves in my patient's conflicts. To mention only a few: his cherishing the values of the hard-working obsessive business executive at the expense of softer and more passive sides in him, his cult of virility, etc. I believe that in general I was both similar and different enough to facilitate a creative interpersonal dynamic between us.

There is an increasing tendency for neo-analytic thinking to ascribe the genesis and treatment of psychic illness to the social psychology of the family. How did this apply in your case?

As it is evident from my case presentation, the parents' role in fostering the patient's psychic illness is fateful. Yet, the relevancies of the parents' influence to the structuring of the treatment situation is another matter. I believe that the parents' influence in this special case came to bear on the patient's treatment mainly via the characteristic transference and countertransference dynamics which it constellated. In this sense the actual family became a more distant problem than holds true for the treatment of patients who are still dependent on their parents, such as adolescents and many psychotics.

If your treatment was concluded what criteria did you use for terminating it? If it is still in process, what guide points would you use to determine when your patient is sufficiently improved to discontinue treatment? Do you feel that a patient should be seen as long as he feels he needs it and is willing to pay the fees?

The main criteria for terminating therapy were, first, a mutual agreement as to its advisability; second, my conviction that the patient's main problems had been worked through sufficiently. I think there are situations in which a patient hangs on to an analytical dependency which the therapist, in turn, may foster. The analyst then has to come to grips with this problem by asking himself how much he, on his part, may have an interest in keeping the patient dependent on him. But each case is different, and generalizing appears difficult in this matter.

Did you make any mistakes in this case -- in the sense of "if you had to do it over"?

I believe I made mistakes which, however, were less mistakes in technique than shortcomings in my experience and life development at the time. Since my technique is, in a sense, sustained and modulated by my over-all experiences in life, I could not do this case all over, even if I wished to do so.

Q. In treating your case did you perhaps feel that the classical distinctions between psychoses and neuroses were breaking down? (This question may apply even if your case represents neither a psychotic or neurotic.)

A. I consider the distinction between psychosis and neurosis to be fluid in any case. The defense and restitutive mechanisms serve in psychotics as well as neurotics to salvage some functioning self at the expense of a reduced adaptation to reality, and of crippled growth. Our therapeutic approach of course has to take into account the kind and severity of the patient's difficulties.

Chapter X

TIME-LIMITED THERAPY FOR AN AGENCY CASE

By John Warkentin and Carl A. Whitaker

"I had a second birth when my soul and body
loved one another and were married."

Khalil Gibran

Long-term psychotherapy is frequently not practical with
clients referred by social agencies. Yet there is currently a national
movement toward the increased use of psychotherapists in rehabilitating
such clients. Tension and conflict have sometimes developed in the
past between the referring agency and the therapist, with one attempting to offer help within the limitations of their budget, while the other
endeavors to get into as deep a relationship as the patient requires.
Many years ago Otto Rank suggested an "out" for this dilemma when
he stated that patients will adapt themselves to any necessary administrative limitations of the therapeutic schedule. The authors
have also noted this but have added the observation that patients will
adapt themselves differently to different therapists.

This case demonstrates how a patient and a therapist were
able to utilize the opportunity offered by the referring agency. Patti
was seen for one preliminary diagnostic consultation by J. W., who
then sent his report and recommendation to the agency, which in turn
authorized ten therapy interviews for Patti.

INTRODUCTION BY J. W.

I first saw Patti on November 7, because she had recently
developed an acute spider phobia to the point that she could not
concentrate, was constantly anxious, and was about to be fired from
her telephone job for "inattentiveness." I saw Patti as a neatly
dressed, quite attractive and friendly woman, age forty-five. She
was mildly suspicious, and inspected my office with curiosity.

Her early history is that she was born into a lower-middle-
class home where her mother was twelve years older than her father.
She grew up physically healthy and her physical health remained good.
There was a tendency toward moderate shyness. She had a younger
sister who got married at an early age to a man twenty-three years
her senior. The two girls had never been close. Patti had begun to
menstruate at age thirteen, had moderate cramps and severe pre-
menstrual tension for many years. She went through high school,
took a short business course, and then did office work until she married.

As a teen-ager Patti had not been permitted to date until age sixteen, at which time she met her future husband, Durden, age nineteen, a boy who had been raised as an orphan. Her parents repeatedly told Patti that boys were dirty and she should be careful with them. At age twenty Patti became engaged to Durden. Her father died of a lung ailment four days after this engagement. Patti married Durden after a short engagement, but normal intercourse was impossible (until after the first baby) because of her strong hymen. She became pregnant anyway within months. The pregnancy and delivery went well, and she had a baby girl. At age twenty-five she had a son, and at thirty-one she had her third and last child, a daughter. At the time of her therapy, Patti's two older children were "on their own," and only Tessie (age fourteen) was still at home.

As a child Patti was very repressed, lonely, and isolated. She had three repetitive childhood nightmares: 1. A tremendous tidal wave is approaching; Patti tries to run away, but the wave becomes larger and finally covers the sky. 2. The large sail of a big sailing vessel comes loose, and falls down to smother Patti. 3. Her mother is pushing a baby carriage on the street, and suddenly both mother and baby disappear into a large manhole.

At about age ten Patti learned to masturbate, and did so until the birth of her first baby when she was twenty-three years old. At that time she began having normal intercourse with her husband, Durden, about once a week with little or no satisfaction. She "always felt unclean afterwards."

When Patti was twenty-seven, she got her first driver's license. At age thirty-six a more significant change occurred in her life. Her mother died at about this time. Patti for the first time looked at herself naked in a full-length mirror. At this time she developed moderately severe migraine headaches and considered herself to have entered the menopause. However, she continued to have some irregular periods. For many years she had been hungering for a man other than her husband, and finally at age forty-one she had an affair with a married man named Ormill. She arranged this affair so that he took all the initiative and carried all the responsibility. In this affair she experienced her first real sexual pleasure, but was constantly upset during the year it lasted because she did not feel guilty over the adultery. After she met Ormill, Patti never again had intercourse with her husband, and three years later they got a quiet divorce.

Patti then worked as telephone operator until this job was threatened by the development of her severe spider phobia. Just before seeing me the first time, Patti had such a real dream of a spider being in bed with her that she turned on the light and tried to find it. She had never dreamed of sexual intercourse prior to therapy She had been troubled by various unreality feelings, such as déjà vu, or that she was not the person talking, or that people looked smaller than their real size. She had never been interested in religion because her father was an atheist. She stated that she was formerly neat, orderly, punctual, and perfectionistic, but was becoming less so in recent years. She was phobic of deep water, elevators, dentists, horses, driving a car, smoke coming at her, thunder, and of course, spiders. She was particularly afraid "that something, not someone, will get to me in bed," and kept a knife under her pillow just in case. Patti consciously associated her current neurotic difficulties with family experiences, and ruminated over such details in her memory as her sister's blatant promiscuity, her father's great fear of death, and her mother's irritability and critical attitude.

My feeling response to Patti in the initial consultation was one of liking and respect. She had had no previous counseling or psychotherapy but was quite psychologically-minded, and I thought her motivation would develop. I felt there was a good possibility that she would achieve enough symptom relief so she could continue supporting herself and her daughter. I also thought there was a chance that I could help her to reinitiate and facilitate her further growth as a person. (For formal diagnosis, see Addendum No. 1.)

In addition to the extensive interview notes which I made at the time, all the interviews were taped, except numbers 2 and 3. C. W. and I listened to the tapes repeatedly, and C. W. then formulated his discussions and summary.

CASE OF PATTI: Interview Segments from Tape Recording

First Therapy Interview, 8 A.M. on Jan. 4:

Therapist begins: It seems like ages since I saw you the other time.

Patient: It has been. And the holidays have passed (embarrassed laugh).

T: Ten interviews, Mr. Smith authorized. That should give us a chance to get some understanding, or some possible changing of your adjustments. November 7, two months ago it was.

P: Is that when I was in here?

T: Uhu.

P: (loud cough; pause)

T: As I was driving to work this morning, I saw that beautiful sky.

P: Oh, did you see it?

T: I thought, it is really a good omen for your therapy.

P: When I came out this morning and looked up, it was just so beautiful that I thought, if I were younger, it would just make me feel like conquering the world. It just gave me the most wonderful feeling. Then by the time I got onto Peachtree, it seemed sort of cold-looking. It changed.

T: I keep thinking, some day I'm going to live in North Georgia, north of here.

Segment 4 minutes later:

P: The only sicknesses I seem to have are from my own tensions, and I think I've gotten over the part of catching bugs, or that I'll be struck down tomorrow, you know (embarrassed laugh).

T: There are two ways of looking at it, one is that if we somatize our anxieties, there's no way to do anything else with them.

P: Uhu.

T: There's no way to resolve somatized anxiety. So, in many ways, free-floating anxiety is something that's much easier to work with, which is what you must be carrying if you're not somatizing it. The other side of it is that some people are so rigidly controlled and so determined that they can't get sick.

P: And that's bad?

T: Well, they do an awful lot of wheel-spinning to stay physically healthy; it's sort of a desperate all-out effort, "I must not be sick."It would be a catastrophe if I stayed in bed for a day.

P: Yes, I think I feel that way somewhat, particularly since I started working. When I was home with the children, if I had a migraine headache, uh, I didn't like it at all, but I felt I had a day or two to get over it, take care of my house and my children; but I can't have that sort of nonsense now, you know.

T: That's the quality I mean; you just expressed it well.

P: Well, I just think that's sort of good because anyone who's had a migraine headache of any severity would be glad to find a way of not having one. And I don't know if that's the reason, or whether even though I'm very tense and full of anxiety, maybe there's a different kind now, or something, so that I'm not so likely to get migraines or something. I feel them starting once in a while, but I seem to be able to channel it into another way rather than to have the pain.

T: You can sure do it with anxiety. You have a migraine coming on, you just get real anxious, and make it. . . . I didn't remember about your migraines, you probably told me.

P: They didn't start till (cough) I was about thirty-six, I think.

T: Yes, that's what you mentioned.

P: And then I did develop quite a fear of them.

T: You had any since you were here?

P: I think I've had two. I know of one; and I've been threatened several times.

Segment about 20 minutes later:

P: I still don't believe all these things about myself. I've done them all so they must be true, but (pause) it seems impossible to me.

T: Sort of as if your experience and your image of yourself don't jibe.

P: That's right. Not at all. Because for years I . . . I never had a high opinion of myself certainly, but I acted as though I did, and I guess I almost came to believe it, except way down inside where no one ever knew about it. Then all of a sudden I do all of the things that society condemns. And actually, it doesn't bother me too much, that about society condemning me. I don't know what it is that bothers me. I guess it's that I, I, I hurt other people.

T: There we go again!

P: (Laugh - cough) Yeah.

T: It's the one thing you keep coming back to.

P: Uhu. I can't get away from it. It horrifies me. There are three nice kids, and a good man.

T: And you are this witch that did all this terrible thing.

P: Uhu. The thing is that I was a witch all along, but they didn't know it.

T: You've got ten sessions. (Patient laughs)

Segment about 9 minutes later is end of Interview Number 1:

T: I'm glad to be working with you.

P: That's good.

T: I'm leaving the making of appointments between you and the secretary. Anything you work out with the secretary, that's when I'll look for you. I have one suggestion about it; we have ten times with each other. It's going to take calendar time as well as interview time to make any change in yourself. You've been saying today that changing your person is not easy. That the image you've had of yourself in years past is sort of permanent. You said several things indicating that you weren't sure you could change anything. That maybe all these things .

P: (interrupts) That is, I'm afraid I won't be able to.

T: You want to.

P: I want to.

T: But you have a fear that you won't be able to. I'd suggest that you plan these ten interviews so that there is some calendar time in between . . .

P: (interrupts) You mean, rather than come in next week . .

T: (interrupts) Yes . . .

P: (interrupts) I have four appointments set up now for a week apart, so change that to two weeks?

T: I'm going to leave that to you.

P: Uhu.

T: And I suggest that you sleep on it before you make any changes in the schedule. But think on it, this belongs to you now, these ten sessions, how you want to use this. I would think it wiser that you come in every two or three weeks.

P: Uhu.

T: You may want to come in next week just to be sure you're started with me. Sometimes people get a feeling that this thing isn't real. If there's a month between appointments, maybe it's not really significant. So you may want to come in next week and then skip a week or two, whatever. So think about it, deal with it as your property, it belongs to you.

P: Uhu.

T: But if you can stretch it over a period of months some-how, I'll be more useful to you.

P: All right. I'll think on it, then. Well, I enjoyed talking with you, too; and it isn't the frightening experience so far that some people had suggested it might be (laughs). I'm still feeling all right.

T: Maybe I won't be an ogre after all . . .

P: (interrupts) No, no, I don't think so. I feel lots . . . I feel a little better.

T: I'll be looking for you.

P: All right. Good-by.

T: Good-by.

DISCUSSION BY C. W.

As we review this <u>first therapy interview</u>, we become aware that these two people are shy with each other. This is related to their previous history-taking visit and the fantasy which each of them carried from that. One might almost say that there was an "instant transference-countertransference feeling tone," and that we're now seeing the results of the undercurrent fantasy that each of them has carried. When the therapist, for example, referred to the date of their history-taking interview, she coughed in a strange, unreal manner. It probably was hard for her to swallow the fantasy to which he was referring. They discussed the weather (George Stephenson noted many years ago that this is a way of talking about each other). The therapist expressed his readiness for this new experience, talking about how good it was when he got up and drove to the office. The patient also had a similar experience to which she referred, and then talked about the chill and fear that she got when she got onto Peachtree. (This is the street on which the therapist's office is located.)

The therapist began to present to the patient his orientation to disease and to the pain of the patient's situation. He talked about free-floating anxiety as being more healthy than somatized migraine headaches. The patient then explained that her migraine was the result of failure to handle her psychological stress. We see a quality of honesty in the therapist as he admits that he had forgotten about her migraine, setting the stage for her to be more honest with the therapist and accept the fact that she had a choice of symptoms. She could either face the anxiety, or she could develop migraine headaches.

Later, in the third fragment, the therapist in his discussion led her to talk about herself in the third person. This may again seem to point to schizophrenia, but it does not. It is merely a reflection of the hysterical dissociative process. In this fragment the therapist shows himself to have some client-centered orientation. This is useful in the early phase of treatment, since he is not putting his full emotional force into operation, but is listening and responding to the patient in a client-centered fashion. The patient talked about her tendency to hurt other people. She did not see this as sadism, nor did the therapist define it. The therapist did not make this kind of diagnostic assault at any time. He did, however, define her pattern and label her a "witch." This was a very aggressive and personal move on the therapist's part. It did not allow the patient the right to find her own fantasy for it. She did accept his fantasy, and it seemed to be a way in which both were able to get closer to each other. When the therapist moved ahead in this more aggressive manner, the patient responded with an hysterical laugh (and I can imagine the therapist's faint smile), again diagnosing the hysterical character of her pathology.

In the fourth fragment of this, the first interview, the therapist has included the last minutes of the interview, in which he functioned as an administrator and discussed the details of their future interviews and her responsibility for handling the appointment schedule. By this role he set the stage for the patient to perceive him in two ways -- not only as a fantasy, but also as a real person. In his discussion about these administrative details, the therapist brought to her his dignity as a person. He discussed it in careful adult-to-adult language, and in this framework she experienced his respect for her as a person. This is in contrast to his concern for her as the patient with her traumas of childhood and the disease of her symptom picture. The therapist's initial history-taking interview prepared him for an early plunge into a relationship with Patti. He was getting affectively ready, and so was she. It has been a good first interview.

SUMMARY OF SECOND THERAPY INTERVIEW, JAN. 18:

Patti was more at ease as she arrived. She admired a small wood carving on the therapist's desk, a faceless female torso with prominent breasts. She spoke of her plans to study algebra, stating, "As long as I have not been to college, my mind is locked."

She came with a written list of her problems in living, as follows: 1. People do not like her for some reason or other. 2. She is anxious and tense most of the time. 3. She is impulsive and afraid of the trouble that this might get her into. 4. She used to like music, but recently music upsets her. 5. She had always liked to read, but now "novels no longer satisfy me." 6. She has had suicidal feelings, particularly since she knows that the financial support from her ex-husband will stop in three years, and Patti is also afraid that she will somehow hurt her daughter Tessie. 7. She fears spiders. She is particularly afraid of fat, fast, dark, hairy spiders. Sometimes she can face spiders, but she hates to kill them. She would not use a flyswatter. She hates to use bug spray because (she said) it gets the spider excited. "The best way I've found is to use the vacuum cleaner." Actually, she stated that she was interested in small spiders, if they preserve their web. It was the big heavy webs with the holes in them that bothered her most. Also, she stated, "If there's one, there should be another, a pair."

At the end of the interview she spoke of wanting to get rid of her anxiety and control herself. At this point the therapist intervened for the first time in a major way and suggested that she should choose: did she want to be without anxiety, or did she want to control herself. (This was an expression of J. W.'s concern that the patient might act out.)

DISCUSSION BY C. W.

The therapist's obvious concern for his patient in the first interview made it possible for her to present a detailed written formulation of her need. She was also able to describe her symbolic phobia in very creative terms. One could almost see her sucking the spiders into that "empty bag"! She was clearly an intelligent and verbal person who was capable of deep interpersonal relating. Accepting her strength, the therapist challenged her ambivalence directly. He will not lose his separateness.

SUMMARY OF THIRD THERAPY INTERVIEW, FEB. 8:

Patti came in comfortably. She spoke of fighting a battle with herself about Jack, a younger man whom she had met, who was already married. The second date with him disturbed her, because she had an impulse to have intercourse with him. She explained, "This lonesomeness is a thing with me now, but you know I've been lonesome all my life." At the end of the interview the therapist again asserted himself by suggesting that she might distinguish between the fight within herself and the struggle she had with the world around about. It seemed, he added, as if she had no life in her except that which was stimulated by her surroundings, and especially by men.

DISCUSSION BY C. W.

Patti was trying to challenge the therapist emotionally, and at the same time she was hoping he would accept responsibility for curtailing her impulsiveness. When she spoke of being lonesome always, she implied, "I expect you to reject me as others have."

Patti also expected J. W. to reassure her in her loneliness, and instead he threw her back on her own resources, thus expressing his respect for her as a person.

Fourth Interview, Feb. 22:

T: (begins interview) I'm going to record this interview.

P: You write, don't you?

T: Yes, but the recording is different.

P: Is it?

T: Uhu. Besides you can't hear what I write.

P: Oh, well ... (laughs)

T: (unintelligible . . . .) It'd be possible to tape it.

P: I've never thought about that. I don't know if I want to hear it.

T: That's part of it.

P: Yes.

T: And then it may not strike you as significant at a later time. You change. Thoughts change.

P: Ahem.

T: To some people it means a lot; to others it means very little.

P: If their thoughts change, or to hear the recording?

T: To hear the recording. A year later, or two years later. Whichever.

P: I can see the advantage of that, looking at it from that point of view . . . the change.

T: Or just to hear what you said last night.

P: Ahem.

T: It may surprise you. I often hear myself say things on the tape that I was unaware that I ever said at any time. A big surprise. But it's on there.

P: I guess that's true because you could be thinking one thing, and the words don't express what you are really thinking sometimes.

T: Uhem. (P. laughs)

Segment about 8 minutes later:

T: You keep talking about Durden as if he were in the room to be considered also, and he's not here. I've never seen him. I've no interest in him. I am interested in you though.

P: Uhu.

T: And to have a woman sit here who's afraid of her own thoughts, that's quite something.

P: Well, but I always have been.

T: But your own thoughts are dangerous to you.

P: They were terribly dangerous a week ago (pause) when this first happened. I really got so scared (pause) at what was happening to me that I had to do something about it, and then something else took over for me, and . . . and now I'm able to manage it. But I think my fear is that maybe this isn't real; that whatever it is, is taking over for me.

T: Well, as long as you are scared of your own thoughts that must make it difficult to go to bed at night and take a chance on having a dream.

P: I haven't had a . . . except for the first two or three nights. I haven't had much trouble with it. I think that I get . . . so exhausted emotionally that I go to sleep, although the first week I did take phenobarbital. I took a quarter-grain four times a day 'cause that was the original prescription a long time ago. And I really, I seldom take it, but I thought during this time I should, and I . . . and of course that kept me going a little bit; and then I . . . after about three or four days I stopped taking it, and I've been able to sleep. But last night was the first night that I remembered dreaming anything; I do dream every night, I know that, but last night was the first I remember dreaming anything that . . . that didn't bother me or that I couldn't remember, and that was that I had met someone. And at first I thought he was younger than I but tied in with childhood, then I found out that . . . that he was about my age and somehow this was connected with Divorcees Anonymous, and that's where Durden met this woman. And . . . there was no sex connected with it; it was just the realization that this man was available, and that he seemed to enjoy my company and that we could talk and laugh together. And at the same time I realized that Durden and the woman that he's going to marry were in the background somehow, but they didn't bother me. (pause) But the strange part of it was I woke up with starting to get a migraine. And that's the trouble with those sneaky migraines, you know. During the daytime I can (laughs) I can control them. Of course, they break out in other ways. There's one . . . I heard about this business, I had a migraine, but it wasn't in the head. It was every place else. But they are easier to cope with now. But this one, I got up and took a pill, and though (T coughs) I am still fighting it a little bit, it isn't going to get the better of me, but . . .

T: All of this was taking place at Anonymous?

P: Yes, I think so. It was sort of outdoors, and there were cars involved, a lot of cars around, and I couldn't find my car. Although, as I was waking up, I remembered where the car was. It was my blue car, and I hadn't been looking for the blue car, the little blue Nash. You know, the old car. And (pause) . . .

T: You were looking for the wrong car?

P: Yes. Uhu. And, of course, my car broke down yesterday morning. I had to leave it at the gas station and have it fixed, so I can see how it all ties in somehow, but I . . . what amazes me is that it worked out pretty well. It wasn't a nightmare.

T: This was sort of a party, I gather.

P: Yes, a picnic type of thing. (pause)

T: What did this man look like that you met? Little, tall, fat, thin?

P: (interrupts) Uhu. He was about a little, just a little taller than I am, and not thin, and not fat, and . . . And he almost reminded me of a . . . a dark-haired man, dark eyes, rather large eyes. In a way I guess he looks something as child stuff but it wasn't the (unintelligible), and it was a relief to me. Don't have to worry about being involved with him, which incidentally I don't have to worry about anyway.

Segment about 2 minutes later:

P: You know, speaking of dreams, the night after I saw you, the last time? For the first time in a long time, you know what I dreamed of (laughs)? It was a Big One, but it was over in the corner, like over in the corner of the wall, but it was in my bedroom, and just sitting there and waiting.

T: (interrupts, but unintelligible)

P: No. Oh, no, not a snake. (spells:) S-p-i-d-e-r. (both laugh)

T: You're being very careful with your thoughts this morning.

P: Very what?

T: Careful.

P: (laughs) I never . . . I never talk too directly about Them, because (both laugh) they're nasty things. And I know what Freud said about Them, too, so I guess it's a reason for my having this aversion to Them, but I . . . I've carefully forgotten that. A lot of things I remember he'd said that might apply to me, and this

one applies to me, too, but I didn't like it. And besides,
they . . . I never read anybody saying anything nice
about Them. They are nasty things. Tessie said an
older man was at school yesterday, and talking to them,
in biology class, and showed them his collection of
insects, all kinds and, of course . . . and, of course,
he had the others, too. She said a whole lot of them.
And he said, "They're all poisonous; although it doesn't
harm you, they all are poisonous." It doesn't surprise
me one bit. They would be.

T: What did Freud say about spiders?

P: I honestly don't remember well enough. I think it was
tied up somehow with a . . . a I don't know whether it
was suppressed sex, or suppressed something, it's . . .
it's something. I don't like it, whatever it was. Because it's associated, been associated with something
else. I would have been able to remember it, but
since its associated with that . . . specie.

T: Sounds as though you are getting worse.

P: With Them? No, I'm just . . .

T: (interrupts) Last time you were able to speak of spiders
rather freely.

P: (interrupts) That's just because I forced myself. I
know you a little better now, and I don't have to make
myself say it. (laughs) But now, for instance, for
years I was frightened of thunder. I mean I realized
how unreasonable it was, because I had read about it
and I understood all about it, but that frightened me.
And now I couldn't care less. I enjoy it. I was thinking
last night when it woke me. It didn't bother me the
least bit. And so many of the fears I had, for instance,
all those years when I was married really to Durden, I
had so many fears. I was so afraid of being alone at
night, and it wasn't so afraid necessarily of some one
breaking in, it was afraid of . . . of something . . . you
know. Not some one, but something. Oh, it was the
most horrible feeling to wake up at night with your
heart pounding. And that's what's so hard for me to
understand now I'm divorced, and I don't have these
fears any more. I can go to bed and sleep at night.
And if there's a noise, I might wake up and be a little
apprehensive, but I think just normally so, and I go
back to sleep again. And . . . when Durden used to
travel and I was alone all the time, I'd even get up and

get a knife and put it under the pillow, you know. Uh . . . and I'd get up and recheck all the doors and the windows, and go and see if the children were all right. And all those fears are gone, except that one you see, which is associated with apparently entirely different things . . . And I guess it scares me because I . . . I feel that I'm a . . . such a different person than I was then, that I keep expecting to revert to it. It's as though I shouldn't feel as good as I do under the circumstances. It's suspicious. (pause) Do you think I'm schizophrenic? That's what I think sometimes. (laughs)

T: You sure talk as if you were afraid what your thoughts might lead to.

P: But the strange thing is, I'm afraid of the good thoughts. I mean, that I like.

T: Uhu.

Segment about 3 minutes later:

P: I do look forward to coming here. And you don't scare the hell out of me, only that isn't the word that was told me. The word began with "s," and I don't like that word, so I don't say it. But that's what I had been warned, you know. (laughs) That that's what would happen to me. But you haven't frightened me in the least; and of course, I do keep expecting that something will be said, or I will say something or you will say something that will . . . and then this feeling will happen.

T: (interrupts) Sooner or later I will turn out to be the monster that you expected.

P: Yeah. I didn't really expect it until I was told this. Not that you were a monster, you understand that. Everybody speaks highly of you and . . .

T: (interrupts) I didn't understand that.

P: Didn't you? I . . . no, not you . . . but the feelings that I would have by coming here, you see. I suppose revealing myself, maybe. These people who have had this experience apparently were upset by the things that they must have said or revealed. And, of course, there again that kind of worries me. If it upset them, why doesn't it upset me?

Segment about 8 minutes later:

T: You want them to have a nicely dressed picture of you.
Not too naked.

P: Yes, I guess so, because the naked one isn't very good.
For instance, Tessie, of course, doesn't know about
my involvement with this other man. In all fairness to
her I don't know whether some day she should know.
Ah . . . most of the time I feel that this is my guilt,
and not one that should be put on her shoulders.
There's no reason for her to know it, except for him
to keep saying, "Well, you don't know the whole story,"
and of course, that's what he means when he says this.
And I don't know that at her age she, ah . . . I don't
know enough about people, or children, I guess, to
know if this is information she should be given or if
this is something she shouldn't find out, and yet, will
she find out sometime anyway? My older daughter
knows about it, and yet she's still . . .

T: (interrupts) We're once more getting something mixed
up.

P: Am I?

T: Uhu. When I speak of telling her the truth, I am not
speaking of a factual history of your life.

P: See when I get it mixed up.

T: You sure do.

P: Yeah.

T: What I'm speaking of when I speak of presenting the
truth to your children, is the way you feel at the time.

P: Even though it isn't a . . . it isn't a . . . it isn't a
fair feeling to someone else? You know what I mean.

T: I take for granted that you are human. Human beings
are not always fair.

P: And they would be able to understand this better than
they would my always trying to . . .

T: I don't know. I don't know what they'd understand.
I'm not interested in them.

P: No.

T: I'm just interested in you. Tessie is really no concern to me. I'm concerned about you and your ideas about these things. Your concept of what gives. Like you said, you don't understand people very well, so you come talk with me about it. We're working on this.

P: I understand other people. I mean, I think I understand. For instance, the people that I worked with fairly well. It's a . . . maybe it's the relationship between me and my children that I don't . . . that I'm not sure of. For years I've spent so much time in giving them the right viewpoint of everything, you see, and (laughs). . .

T: You know, I had a real funny thought.

P: Uhu.

T: I was talking to a woman not quite your age, but the same bracket, who was very much concerned to see people naked. She had an obsession about it. Men and women -- she wanted to see them naked. And this went round and round for her. And there was something funny about it. I asked her one day, "Do you ever look at yourself in the full-length mirror without clothes on?" She said, "Oh, heavens, no!" (P laughs) And I suddenly had some insight into what she was trying to see.

P: Uhu. I can remember being like that. Not wanting to see people naked. If I did, I didn't realize it. But I can remember the first time I looked at myself naked in a full-length mirror, and . . . and that was when I was thirty-six or something. And, whatever it was, started changing in me. And that was the first time I didn't . . . and I wasn't horrified at what I saw. And . . . and . . .

T: You horrified now?

P: No.

T: You were thirty-six before you looked at yourself naked?

P: Consciously. May have done it accidentally, you know, or something, but I can . . .

T: Deliberately.

P: Yeah. Uhu. And that was at the time when my migraine started, and all these thoughts that you are supposed to keep hammered down started coming forth. (laughs)

T: You are awakening.

P: Yeah. (laughs)

T: Had you thought of it as that?

P: Not then, no. I just didn't know what was happening.

T: Now, I mean.

P: Now, yes, now I feel that way. But as I say, I just
trust that . . . it doesn't seem as though I should . . .
this is a good feeling . . . that it's like a relief, and
I shouldn't have it, you know. (pause)

T: The release is looking at yourself? Or the release is
what happened when you were thirty-six?

P: When I was thirty-six the release happened, and now I
think I can look at myself, and that's a release now.
At the time, I don't . . . I didn't look at myself. I was
aware of . . . of something happening, and I think
that's what it was. Migraine started, because I was
trying to suppress whatever was happening.

Segment about 2 minutes later:

P: Seeing what it is that's wrong about my relation with
other people. I realize that it must be me because
I . . . you know, I had decided not to make good
friends with people, because you lose them. They
move away, you move away, or something, and so,
in order to do that, or to avoid that, just don't get
too close to people. Be friendly with them, but if you
find that you are getting a little close, then hold them
off. Then, of course, I guess I need someone, such
as Ormill, or a child, and then I go haywire. But I'm
being able to work with the relationship with Jack,
mostly, of course, I haven't had much choice. His
superego is better than mine, you see, so mine
doesn't have to work as hard as it might have to.
I don't know if it would do the job anyway. My ego
is a threat for a while, it can be strong when the
superego is not getting a chance to work, I guess.
Now I sound confused and mixed up, that's how I feel.

T: I was still running by what you're saying about, there's
something wrong in your relationship with other people.
You've used that phrase over and over.

P: Well, I think that, ah, I suspected this, but it wasn't till you put it into words, and maybe I misunderstood you. You know, something about there are no (unintelligible) over the other people, and this is what I don't understand. I didn't think anybody would live just by themselves, alone, and not have a relationship with other people but, and this, I don't understand this, and yet I don't get the, the satisfaction. I know, because if I have relationship I expect too much of this relationship, and it doesn't come up to what I expect and then I become unhappy and want to push them away. That doesn't explain it to you.

T: I'm listening closely.

P: I don't know myself. I didn't really know that other people were able to handle their relationships with others differently than I do, and I don't know what the difference is. If I don't find out what the difference is, how can I work with it? Why can't you tell me?

DISCUSSION BY C. W.

The fourth interview is considerably different from the first. They certainly have been moving in the relationship. The therapist started out by rejecting the patient, saying he didn't bother to tape the other two interviews, and she immediately cut back at him, saying, "You do write, don't you?" This negative transference (and what I should like to call negative countertransference) was a struggle between the two of them to see whether she could make him break through his technical role. She says, in effect, "You are as dishonest as I am." She talked then about the shock of her husband's remarriage and said in an upside-down manner, "It isn't that I wanted him back." She then described beautifully how the hysterical person learns to repress as a life pattern. It seems in this early phase of the fourth interview that the patient was about through "trying to cope" with life, trying to manipulate it, to handle it, to understand it, and to manage it. The therapist then used his person, his symbolic significance to her, as a wedge to pry out of the interview some of her concern with "social therapists" (boy friend and ex-husband). This is technically called manipulation of the transference. But I should like to emphasize that the therapist did not do this as a trick. It was not a deliberate move; it happened in his feelings. It was not something he calculated and then did to her. He merely expressed to her what had happened in him. J. W. hinted in a subtle way that he was getting jealous of her talking about previous "therapists," and the patient immediately talked about her new boy friend, Jack. You get the feeling that she was simultaneously talking about the therapist as well as the man she met outside. She used the transference relationship to the therapist as a way of manipulating her outside life. She identified the therapist as though he were a member of Divorcees Anonymous, and identified the interview as a picnic ("a happy time where one is irresponsible, out in nature, and is apt to get pregnant"). She talked about the person she was involved with as being like her general practitioner, e.g., the therapist. She then went on to talk about a dream in which there was "a Big One just waiting in the corner of my bedroom." (I'm sorry you can't see the actual position of the therapist's chair, which is clearly in the corner of his office, or it would be more obvious to you that he was the Big One.) She went on to say, "They are all nasty things," and one gets the feeling that she was simultaneously talking about penises and spiders, and possibly even about her own tough hymen. She talked about her previous phobias, and the newest ones -- that she was afraid of good thoughts, that she was afraid of the therapist, and that she was afraid of disrupting her previous handling of life. She talked about the therapist again in another abstract way, referring to her desire to save face with her daughter. She pondered the difference between truth as a factual problem and truth as an existential facing of one's feelings of the moment. Then she became historical again, and talked about having seen herself naked for the first time when she was thirty-six, and how this precipitated headaches. She did this in the framework of beginning to see herself naked in a new way in this therapeutic relationship. She intuited that she was going to have some new kind of aches from that -- I suspect heartaches. In the final minutes of the interview she used several psychopathic (impulse disorder) mechanisms to handle the hysterical aspects of her living process. She wanted the therapist (whom she assumes to be also manipulating life) to reveal "the secret" of how to cope with life successfully. She described her own pathology in this area. She had tried not to get close to people because they will move away. She realized that she doesn't want to get close to people, because she had always tried to use them as therapists and found that this didn't pan out. She got involved with the ex-boy friend, and thus lost her capacity to be cynical and got "out of control." She was, in effect, saying to the therapist, "You're next; I may get out of control with you." She spoke of slipping back into the hysterical framework again and that the therapist should be able to give her the key -- again referring to her desire for some kind of secret symbolic weapon to make her "cope." We see that the two of them have struggled toward a way of relating which will be satisfactory. Each one was sensing that there was a dangerous climax building up, and that this climax was getting closer all the time.

Fifth Interview, March 8:

     T. begins: Hi. (after initial silent pause of a minute)

     P: Hi (laughs). I always need a few minutes just to sit. -- I'm almost afraid to say that I think I'm doing better

because you know I might get struck down for it. And so
many awful things have happened, that is, awful to me,
you know, not to anyone else. It amazes me that I'm
still able to cope. I don't know if I'm coping with them
or not, but I'm not getting hysterical about it, and, and
if I think it's time I ended my life, I think about it
sensibly (laughs), not run off someplace and do it. I'm
not going to do it anyway. So it seems to me that maybe
I am, well, there are times now when it's enough just to
be alive, you know, whereas before I had to find a reason
for it. And now, I can't think of any reason that would
be worth while, if I stop to think about it. I found myself
enjoying things, and, and I can talk with people and know
what they're saying. For a long time I couldn't do that.

T: It shows on you.

P: Does it?

T: Uhu. You're prettier.

P: Uh, well, that's good. Several people have mentioned
a change in me. They don't say what it is. At work
(unintelligible). And I don't know what it is, except
there are hostilities flying all over the place. I guess
they like me better that way. And it is easier to
manage. The trouble is, there's so many things wrong
with me, you know, and we have such a short time, and
I don't see how I can possibly talk about them. And,
and there's one thing that I wondered if I could get
straightened out, it would help me manage better.
You see, I'm no good. And I know this, and other
people probably don't know it because I've had to put
on this act for so long that I fool people. And so they
think I'm clever, nice, and all these things that go
along with being an acceptable person. But you see,
all this time I know underneath that I'm not any good,
and I can, and, I wondered if the reason for this is
whether it's really true, or as I remember. My
mother always told me I was no good, I wasn't any
good to look at, and it bothers me sort of because I
never have. And that nobody would want me around,
and I couldn't do anything, and I should stay away from
people because they wouldn't want me. Nobody could
possibly like me. And I can remember that so clearly.

Segment about 2 minutes later:

P: There are many times when I'm hopeful. And when I
look back, and the few times we've been together, I
realize that I feel better. It's just that I can't

understand why. And maybe that should be, maybe that's the way I should accept everything, that it's enough that it happened, and I don't have to find a reason for it.

T: The big "whys" you can't find anyway. The little "whys" we can discover, like if your car doesn't start, you can find out why it doesn't start.

P: Uhu.

T: But as soon as we get to bigger things, like why should you live or why should you die, then it doesn't work any more. Then the "whys" give out.

P: That's when you really become distressed.

T: Maybe.

P: That's when I really become distressed, I guess.

T: You can change the question to "How can you live?" "How can you die?" Then it becomes profitable. (pause) You were talking as if it wasn't right to think about your death.

P: I don't even remember what I said, but it hasn't been until (pause) I think it has been fairly recently that I've been able to accept . . . to think about it. And a lot that goes along with it, I think, is my feeling about religion, that . . . that there's nothing afterwards. Then what's the point of going now. You know, that's (unintelligible) so what's the use, where does it get you? And, I think that has something to do with my feeling about death. I'm changing a little bit on that. I can think about it now without becoming horrified. I guess that's the first time that I have even put it into words. But it's just as you said, it's a big question. And I know now it's no point questioning it anyway, and I'm here, and if I can get some enjoyment out of being here, I don't question that either, just go ahead. But I've always been afraid to before.

T: I certainly enjoy your being here. Hope you do, too.

P: I do very much. Of course, there's another thing that bothers me. I do enjoy it, and I like you as a person, not just as a doctor. So then I think, well, there's just a few more times I can come and see you, so why bother coming at all. I might as well stop it right now, and then that'll be, then I'll be through with that, you see.

Then I won't have to worry about that any more. I'm not going to. I'm just explaining what happened. (laughs)

T: Uhu.

P: Really, I am surprised that I have managed as well as I have, I guess with all the . . . (laughs) when I realize all the thoughts I've had for so many years.

Segment about 2 minutes later:

T: You brought to mind the picture of a little boy of about six years old, I guess, playing in the back yard, near the steps of the house. And he was doing something with his father, and then he got angry at his father. He went into the basement, got a hammer and collected all his toys, and started to pound them to pieces, one by one.

P: (pause) (unintelligible)

T: And he probably hurt his father more that way than if he had attacked him directly.

Segment about 3 minutes later:

P: I don't know how you help me. It must be just because I can talk with you. You certainly don't tell me anything in so many words. You suggest something once in a while, and then those stay with me.

T: I was going to suggest something to you today. That it might make a good bit of difference to you if you could stop this worrying about what's wrong with you -- and go back to just looking at yourself like you did nine years ago, the first time you really looked at yourself in a full-length mirror.

P: I just am afraid of what I'll see. I'm so sure it's no good.

Segment about 2 minutes later:

P: I don't think I'm putting in as many blocks in the road but . . . they're still there. I just don't look at them much.

T: They may not even be there.

P: No, maybe they'll disappear.

T: Maybe you're seeing things.

P: Yeah.

T: You've been delusional in various respects. Why not in respect to the blocks in your road?

P: Well, because I think that I . . . the goals I've set for myself are too high. I don't see how I can possibly live up to them, but they're what I want.

Segment about 1 minute later:

P: But why would a mother say those things to her child unless . . . unless they were true?

T: To the mother, you mean. (pause) They were true to the mother, you mean.

P: Well, no, I guess that isn't what I meant, but I see what you mean.

T: Well, who else would they be true to, except to the mother?

P: Well, if they were there?

T: Yeah. (pause) For the mother they were there.

P: Uhu.

T: And she's dead and gone.

P: Maybe she's (unintelligible) . . . . . . They weren't true.

T: You weren't so sure you wanted to let her sayings die with her. Huh? I was just checking how long she's been dead. She's good and dead.

P: Yeah. Let me see, about . . .

T: (interrupts) Nine years.

P: Yeah.

T: Which is the time you first looked at yourself naked.

Segment about 16 minutes later:

P: You know what I wish I could change most though?

T: No.

P: I've said this before. It's that shaky feeling inside.

T: Uhu. (pause)

P: And I've read enough to . . . so that I think it's repressed. Things that I don't even know about, I guess.

T: I wonder if some of this shaking might not be from the dreams that you're unaware of.

P: Dreams you mean that I have now, or have had?

T: Both.

P: Shall I tell you something funny? (laughs)

T: Uhu.

P: I hope you think it's funny.

T: I was always interested in funny things.

P: This is a dream last night. And I don't know whether I've dreamed about you before or not, but this one I remember. And part of your treatment was sexual, and . . .

T: (interrupts) That's encouraging. (P laughs)

P: That was fine, and I accepted that and went along just fine.

T: Can you be more specific? Just how was this?

P: Well, we had intercourse . . . ah . . . it was . . . there wasn't any passion with it really. It was something that would be good for me, and you didn't seem to mind; but . . . in fact, you liked me well enough, so it was all right, you see. But, afterwards what made me smile when I thought, "Well, now if he has, say, six . . . five or six women in one day, I wonder how he manages that many?" (laughs)

T: In your dream. (P laughs)

P: That's when I woke up. I was sort of smiling. I rarely wake up smiling. (laughs) . . . So you're really quite a man, you see. (laughs)

T: I feel highly flattered.

P: (laughs) Well, you should.

T: At my age that's a wonderful compliment.

P: Well, you see you are quite capable, at least in my dreams.

T: I like that very much.

P: Good. I do too, incidentally.

T: Was our relationship complete, the intercourse to orgasm?

P: Yes, but as I said, it was . . . sort of therapeutic. You know . . . it . . .

T: (interrupts) Clinical.

P: Uhu. We both enjoyed it, you know, but we both realized that this was something that was good for us. Or . . . good for me, and it did you no harm, apparently.

Segment about 7 minutes later:

T: I think of this relationship with you as intercourse. I feel it as that at moments. I think of it as a real profound encounter. Something that has a lot of meaning to both of us, even though it is for your benefit, just as you dreamed it. We're agreed about that.

DISCUSSION BY C. W.

Interview Number 5 is unique. This was the core experience. In this appointment we see that the therapist switched, in spite of himself, into a real relationship with Patti. The professional therapist would naturally want to protect himself from intense involvement in a situation which is administratively limited.

Patti described the paranoid-like delusion characteristic of many persons in therapy, when she said, "I'm afraid I will get struck down if I'm happy."

During this interview the therapist developed a series of three hunches. First, he reflected his intuitive sense that there was an upcoming profound junction of their feelings for each other. He said, "You seem to be showing evidence of a change." She answered, "We can't do it in the time we have available . . . . It's really enough to be alive." She once more asked the therapist to admit that her life was an act. Then she moved in the fantasy of maternal rejection which, although not clearly emphasized, is a fantasy as universal as that of sex trauma by the father. Some patients describe it as the fantasy of being an adopted child, or of being an orphan, or of being illegitimate. In this case it came out more obtusely, as the spider phobia. She said, "I'm no good. Mother told me I was no good." The therapist projected this into the therapeutic relationship (perhaps differently than many other therapists). He then talked about his acceptance of her hopelessness. It's as though he was agreeing that if she wanted to stay hopeless, it was all right with him. (J. W. wrote a paper entitled, "Support Through Non-Reassurance," and this is a beautiful example of how he does it.) The patient seemed to catch his existential flavor, and she herself talked about living without reason, that is, without essence, without a purpose. One just lives to be alive.

The therapist then, on his own initiative, moved into the consideration of death and his own feelings about death. This was his hunch number two, his perception that the patient was ready to deal with the ultimates. In this he did something rather unique. He said, "I like seeing you." This juxtaposing himself as a person and as therapist provided a contrast of profound significance to the patient. Patti responded to this as though in panic, saying as she had before, "I had better quit while it's still hopeless." Shortly thereafter she spoke about death again, as though this universal phobia had already begun to replace the phobia of spiders -- death as a fact, rather than death as a fear of spiders. The therapist took advantage of the patient's involvement by offering, as though it were a fantasy, a story of his own home life, which he told in the third person so it would not create intolerable fantasies in the patient. Then, tackling Patti's paranoid feelings by acknowledging her power to hurt him, he explained in an inferential manner the paranoid mechanism of projection. There followed a considerable discussion of the patient trying to make the change-over from searching herself for blemishes, like a monkey looking for lice, to just looking at herself for the satisfaction of participating. She kept talking for a while, and J. W. shared with her his boredom at her talk, indicating his capacity to share negative feelings or indifference with her. One more thing that moved them closer to the core phase was his inferentially calling her crazy, by suggesting that the block she saw in the road was an hallucination. J. W. is neither nondirective nor is he directive; it's as though his way of sharing himself, of precipitating a person-to-person quality in the relationship, is part of both. It involves a respect for the patient, and at the same time denies any superpower in the therapist. Another therapeutic technique which is noted here is that enigmatic or para-doxical move the therapist made when the patient said, "If mother says I'm no good, it must be true." He agreed, thus giving her a kind of "intravenous interpretation," and then noted that mother had been dead for a long time. The quality of his voice on the tape recording was such that it's obvious he was talking out of his own counter-transference, which at this point was useful and not damaging to the patient.

Patti stated that her greatest need was to get over feeling shaky inside. The therapist intuited that the core was closer, and hunch number three suggested that her shaking was based on a dream. Then she began to recall the dream, which is a beautiful description of what therapy is all about. The therapist dared to take this thing personally, saying, "I like that," as though he himself were participating in the dream. She agreed in her slip, "It was good for us." One wonders if this is an indication that dreams during therapy are something like acting out experiences. They are jointly designed by the two people involved, or as we sometimes say, acting out is at the direction of the therapist. The therapist deliberately tried to alleviate undue anxiety in Patti by his open acceptance of his responsibility.

In the dream she said, "It did you no harm." It is as though she were describing the aftermath of the six-year-old's fantasy inter-course with her father. She wanted to be assured that this wasn't going to make any difference in the relationship between the parents. Another patient many years ago said that the trouble with most therapists is that "they won't stay for breakfast" afterwards, as though many therapists could "sleep" with their patients effectively, but that they were then unwilling to face this on a conscious basis.

In summary, this crucial segment points up the characteristic qualities of the core phase. This patient dealt with her life's metamor-phosis not only in the dream, which is kind of a paradigm of the whole interview, but also in her joint identification with the professional therapist. She dealt with laying mother to rest. She dealt with her own values in life and with her own death. And, finally, she faced the unconscious-plus-conscious relationship with her therapist.

SUMMARY OF SIXTH INTERVIEW, MAR. 21:

The patient came in hesitantly, and after some casual comments said, "I'm afraid of being too personal with a doctor." Therapist retorted by, "You just like to cultivate your guilt feelings, and you seem to do it deliberately." Patti immediately retreated to talking about her need for a new car and added, "This one is all worn out, it doesn't start in the morning." The therapist carefully denied the symbolic implication to this, and the patient again retreated to he outside world, noting that her ex-husband was about to remarry and then wouldn't take care of her car. She had written to Ormill for some money. She then added, parenthetically, "I used to get so angry with him, and I'm surprised I don't get angry at you." The therapist returned to the fact that she was controlling her human relationships by guilt feelings and by punishing herself.

Near the end of the interview the therapist got in an argument with the patient, insisting that a marriage license was not the most important thing to a marriage while she insisted that it was. The therapist told her she was in error about human relationships, feelings were always mutual; then, when the therapist caught himself in the argument, he stopped and asked about her dreams. She said she had had none, but she was less bothered by sex since the last interview.

DISCUSSION BY C. W.

In this <u>sixth interview</u> the patient went through what is usually called the second-interview phenomena. After the intimacy of their previous core phase interview she came back fighting, talked very clearly about not wanting this to be soured and not wanting the level of intimacy between them to go any further. She said that she had always been angry at someone after an intimate relationship such as they had last time, and it surprised her that this was not true today. Each of them talked on a superficial level because they were both basking in the fantasy memory of the past interview. The patient related that in the early part of last week she had a wonderful time, the world was bright, things seemed all right. In the latter part of the week things were not good at all, and she talked about her guilt, identifying it with the guilt about her affair. She tried to justify that affair on the basis of her husband's bad treatment of her. They discussed at some length her deliberate use of her guilty feelings, and the aggravation of them so that she could keep herself in line socially. Dr. Warkentin then stuck her with a classic kind of statement. It's an existential thing he said: "My feelings last time were like yours." "There were only two consciences in the room at that time, yours and mine." And, "All feeling states in face-to-face relationships are bilateral." In doing this, he gives her a focus for future fantasies. He suffered no second-interview retreat.

She talked about being more bothered with sexual feelings for other men during the week, and she also spoke of being less bothered by sexual feelings. The fifth interview had reopened fantasies about her husband and about her boy friend, and she talked about her effort to control future behavior by guilt over these fantasies. The therapist then accused her of worshiping her guilt. The patient was in effect trying to find out what the last interview would do to her life. She was afraid that it would make for more pain.

Hope arose in her for an expanded life, but she did not yet quite dare to make another move until she could re-evaluate the whole situation.

Seventh Interview

Segment at beginning of interview:

T: We have three more after today. Three more.

P: Uhu. (T coughs) Well, I don't think about that, 'cause I don't like that. (laughs)

T: Sometimes I get the impression that you play games with yourself.

P: Yes, I do. Uhu. (long pause)

T: Did you get Durden married?

P: Yeah. I feel better since he's married. (laughs) It was a bad week though (laughs) up until then. I don't know why, but soon as he was married, I was all right.

T: You were just scared you'd mess it up for him.

P: I was? I don't see how I could have at that point. I don't know what it was. I never could understand why it bothered me so. And I don't know how it bothered me. Just had me upset. And as soon as he was married, I couldn't care less.

T: Maybe you just kept fantasying sort of unconsciously just how they would do it after the wedding.

P: Perhaps that's how it started turning my stomach. (both laugh) See, I've never been interested in Durden that way. I just don't know. He's never been a man to me, you see. (pause) I hope she enjoyed the trip. (pause) But I really do feel that -- not just saying that. And I don't mind his being married, or gone, or anything now. I feel much better. And the children do, too.

Segment about 6 minutes later:

T: Did you dream about it?

P: About the car?

T: Uhu.

P: No. (pause) I had a dream, but it wasn't about the car. It was about fishing.

T: Sounds interesting. How did it go?

P: Well, you know I never have fished, and I don't know that I care anything about it. Everything's sort of murky, and . . . and . . . you know, when I dream sometimes, there are . . . are two of me. There's one sitting watching what the other one is doing.

T: Uhu.

P: And that's what was happening. And I was just sitting in this little dory of a rowboat fishing in the water. It wasn't too deep, as I remember. And the only thing I can . . . that I said was, "These professional people think they know so much." (laughs) And I don't remember any more. The other one was just on the bank, just listening or watching, and not really paying much attention, not thinking much of what the boat was doing, or . . . (Unintelligible)

T: Uhu.

P: I remember one time before I did the same thing about dreaming. I think this was about a month ago and . . . one of me was writhing on the floor and suffering and having just a terrible time, and the other one just . . . stood over on the side of the room, or sitting on the side of the room and couldn't care less. Just watched and looked around and . . . and the one that was suffering so, finally almost just gave up and went off to a corner, and the one that was watching said to herself, you know, "Well, good place for her. I'm glad I'm rid of that thing." (pause) That's funny.

T: Well, maybe this is what's going on with you.

P: I have sort of had that feeling.

T: In the first dream about the rowboat, one of you was in the boat, one of you was on the bank.

P: I couldn't make any sense out of that. I could the other one.

T: How were you dressed in the fishing dream?

P: I can't remember that. But I can in the other one, but I can't in this one.

T: O. K. How about the other one?

P: I had a black skirt on and a red sweater.

T: Both of you? . . . Or is this . . .

P: (interrupts) No, this is the one that does all the action. The one that's watching, I never see. I am with that one . . . It's the one that does all the action that I can see.

T: (pause) Were you catching any fish?

P: Hm . . . No.

T: Seemed like this was serious fishing, or were you just having a good day?

P: No. It was . . . it was serious, but I can't believe it was really fishing. I know I had the fishing rod.

T: Had the flavor of you might well catch some fish?

P: Yeah. But it might not be fish. That's the . . . I mean . . . I had the rod and I was in the boat, and I was on water, and it was sort of dark and murky, but I don't know that I really expected to fish. It was something.

T: What could you have been expecting besides fish?

P: (laughs) I don't know. A man?

T: "A man is for the woman made."

P: (laughs) I wish he'd hurry up and show up. (pause) No, I didn't understand that dream. I don't know what I was fishing for. (pause) But usually the only dreams I remember are those that make some sense to me so maybe at the time it did. (pause) The mixed-up ones I don't remember. And I guess . . . I guess I dream all the time anyway. I have a fine time all night long dreaming, but I don't really remember them. (pause) I think dreaming is good for you. I think it's good for me. Get rid of a lot of something.

T: I don't know about getting rid of anything.

P: Well (laughs). Exposing?

T: Maybe. Or just experiencing? (pause) You know, life is relatively short.

P: Isn't that true.

T: And what's in it for you? If you can do some experiencing in your dreams, so much the better.

P: But since I've been feeling better, I don't seem to . . . I don't think I dream so much. Most of it's . . . I think it's when I am very unhappy or depressed that I dream. I think. (pause) But it's good to be feeling better.

T: I sure (unintelligible) . . . take part credit.

P: I want you to, because you had a lot to do with it. I don't know why or understand any of that, but I just know that . . . that a . . . it's just a feeling of knowing that you're there that even though I never call you or I only see you every other week. But it's just, . . . it's like, it's as though someone is there; and, I guess, if something bothers me, I can see your face, and I . . . can can see you doing that.

T: You can talk to me.

P: Yeah. I tell you a lot of things. And when I get here, I don't . . . they aren't important any more . . .

T: I think it's one of the benefits of psychotherapy -- a fantasy to talk to. It sort of provides a medium in which you can hear yourself some more.

P: Especially after you get to know them. Or after I'd gotten to know you a little better, then I could see your expression, see the way you . . . 'course you really haven't that much expression, unless something amuses you, you know. (laughs) I know you are thinking all the time.

T: Cagey-like!

Segment about 2 minutes later:

P: Why don't you ever say what you're thinking?

T: I was just thinking that you're getting prettier.

P: That's cause I feel better. And I don't know why, because nothing is any better than it was actually, except that I am. So I guess the other things don't matter so much, that I used to build up on. (pause) I don't need them anymore. I'm better. I don't have to find something to worry about. Although I still have plenty of things, you know. (laughs) (pause)

Segment about 18 minutes later:

P: It bothers me that some men are men to me . . . a man to me. And I have to watch out for that. You know, the man next door. He doesn't interest me at all. So it isn't just a man.

T: And this is not exactly a compliment -- when a man's a man to you.

P: Yes it is, as far as I'm concerned.

T: But it's wrong.

P: Yeah. It's wrong that I should sexually be interested in a man that I shouldn't be.

T: So this is a very mixed business.

P: A very mixed business.

T: It would really be so very much simpler if you could just maintain a childlike feeling at all times. You know, like a five-year-old girl that sees there's a difference between men and women, but doesn't get wrought up over it.

P: Yeah. She shouldn't be wanting to go to bed with . . . a man that you like.

T: So it could really be sinful every time you come to the office here. (pause) Because you have a sort of warm feeling about it . . .

P: Yeah.

T: Which is really a sinful feeling.

P: Yeah. I got into trouble with that time I talked about my dreaming about you. (pause) And then I realized that I had to be careful. And then, of course, I also know that most women have this same reaction to their psychiatrist, but I felt that would interfere with any good I might be doing, and I had to . . . keep this feeling under control.

DISCUSSION BY C.W.

In the seventh interview, the patient was immediately faced with the doctor's structuring remark, "I'll see you three more times." You will notice that she failed to keep the next appointment, as though to retaliate. The patient was now moving away from the core experience toward an existential person-to-person relationship with the therapist as a person who can teach her and help her with her learning about herself. In this interview she faced some more of her evasiveness with herself and more of her ambivalence about her husband. She responded to her fantasy of sex between her ex-husband and his new wife as "turning her stomach, " and immediately added in the next sentence that he didn't mean anything to her and that she was glad to be rid of him. Later on in the dream sequence she again showed how adequate she was at repressing. She talked about fishing for something, not fish, and then wondered if it could be a man; and then said, "I don't know what I'm fishing for, " as though she had carefully forgotten what she had just discovered. In the dream sequence you notice also her capacity to sense three selves -- one who was writhing (or fishing), another one who was looking, and still a third one who said to herself that this kind of thing is obviously a way of "getting rid of a lot of something, " i. e. , the painful presence of herself.

The patient said she was talking to the therapist outside the appointment. This followed directly his helping her to project her dream into the present tense. We see how the therapist can convert a memory into an existential bit of relating. Why did she find it possible to talk with him outside the appointment, and how did this help her to find herself? Part of it was just simple transference, part of it was the enigmatic quality, the aloofness of the therapist, and part of it was the fact that now following the core phase she had introjected the therapist, and he will be with her like her original parents -- forever.

In the latter part of this interview she asked, "What are you thinking?" It is as though for the first time she wondered about him as a person. And then he became a person for her. He told her about his past life; and he told her about his seeing her as a pretty woman. In essence two things were taking place: They were post core and heading toward ending; and, if you will, the therapist was "staying for breakfast. " He was saying to her, "This is not an affair you and I are having -- this is a marriage; this is a responsible relating between two people. " He was helping her in the continued transition from transference to person-to-person relating. One wonders if maybe this is what frightened her into not coming back for the next interview.

She talked in the latter part of this interview about the change in her, and said, "I'm better. I don't have to find things to worry about. " It's as though this discovery constituted a freedom from the need to manipulate herself into having guilt enough to be a good girl.

Patti has gone through an interview in which she was more of a person. At one point she talked with the therapist as though she were a colleague, after he had shared with her a fragment of another patient experience, and she commented on it with a kind of respect for her own opinion, a kind of challenge to his superknowledge. She left with an orientation toward the outside world, and with new readiness to use this relationship as a prototype for the kind of relating she would find "outside. "

Eighth Interview, April 17:

Patient failed to keep this appointment. This interview was not made up. In other words, this meant she had a total of only nine therapy interviews.

We assume that her forgetting the appointment was not consciously deliberate but that it was purposeful in the process of her therapeutic effort with J.W. If we assume that the core experience was Oedipal, can we then assume that this denial of conformity was a teen-age-like rebellion against the System? The aggressive time limitation by the therapist is relieved of its dominant force by Patti's aggressive move, which castrated the therapist, thus enabling the patient to end her therapy and leave her therapist without excessive anxiety.

Ninth Therapy Interview, May 3:

T: (begins interview) I was certainly disappointed when you didn't show up last time.

P: Yeah. I know what you thought.

T: I thought you didn't love me anymore.

P: Do you now?

T: Well, it's hard to know. You're here. You got here two minutes early.

P: It didn't do me any good. You saw me fifteen minutes late.

T: That's true.

P: I don't need to be punished. I punish myself (unintelligibl

T: I thought maybe you'd get over that.

P: I had done very well, until I missed my appointment. And it won't do me any good to tell you how horrified I was when I realized it, 'cause you won't believe it. You'll say it's something . . . deep-seated, something or other.

T: That's right.

P: Yeah. (pause) It took me . . . why it took me over a week to get over that. I'll probably never get over that. (laughs)

T: There's no way ever to catch up on those things.

P: No . . . No.

T: Have to live with it.

P: Yeah. (laughs) You're a big help.

T: I try to be.

P: Uhu. You have been. (pause) Up until this. You know, I'm still not sure about . . .

T: It's interesting that you make it punishment, instead of permitting me to have human feelings like others.

P: (unintelligible)

T: Why, you've worked at this, you know, all along.

P: Uhu. Since I've known you, you mean, or . . . or . . .

T: Uhu. (pause) Yes, that's what I mean. You've always insisted that I wasn't human -- I was a doctor.

P: Uhu. (pause) Well, you would be . . . you are human outside, when you're not being a doctor. Are you always a doctor?

T: I'm never a doctor . . .

P: (interupts) But with me you have to be a doctor. That makes a difference.

T: It won't work.

P: Well, you must have known that it wasn't because I didn't want to come here on that Tuesday.

T: Of course.

P: Some other reason. (laughs)

T: Sure.

P: Well, maybe, that I don't know about, but it certainly wasn't because I didn't want to come.

T: Of course, you just didn't look at the card.

P: No, I didn't, because I could see the card so plainly in front of me, and I knew it was Thursday. I had had one on a Wednesday, and that took care of the one that was not a Thursday. And you know, I make the appointments, three appointments in advance, so that means . . . I'm about six weeks (unintelligible).

T: Of course you could. That sounds good. I like to think of you as careless.

P: Well, actually I'm very careless . . .

T: (interrupts) Glad to hear it.

P: It's something I had to . . . I've had to fight for a long time. It's another one of the battles. (laughs) You know, it's a very difficult one, 'cause it's so much easier to be careless.

T: But you'd rather do it the hard way.

P: No, I would rather . . . I have to, to survive or something. Can't go around forgetting appointments and . . . and just not doing anything 'cause you can't be bothered.

T: (interrupts) It's quite a . . .

P: They wouldn't have put me on the (unintelligible), if I were like that. I wish they hadn't. (laughs)

T: Look what an exciting interview we are having, just because you missed last time. (P laughs)

P: I didn't like missing last time. I missed more than just the . . . an hour . . . A lot more.

T: Maybe you got more.

P: Uhu.

T: That may have been your most important appointment with me.

Segment about 18 minutes later:

P: I have a feeling that there's something wrong with this. (pause) No, that you feel that there is something wrong with this wall. And I feel that it's necessary to me. And . . . and, if you said, "Break down that wall," I don't know. I might do it. (pause)

T: A little while ago. (P laughs) Now we can just enjoy it.

P: Well, I enjoy it anyway. Except I think it's one-sided. (pause) I know it has to be that way. That's what I'm here for.

T: You'd rather not believe that I enjoy it also.

P: (coughs) Why you must, because you (coughs) wouldn't be a psychiatrist, if (coughs) you didn't enjoy working with people, but (coughs) you have them all day long.

T: You almost choked on it.

P: Yeah. I almost choked on it.

Segment about 3 minutes later:

P: I want you to like me better than someone else. That's because I'm not sure of myself, you see, with anybody. And I need this feeling. But that's one of the things I'm coming here for . . . so I won't feel this way. It really has nothing to do with how you feel; it's . . . it's all my having to figure this thing out.

T: If you could just be sure of that. (P laughs) That's all there is to it, is your figuring this out.

P: That'd make an awful mess of that wall. (both laugh) You ought to go over to the Russian Zone.

T: I can tell you how to keep your wall.

P: You can tell me how, but does that mean that I should?

T: Oh, that's up to you.

P: Oh, how do I keep the wall?

T: It's your wall.

P: Yeah.

T: Just not look at me. If you study your coffee cup, and look at your knees, and look around the room, and concentrate on your cigarette.

P: Oh, I like to look at you. I do all those things.

T: Oh, that messes up the wall, if you look in my eyes.

Segment about 11 minutes later:

T: I had another picture of you today. And it came back a couple of times, so I guess I should share it with you. I had a picture of you and your father. You were about four years old, and father had sort of teased you into climbing into his lap and held you there for just a moment and then very abruptly picked you up and set you off on the floor.

P: It feels as though it happened, and I can't remember it happening, but it feels that way.

T: And that you had no idea what was going on. All you knew was that he teased you into loving him, and when you put yourself into that body and soul, something awful happened.

P: (pause) (unintelligible) (long pause) (with tears) That's the way I feel about (pause) my relationship with everybody.

Segment about 2 minutes later:

T: I was assuming that if this ever happened with your father, or anything like it, you must have assumed then that whatever awful thing this was, was within you.

P: Yes. If that's . . . if something like that happened. Must be . . . because . . .

T: Because you were awful.

P: And I can't get over that feeling no matter how I try. (coughs) I just . . . (coughs) You know, I do try to convince myself that I'm not as bad as I think I am.

(pause) Well, I don't know what it is that's so bad about me, it's just . . . it's just there.

T: A four-year-old can't figure these things out very good.

DISCUSSION BY C.W.

The <u>ninth interview</u> was definitely "interpersonal, " as though Patti and J.W. were for the first time more nearly peers.   There were no long speeches; it had a real give-and-take quality.   The therapist responded with sarcasm to the patient's missing the previous appointment.   She seemed well convinced that there was no possible way of apologizing, and seemed to enjoy his "gigging" her about this.   The therapist suggested that the missed appointment may have been her most important one.   This is a pattern of teaching that could give her some sense of the fact that her inner experience was more important than her magical dreams about the interviews.   The therapist also noted for her that he was punishing her so that she might stop punishing herself.   Patti spoke of forgetting to look on the appointment card given by our clinic with the date and the hour of her next appointment.

She indicated her perception of the therapist as a separate person by asking him if he had a wall of defenses, like the one she suspected was building up inside her.   This led to a give-and-take between them which seemed related to their bilateral unexpressed fantasy of having sexual relations.   She talked about her feeling that the interview was over, as though they could now move to a social relationship.   There was a moment of confusion.   The therapist moved beyond this by becoming enigmatic, talking upside down, and being sarcastic.   In his telling her how she could build a wall in all of this, he was helping her to handle the panic of her fantasy, and also to develop her capacity for separating from him at the end of therapy.

We have included here a fragment in which the therapist offered his fantasy of her sitting on her father's lap.   This could be regarded either as a free association by the therapist, or as a deliberate formulation from the core (fifth) interview.   I see this as the therapist's effort to help her struggle with herself at the present moment.   Patti began to cry.   The therapist then flipped from being "father, " who had bumped her down out of his lap, to being the disapproving "mother, " who said that Patti was bad.   This resulted in a fairly significant re-enactment of the Oedipal triangular dynamics, but this time in the new framework of freedom and objectivity that the patient had attained.

We see then that by the end of this interview they had reaffirmed their roles.   The patient used the therapist in his professional function. The therapist, with some pain, faced the indications that his "child" was preparing to leave home.

TENTH (FINAL) INTERVIEW, MAY 16:

P: (begins) You know, I've heard about your cow. (This is reference to a new picture in J.W.'s office entitled "The Red Cow.")

T: And you like my cow.

P: Yes, I like it better than the (?) cat. I think it's quite intriguing. I don't really care for pictures of animals, but that's different.

T: It's not really an animal.

P: Yeah.

T: And it's not really grass either.

P: No, I like it. Something about it . . . very intriguing.

T: I've been very pleased with it.

P: Yes, I would think so.

T: It's from a girl that I'm very fond of, one who knows the artist who made that cut. I think it's a woodcut it was made from. (pause) Was it especially difficult to come today?

P: Oh, well, I didn't know it was going to be until I started coming. (pause) But I thought I should tell you how much good you've done for me. I owed you that at least.

T: You mean you're here for my benefit today.

P: Yeah . . .

T: (interrupts) Sure that I feel . . .

P: I know. (laughs)

T: All right about it all.

P: (laughs) No, but if you have a patient, I should think you'd like to know whether you've helped the patient or not. (pause) You don't want an old (unintelligible).

T: I'm still sort of stuck with the question, is that why you're here today, to thank me, so that I'll feel good. That I'll . . .

P: (interrupts) No, I don't think that it's . . . so that you'll feel good. I don't know whether you feel good or not. It's something I owe you. You agreed to take me on referral from the agency, and you've done me a lot of good.

T: Now you are indebted to me.

P: Yes, in a way. But that isn't worrying me, that I feel that way. I'm glad you helped me. I don't think that I'm indebted to you. (laughs) Why don't you like all this?

T: I was thinking back many years ago, I was dating a girl that I sort of liked. And we did some necking, and in the course of the sex play she had an orgasm. She said, "Thank you, thank you."

P: Well, maybe you can see . . . the similarity.

T: Didn't seem quite appropriate. I sort of felt sorry for her. (pause) I've often thought back to this experience, and something reminded me. (pause) Sort of a problem of how we see human communication in relationships.

P: Well, mine haven't been very good, I guess for . . . some years, but I think they're better now, and that's what I wanted to tell you. (pause) You don't like anyone to thank you, if you've helped them?

T: I'm sure listening to you. Trying to adjust myself to what you're saying.

P: (pause) Well, anyway, I won't go on with you. But you do make it difficult for me to tell you how you've helped me, because you get me . . . wound up with feelings I don't . . . I don't want to (pause) not have present. Certainly you understand that.

T: Yeah, that's what concerns me. I think I might understand that. What I understand I have difficulty going along with. (pause) It makes me feel sorry for you.

P: I don't want you to.

T: I don't want to either, but that's still how it comes out.

P: But this experience has been good for me. Why would you feel sorry for me? It's part of a learning process, isn't it?

T: The same way I felt sorry for this girl years ago.

P: That just makes me angry.

T: To me it's such a major misunderstanding . . . in the relationship.

P: Well, no . . . there's no misunderstanding. I don't feel that there's a misunderstanding.

T: (pause) You ever bake bread?

P: Only a couple of times. I'm not proficient at it.

T: Have you baked bread without any salt whatsoever?

P: No, but I know what it would be like.

T: That's what you remind me of. (pause) No saltiness. Or at least, that seems to be your effort; that's what you want to achieve.

P: Would you feel better if I broke down and cried (unintelligible)? Would you understand it more if I broke down and cried and said that it bothered me because I wouldn't see you again, wouldn't be able to come back anymore?

T: That's my feeling . . .

P: (interrupts) You know that.

T: That's my feeling about you. (pause) But I'm sorry that I will not see you again. I'll miss you. (pause)

P: I don't feel sorry for you, you see, because . . . you see . . . you have a full life, and for me, it's a little more difficult to lose someone. So I have to hide it more. It doesn't do any good . . . to show your feelings.

T: I always try to, anyway.

P: I can't show my feelings when (pause), I know I show them anyway, I know I do . . . by denying them. That's the way I feel. I try to hide them, and I feel that I'm not hiding them.

T: On top of that you try not even to have them.

P: Yes.

T: Certain ones.

P: And I thought I had done extremely well . . . until last night . . . and this morning. (pause) Then I became petrified because I thought maybe I didn't have the right date on purpose without knowing it. So I checked again last night, and it was all right.

T: (laughs) Well, we were together on that.

P: And the only reason was . . . and . . . this sounds silly again . . . because I didn't want to hurt you, and certainly wouldn't hurt you, if you'd see . . . you'd know I had done it for some obscure reason . . . 'cause I really didn't want to come and see you again. It'd be easier the other way. (pause) But in spite of . . . or maybe it's a good thing that this happened to me. (pause) I can see it clearer now, whereas before I knew you, I would have been confused again by what has happened to me. (pause) Or maybe I'm just kidding myself, don't know. Or talking myself out of it, but . . . Well, let me tell you anyway. The biggest thing (unintelligible) telephone . . . the conversation in the other room. I'm one person now, and I used to be two all the time. And I realize . . . that after a while after my last visit here that suddenly I felt just like one person, whereas before I hadn't realized how much I felt like two people. And one was always watching the other, and . . . and neither one had any use for the other. And . . . now that's gone. I just hope that I'll stay that way.

Segment about 4 minutes later:

P: But I've been able to get through all this without feeling I had to go kill myself . . . or try to find someone else to . . . take over . . .

T: I liked your feeling about killing yourself.

P: I thought that was bad.

T: Well, I didn't.

P: You didn't tell me. Why didn't you tell me?

T: I'm telling you now.

P: Once I . . . once I felt . . . a week ago . . . I chased it away fast.

T: It means to me that you have in mind that death will not happen to you. Something you will do. You'll do your own dying, whenever you get around to it.

Segment about 10 minutes later:

P: Whatever experience I have (coughs) makes me have . . . continue with this feeling of pity for other people who I think are going through some sort of struggle within. My experience with (unintelligible) . . . Well, in my learning to love you has increased that feeling for other people. (pause) And I know that they say that "it is better to have loved and lost," you know, "than never to have loved at all." I guess it's good for people. I don't like it for me.

T: Maybe you haven't lost yet. (pause) Maybe you can take it with you.

P: Well, I . . . well, I expect so. But there's a sadness with it.

T: Uhu.

Segment about 3 minutes later:

P: You don't care whether you've done something for me or not, is that it? Every time I try to show you how you've helped me . . . you (laughs) . . . you change it around somehow. You're (laughs) . . .

T: The look in my eye changes. (P laughs) I would assume so. (pause) Yeah. You've done as much for me as I have for you.

P: I have?

T: Uhu. (pause) Yeah, I really think that it's quite mutual. Quite reciprocal. Has been precisely as satisfying to you as it has to me. Precisely as frustrating to you as it has to me. Precisely as pleasant and unpleasant. (Long pause)

P: I hate it being the last visit. But even yet, even if they said, "Well, you can have ten more visits," I wouldn't take them.

T: I was thinking of that before I called you (from the waiting room) this morning.

P: Thinking about what?

T: That one of the very important things in this relationship between us was the limitation.

P: Uhu.

T: To ten visits, which you cut to nine. (P laughs) At least it didn't happen to you. You did it. All of this I'm pleased with.

P: Well, I realize that the time had something to do with it. (pause) In many ways it's much better for me not to see you anymore for myself. (pause) And then, when I came here, I came determined to . . . help myself in any way that you could offer me help . . . and to have my mind as open as I could, to see anything you might . . . and it sure did frustrate me when you would tell me something, and I couldn't feel or see it. And it would infuriate people like this friend of mine who's been going a long time to a doctor, and I act so much better in a short period of time. And I told them it was because they had a year or so to go, and I didn't. I only had ten visits. I only had a short time.

T: To make the most of it.

P: Only I tripped.

T: I didn't notice that. When was that?

P: (laughs) Well, you know it now. In how I feel about you. I knew the first time I came to see you that I liked you and trusted you. But that's where I intended for it to stay. And then . . . and then this other feeling gradually grew. See?

T: (interrupts) This is wonderful.

P: No. I don't want it.

T: I don't believe that you don't want it. Everybody wants it . . . you want all the feelings there are -- the murderous ones, the loving ones, the jealous ones, the fearful ones, frustrated ones.

P: I've had them.

T: Uhu.

P: And this one.

T: Isn't that wonderful? Got a whole keyboard.

P: (laughs)

T: No dead keys.

P: Only one.

T: I hadn't noticed. Which one is that?

P: (laughs) A relationship that would be satisfying for me.
(pause) And I don't expect that is going to happen to me,
so I guess it's a good thing that I have all the others.

T: Sometimes you flip over from expression of feeling to
referring to an over-all life arrangement. And I keep
talking just about feelings.

P: Uhu.

T: And it's the feeling keyboard I'm so concerned about --
that you have no dead keys there.

P: (interrupts) And there's also a feeling of security in
loving someone, and helping that person love you back.
You feel secure in that. That is an important feeling.

T: I certainly think so.

P: (unintelligible) That I can understand, it seems to me it
would be good. And I look at people and wonder if they
have that. And if I think they have it, I am very glad
for them. It isn't that I envy them, I'm glad for them.

T: Well, you're getting better in terms of looking in people's
eyes (P laughs). Maybe after a while you can feel more
secure in what you see there. (pause) We'll have to stop
today.

P: Well, you made the last visit better than I had expected

T: Could have been worse.

P: Could have been worse. Good-by .

T: Good-by.

DISCUSSION BY C.W.

The last of these ten interviews is characterized by a profound struggle between Patti and J.W. The interaction had become more free and full of feeling. In the ninth interview the therapeutic interaction was still relatively professional, even though it was clearly moving toward a present-tense, person-to-person exchange. Now in the tenth interview it seems as though the therapist and patient are taking leave of their functional roles and seeking each other as friends. The therapist was awkward rather than technical, and we judge that this was a very live experience for him. He was no longer "doing therapy." As I listened to the entire tape recording it became rather painful at times to follow the desperate efforts of these two people as they attempted to say their good-bys with some dignity.

Patti had obviously arrived to say her "thank you's" as a good little girl should. This would be the safest role for her in these final minutes, so that the powerful sexual undertow of their relationship might not find expression. The therapist was very rejecting of her efforts. He seemed to be searching for the adult woman in Patti, or at least an adequate adolescent daughter's warmth. He suggested that she should be more "salty." He told her that he felt like crying, and said directly with deep feeling, "I'll miss you." As the therapist thus left himself without professional status, the patient felt obliged to assume the role of control person for both of them and said, "I can't show my feelings."

By comparison with the early interviews, we find their relationship to have undergone a thorough reversal. Patti was clearly sensitive to this, when she said to J.W., "I am petrified, lest I hurt you," thus indicating her awareness that he was now vulnerable. Then she added, as if it were a consequence, "I'm one person now."

Patti's sense of integrity and uniqueness might be thought of as evidence of a transference cure, a flight into health. The therapist thought this unlikely because of the depth of his own feeling with Patti.

The therapist next appeared to try to seduce Patti into becoming a regular patient again because her experience was still so limited. She denied this by reminding him that she was now trying to get something for herself, and that she could participate as she chose. Then, on second thought, she spoke of suicide once more, as if to provide an excuse for continued therapy. This time the therapist refused and told Patti that she is able to take responsibility for her own death, as well as for her life.

Then they laughed in a comfortable way about all they had gone through together. They knew that the crisis was past. They also about how he had contradicted her. They also returned to thoughts of death, probably because they faced the end of their therapeutic relationship. Once they had agreed on this, she could tell him with much feeling, "I've learned to love you." It seemed clear to me that by then they had both transcended mere sexual feeling and had found each other with mutual respect as people.

In the last few minutes of the therapy they agreed in their acceptance of the administrative ending of their relationship. She reassured him by saying, "If there were ten more interviews, I would not take them, ----- and it's much better for me not to see you any more for myself."

CONCLUSION BY C.W.

We have described a therapeutic process limited by circumstance to ten interviews. We postulate that the therapy was effective in symptom relief and was also growth-promoting for the patient. We have discussed the process from the viewpoint of the relationship between the two persons involved.

This case presents a sample of experiential psychotherapy. It is essentially a routine process which is typical of psychotherapy as practiced by J.W. and of patients treated by him. It differs in its condensed form and capsule-like quality. J.W. was concerned in planning this series of interviews lest they result in nothing but a transference cure of the symptoms. Under the threat of the time limit certain specific variations took place. J.W. did very little in the development of insights into the dynamics of the patient and her illness. The therapist and patient did very little deliberate working through of the symptoms or of the dreams. They did not even investigate the core phase dream reported in the fifth interview. There was no investigation of the patient's history beyond the initial fact-finding appointment. Finally, J.W. quite clearly denied his personal curiosity about this patient; both of them related to her present life.

It seems clear that the process of change in this patient was initiated nine years earlier when her mother died and that this therapy resulted in a rebirth (second menarche?) after nine years of relative menopause. We assume that the depth of the therapeutic relationship in the fifth interview made the difference between a transference cure and a break-through out of her stalemate in living. We assume also that J.W.'s obvious respect for this patient was one prerequisite for a good prognosis in therapy.

This case raises several moot questions:

(1) Is it possible that any other psychotherapy in a similar setting would have gotten at the therapeutic impetus possible for that patient and that therapist? That is, is the limit of gain in the relationship and not in the time as such?

(2) Is it possible that any therapeutic process could be as adequate in ten appointments as it could in an unlimited number, if the consenting parties really accept the time limits as final? (In my opinion, such acceptance may only be based on whether the limitations are really necessary.)

(3) Is it possible that any therapist challenged by similar time limitations might develop a similar pattern with similar results?

ADDENDUM

Q. Did you formulate a specific diagnosis before you began psychotherapy, or was it made after psychotherapy was in progress?
Do such pre-therapeutic diagnoses inhibit or facilitate taking a
patient into treatment? Are your diagnoses subject to revisions
as psychotherapy proceeds, and do they vary depending on the
way the patient responds to the treatment? Do you distinguish
between diagnosis as such and simple spontaneous diagnostic
reflections?

A. Yes, following his diagnostic consultation with Patti on November
7, J.W. sent the following report to the referring agency:

1. Is an attractive, friendly, likable person of average intelligence and above-average social capacity. 2. Good physical
health. 3. Neurotic problems since early childhood. 4. 000-x06,
Agitated Depression, chronic, mild, with pathology in all developmental areas. Presenting symptom is spider phobia. 5. Motivation for therapy is present but needs to be encouraged. The
agency responded to this report by authorizing ten psychotherapy
interviews for Patti.

A few years ago both authors were accepting patients for therapy
without even as much diagnostic study as in Patti's case. We
found that when it began with the first face-to-face encounter we
more rapidly developed the intense interaction necessary for
therapeutic movement.

However, we have gone back to making a professional evaluation,
usually in the course of three consultations (except in instances
of administrative limitation as in Patti's case). The "diagnosis"
enables therapist and patient to identify the nature of the therapeutic task, provides a basis for planning of interviews, and contributes to the comfort of the therapist. The "diagnosis" also facili-
tates communication with the referral source, and thus places
the therapist in the acceptable framework of the health work in
his community.

The diagnostic consultation with Patti probably delayed the development of intimate sharing in therapy, but it was a temporary minor
obstacle. In the course of the therapy, many partial dynamic formulations crossed the therapist's mind, and he shared these as
occasion arose. He tried specifically to identify changes in the
growth effort of the patient during therapy. Generally, as our
patients become profoundly involved, especially as we continue
in long-term treatment aimed at character change, we repeatedly
find such major oral dynamics operating that we think of the patient
as "schizophrenic"; this feeling in us has no connection with the
original diagnosis, but constitutes our awareness of the patient's
"wholesale involvement."

Q. Did you approach your patient with a consistent and verbalizable theory or set of hypotheses on personality structure and/or the genesis of psychic illness? Was such theory used directly (or indirectly) in selecting the patient for treatment? How was it applied in the treatment and how effective was your theory in reaching the goals of treatment? What do you see as the function of such hypotheses or theories?

A. Our concepts, hypotheses, attitudes, and particularly our personal experience, are the major factors which control our interaction with patients. The therapist's faith in himself is obviously expressed via his theory of psychopathology. Therefore, our view of life and human nature determines rather "automatically" our selection of patients and procedures with them. We do not select patients on the basis of psychopathological category, nor genesis of the illness.

We hypothesize that: 1. All persons seek to grow emotionally, at all ages, and in all relationships. This biological drive for growth is a most underestimated phenomenon in modern society. However, the expression of this drive is variable. 2. All functional pathology and symptoms constitute a cry for help. 3. All possible psychopathology is currently operative in the patient to some degree. 4. A person's character structure, the direction of his growth efforts, and his psychopathology arise from the matrix of his "family" experiences. His "significant others, " including the professional therapist, continue to constitute his source of "becoming. "

The purpose of our hypotheses is to conceptualize our function so that we may remain anchored in our own realities. We thus maintain an objective perception of the subjective experience within ourselves. It is our way to connect past learnings with patients to our experience with the present patient, so we might resonate affectively. We are less hesitant when we can anticipate further possible movement with the patient. Finally, our theoretical agreements and disagreements with professional colleagues enable us to discuss patients together, and to use a colleague as a consultant.

Q. What did you think of the prognosis of your case before you accepted the patient for treatment? What did you think during the first several interviews; and during the latter stages of treatment? Do you feel prognostic judgments about ultimate health or ultimate illness are useful? Can we dispense with a prognosis as a formal event in clinical treatment?

A. In Patti's case the prognosis for symptom relief was judged to be good on initial examination. Her participation confirmed this. A good outcome seemed assured after the fifth interview.

We try to formulate a prognosis in writing as "part of the diagnosis." Not the diagnostic category, but the expressed motivations of the patient establish whether it is wise to proceed into therapy with the patient at a given time. The willingness of a patient to write dreams, to free associate, to share embarrassing thoughts and feelings, are significant prognostic "straws in the wind."

The feelings of the therapist are equally influential in determining therapeutic results. His sense of a healthy readiness for relating to the present patient, or his sense of aversion and futility, or his possible early overinvolvement will identify how the therapeutic interaction might develop. One value of the formal prognosis is to force the therapist to recognize the possibility of failure, to remind him that any patient can defeat the efforts of any therapist.

Q. What particular therapeutic techniques did you apply in this case? Which of them were most effective and which ineffective, and for what reasons? Did you attempt any technical innovations on an empirical basis? When did you feel that a "peak" experience or turning point occurred?

A. The gross limitation to a total of ten therapy interviews with a relatively disturbed patient was a major innovation. In meeting this task the therapist endeavored to utilize every transference opportunity and the full impact of his countertransference affects. Then, following the core phase in interview five, the therapist increasingly utilized the existential techniques which are part of his work with relatively secure patients.

The core phase (major turning point, climax) in this therapy was neatly defined in the patient's sexual dream. The significance of this dream was not only that she had it, but that she shared it with the therapist, and to some degree re-experienced it with him. The dream served to cement a profound identification, which established the therapist as her prototype.

There must have been ineffectual techniques. These would be those not emerging from the feeling state of the therapist at the time. We now find it impossible to identify specific instances.

Q. Did you feel that Freud's formulation of transference and countertransference were sufficient to account for the therapeutic encounter with your patient? How would you describe your encounter?

A. We find the concept of transference to be adequate in understanding the early phases of treatment. After the relationship becomes person-to-person, movement of the therapy toward ending may be explained more effectively by reference to nontransference factors.

Q. It has been said that psychotherapy is a white, middle-class, urban phenomenon which does not necessarily apply to other social stratifications or cultures. In what way did your patient's cultural background influence his illness and treatment? In what way did your own cultural background assist or deter the treatment?

A. It is our experience that the professional therapist is able to contribute to the living of any other person, despite stresses arising from differences in race, culture, social class, or language.

The comfort of the therapist, and probably his efficiency, is greater when his identification with the patient is facilitated by their similarity in background and culture.

Although Patti came from the "lower middle class" and the therapist from the "upper middle class," the latter had no problem identifying with her.

Q. There is an increasing tendency for neo-analytic thinking to ascribe the genesis and treatment of psychic illness to the social psychology of the family. How did this apply in your case?

A. Patti's history and therapy were conditioned quite obviously by family patterns. She came to therapy at the time when her childhood (family) patterns were at last thoroughly disrupted. She could neither correct nor reconstruct her original family model. Her efforts with the therapist were directed toward learning how to construct a new model for a possible family-to-be.

Q. If your treatment was concluded what criteria did you use for terminating it? If it is still in process, what guide points would you use to determine when your patient is sufficiently improved to discontinue treatment? Do you feel that a patient should be seen as long as he feels he needs it and is willing to pay the fees?

A. Therapy was terminated on schedule with the tenth interview. In subsequent years there was no indication that Patti needed or desired further psychotherapy. There was no evidence of negative or positive transference residuals, which would have been symptomatic of a transference cure.

Q. Did you make any mistakes in this case -- in the sense of "if you had to do it over"?

A. Our usual procedure would have involved use of a consultant in the second or third interview. This was not done with Patti because of the administrative restrictions.

There must have been errors in this therapy which are not now evident to us. For example, the therapist's judgmental attitude might be regarded as an error. However, Patti's therapist would have done less than his best if he had not presented him - self as openly as possible. He is actually a compulsive person, and it would have been dishonest for him to pretend otherwise to the patient.

Q. In treating your case did you perhaps feel that the classical distinctions between psychoses and neuroses were breaking down? (This question may apply even if your case represents neither a psychotic or neurotic.)

A. We have found the classical diagnostic distinctions of little help in facing the therapeutic task with a specific patient. It has been said that "no patient can be insane twenty-four hours a day. " We agree, and would add that nobody can be sane for twenty-four hours a day.

We see our culture as becoming gradually more honest in acknowledging the psychotic and neurotic processes going on in each of us.

PSYCHOPHYSICAL REACTIONS

Chapter XI

THE THERAPY OF ESSENTIAL HYPERTENSION

by Harold Kelman

INITIAL CONTACTS

Knowledge of this fifty-one-year old banker began three years before our first meeting in September, 1961. Awareness of him and his wife was augmented by friends and a former patient who urged me to work with him.

In my waiting room, I met a well-proportioned, good-looking, carefully groomed, tight-smiled man, who jumped up to greet me. He felt taller than his seventy-three inches, walking with the stoop of people sensitive about their height. He anxiously waited to be told where to sit. When I indicated the chair opposite he leaped into it, bending across the desk, his eyes desperately clutching at me. His tasteful dress felt like the clothes that should be worn by a man in his position. Needing to please and do the correct thing permeated his being.

PRECIPITATION FACTORS[1] AND PHYSICAL HISTORY[2]

To my "Can I help you?" he said, "I had two convulsions the night before I was to leave on my vacation in July. The same thing happened last year. Just before I was to go on vacation, a blood vessel in my right leg closed off and I had to be operated on." He immediately followed with his physical history.

The doctor for the extended family and friends "became a sadist as he got older. All my family became hypochondriacs because of him. One day," when Mr. Stein[3] was twenty-eight, "I came into his office. He looked at me and said, 'You look terrible. You haven't six months to live.' Once when he was on vacation, at my wife's insistence, I changed over to Dr. R, who was taking his place. He took everything so casually. I no longer was hypochondriacal. I began to be worried about my wife." The essentials of her extended mental illness followed, including hospitalizations and unsuccessful therapy by experienced analysts until she began seeing Dr. A three years before, with steady improvement.

1. Kelman, H. The Process in Psychoanalysis. Chapter I, "The Initial Interview." New York: American Institute for Psychoanalysis, 1963.

2. Kelman, H. "Clinical Psychoanalytic Concepts of the Etiology of the Neuroses." In The Etiology of the Neuroses. (A symposium by the Society of Medical Psychoanalysts.) March 17-18, 1962 (to be published

3. All names are pseudonyms.

While Dr. R was on vacation, Mr. Stein developed symptoms in his right leg. This was erroneously diagnosed by one surgeon and in July, 1960, he saw, on the recommendation of his wife's friend, Dr. T who has been his physician since. Dr. T referred him to a second surgeon. An emergency excision of a thrombosed popliteal aneurysm saved his leg.

This awesome history of associations with physicians, physical and mental illness, began with his father who attempted to play family doctor. He was severely phobic, obsessional, and hypochondriacal, terrorizing Mr. Stein with his temper and shouting. Intimidated by his wife, he obediently carried out her delegated chastisement of his son. As soon as Mr. Stein sees a doctor, in his office or at home, he becomes anxious and his blood pressure rises.

He was heavy before his double mastoid at eight, thin until eleven, and then very fat up to sixteen. Nicknamed "Fatty," his painful shyness was made worse by ridicule and by his awkwardness in athletics. Suddenly at sixteen, he shot up five inches. Again he was at a loss with his body, thereafter having frequent struggles with being overweight--up to 230 pounds. In his late teens he became a good tennis player and preferred singles. Secretly and sanctioned, he could enjoy releasing his aggressiveness and hostility.

His shifting physical states reflected his mounting tensions, as did his blood pressure, labile at eight, confirmed as hypertensive at twenty-five, and 240/120 the night of his seizures. His parents, siblings, children and many relatives had hypertension. By twenty, he smoked three packs of cigarettes daily, cut out one year before because of hypertension and vascular changes. This increased the torture of dieting necessitated by easy weight gain.

FAMILIAL SOCIOECONOMIC EVOLUTION[4]

To a question about Stein House, in which he was an officer, he poured forth with pride the history of this family banking business, originating in Germany a century and a half ago. For his era and milieu, his father, a lesser light in the bank, married late, the second choice of Mr. Stein's mother, a beautiful, unhappy woman, painfully shy, jealous, possessive, still in revolt against her family and their mores. Silently, through her fears, she dominated and warped the lives of her husband and children.

---

4. Kelman, H. The Process in Psychoanalysis. Chapter II, "The Life History." New York: American Institute for Psychoanalysis, 1963.

When Mr. Stein was five, Charles was born; at eleven Evelyn; nd at fourteen Joan. Toward Evelyn he has a benevolent fatherly ttitude. Joan has played a minor role in his life, but Charles has een his nemesis, a bully with a violent temper, never disciplined by is mother.

Mrs. Hirsch, a beautiful, driving outsider, instead of effacing erself, contrary to the clan mores dominated many insiders, includ- ng Mrs. Stein. Her son, a bully, made Mr. Stein's life a hell. Mrs. tein forced her son to dress identically with several cousins stensibly as proof of family closeness, but actually to mold him and ipe out his identity. Nowhere did Mr. Stein seem to have a court f appeal.

In the Stein evolution, the value systems of being German, ewish, having wealth, and even of the clan itself, fell away. Good orks, through educational and social service organizations, re- ained a value and a focus for many of their social and personal elationships, except those continued from childhood. The latter ften dragged on through inertia and a fear of leaving the known, though many of them no longer were meaningful. Factors favoring Alienation in Our Times"[5] were intensified by those unique to that ass, to the Stein family, and hence to Mr. Stein.

From age nine, he was sent to a boarding school in the city here he felt isolated and lonely, coming home for weekends which e shortened to arrival on Saturday midday and departure on Sunday fternoon. His school and college grades were average because of motional blocks. He married in his early twenties. His two sons nd older daughter have hypertension; the younger does not. The ons work in Stein Bank as does one son-in-law. As he mentioned is closeness to his mother in the last years of her life, he teared, hich from childhood he did frequently. Almost immediately he lded with pride, "My father began to live after my mother died. e was a different person. Those were the happiest years of his fe."

Toward the end of the session, with an intensity of feeling, e related two incidents which occurred the summer he became ree. While he was sitting on a "potty" in a Berlin railroad station, is parents left him with his governess, as he screamed in terror. ortly thereafter, in Rome, he again was left with his governess, reaming, as his parents crossed the piazza for refreshments. e had wanted to go with them for ice cream. He inferred the governess as Katie Boyle, who he knew had been kind to him, but he could not call her being there.

Kelman, H. Alienation: its historical and therapeutic context. Am. J. Psychoan., 1961, 21 198-206.

STRUCTURE OF HIS WORLD

"My friend, Mr. B, whom you know, said I was to call you about an appointment," on the phone; "Didn't Mr. B tell you about me?" when I asked "Can I help you?" in our first interview; my knowledge that his internist for months, and his wife for longer, had suggested that he begin analysis; his insistence that his wife urge Mr. B to talk to me to arrange an appointment for him, tell us that Mr. Stein is centrifugally directed, other-oriented, and that his center of gravity is outside himself, in others. He needs to avoid decisions and the responsibility for them, to efface and hide himself. He attempts to evade and forestall anything suggesting change, which would threaten his rigidities, evoking fears, His feelings of weakness and defenselessness and his centrifugal orientation preclude his being overtly assertive. What refers to him must be contracted and restricted; to others, expanded and enhanced. Imminently, he feels threatened with world dissolution; no"They" around whom to orient, his frail "I" feeling dissipated. Verging constantly on mounting anxiety, he must have tangible persons and abstractions made into graspable concretions.

Extremely alienated and self-effacing, he used externalization as a defense against the coerciveness of a tyrannical system of shoulds and intense perfectionistic standards and to mitigate the consequent self-hate.[6, 7] His world was one of immanent criticism and attempts to forestall, avoid, and minimize it: by giving way to others, by hanging back so that the initiative was forced on them, by immediately doing what was asked, by frantically sensing what mig please them and doing it at the right time. His world was filled with doubts, uncertainties, and irritations which had to be denied and hidden. The needed support and frightening threat of the other were intensified by my being a doctor and an authority, further compounded by the terrifying implications of his being in analysis.

CONDUCT AND PATTERN OF SESSIONS

His initial and subsequent comments indicated physcial illness as a topic of crucial import. Alert to new topics for immediate and future exploration, pertinent questions helped maintain the contact, the flow of associations, opening him to himself and to

---

6. Horney, K. Neurosis and Human Growth. New York: W. W. Norton & Co., Inc., 1950. Cf. page 1, Chapter 3, The Process i Psychoanalysis.

7. Kelman, H. The Process in Psychoanalysis, Chapter 3, "The Process in Analysis." New York: American Institute for Psychoanalysis, 1963.

me, and to obtaining more life history, past, current, and future.
Assured, not reassured, at the end of the session he was daring to
ask, with the memories from age three, "Will you abandon and
desert me for your pleasures like my parents did, when I am
powerless?" Throughout he had been asking, "Will you be like so
many of the doctors I have known?" "Will you misdiagnose my
condition and harm me?" "Will you understand me and my needs?"
'And above all, will you criticize and reject me?"

Openness to continuing testing, chancing, and error were
essential to learning the language and structure of his world, rooted
in his biology from birth,[8] toward transforming his experiencing
of the world from being rejected to being accepted.[9] Hungering for
being accepted does not equal having the capacity for it. Not pacing
he resolving of patternings of feeling rejected and strengthening
hose of being accepted can be as disastrous as too much water or
ood too fast to a dehydrated or starved person. Even experienced
herapists are driven to despair by the malignant ingenuity of so-
called masochists[10] in provoking rejection. Possible progress is
proportionate to the therapist's biologically being and experiencing
he radical organismic reorientation in his patient's shift from
eeling rejected to feeling accepted, in changing from being
compulsively centrifugal and centripetal, dependent, independent
and interdependent, to becoming more spontaneous and flexible in
hese ways of being and moving, and in these forms of relating;
rom feeling lonely, isolated, and alone to being comfortably himself,
alone and with others; from feeling helpless, to feeling and being
able; from feeling himself an alien object of hostility, to experiencing
world in which healthier cooperating and conflicting can obtain.

Having to unload what was in the foreground was immediately
evident. It was followed by slowing down to silence, to becoming
shrunken and withdrawn. When relief from me was not forthcoming,
e became frantic. As he dared, he moved from silent appealing
o unspoken demanding, while repeating the same verbalizations,
pproaching a stereotypy.

. Scott, J. P. Critical periods in behavioral development. Science,
   1962, 138, 949-958.

. Kelman, H. Discussion. Schizophrenia: A human situation,
   by Siirala, M. Am. J. Psychoan., 1963, 23, 61-63.

). Kelman, H. "Masochism and Self-Realization." In Science
   and Psychoanalysis, Vol. II. Individual and Familial Dynamics,
   Masserman, J. H. (Ed.) New York: Grune & Stratton, Inc., 1959.

My continuing response was the greatest possible openness for wider and deeper contacting, for palpating the subtlest changes in his tension level, and for experiencing his emerging patternings. Only by the most implicit means, through what I have subsumed under open contacting, the pure research viewpoint, the phenomenologic approach, being passionately objective and dispassionately subjective, being the ultimate of the impersonal which is the ultimate of the personal, might it slowly filter through to him that I was being trustworthy. By continuing to open ways for his moving on his own, always alert to his responses to inform me whether I was within the range of his possibilities, leading to accruing trust, a relationship [11]was being formed while the therapeutic process was gathering momentum in constructive directions.

Through considered pacing and timing he could integrate his changing perceptions of himself and his past as more information and memories emerged. I would allow him to go on without comment or question, extending the time of his silences. His tolerance for being abandoned and alone steadily increased as it did for increasing the number of sessions. At his preference, we started at once a week, with my indicating more would be desirable when available. After two months he accepted a second when offered, and eagerly the third, one month later. After two weeks of the three-session schedule, I allowed him to be on his own significantly more than heretofore. He knew he could call me if he became too upset between sessions. Also, he had shown greater resourcefulness in dealing with attacks of jitters on his own.

In this session, after talking forty minutes, with lengthening silences, about current happenings, the words and their equivalents to "being in the dark," "not knowing what to do," "I was frightened," "there seemed to be nobody I could turn to, " and more appeared in his associations. Right there with me, in broad daylight, he was experiencing himself as that helpless, frightened little boy, hiding under the covers, abandoned, about to be assaulted by an ominous something with no one to turn to. It revealed how easily that terrifying perception of the world was precipitated.

During the first year almost every session opened with a discussion of his last attack of "jitters." He had to keep talking about them until he felt relaxed. He worked through a spectrum of fears and anxieties as he became the experiencing subject objectively aware of their physiological components and of the symbol forms

---

11. Kelman, H. The doctor-patient relationship in therapy. Am. J. Psychoan, 1955, 15, 16-19.

pointing to them as description and conceptualization. He saw he made sense to me and in time was able to make sense to himself. He began to have a phenomenologic attitude toward his own happenings with increasing zest, curiosity, objectivity, and acceptance of the concomitant discomforts. With the relaxing happening as a learning experience, verb forms pointing at pulsating dynamisms began appearing, e.g., contracting, expanding, opening, closing, producing, reducing, increasing, decreasing.

Crucial for such happenings is my notion that symbols are processes having experienceable substantiality and content as well as describable, abstractable, and conceptualizable aspects and that symbolizing[12] is a process, an aspect of the universal forming process[13] and constituted by a sequence of connected levels from depth to surface, from the pre-ratiocinative to the highest order abstractions and vice versa.

What supported and expanded this process was helping him to communicate more freely and openly. This meant learning to unlearn what he had been taught since infancy. "Children should speak when spoken to" had been beaten into him with blows and terrorizing. To be permitted, even to be asked to speak freely and at will, was frightening and incomprehensible. With gratitude he could say in the sixth month, "You are an ardent listener," and a month later interrupt me as I was about to comment, with "I'd like to say more about that. After all there are only fifty minutes to a session."

About this time I left him blocked and silent for some minutes. He burst forth with, "You don't want me to babble like an idiot?" This opened the subject of his incapacity for small talk and that he had no recallable experiences of having babbled as a child, which he knew from his experiences he had encouraged and enjoyed with his children and grandchildren. His ability to do so came slowly and painfully. About six months later, with delight and tears in his eyes, he said, "I certainly have been babbling. I didn't think I had anything to talk about." About a month later, he couldn't get started. Toward the end of the session he announced

12. Kelman, H. Life history as therapy - Part I. Evaluation of literature. Am. J. Psychoan., 1955, 15, 49-70; Part II. On being aware. Am. J. Psychoan., 1956, 16, 68-78; Part III. The symbolizing process. Am. J. Psychoan., 1956, 16, 145-169.

13. Kelman, H. "Toward a Definition of Mind." In Theories of the Mind. Scher, J. M. (Ed.) New York: The Free Press of Glencoe, Inc. 1962.

with pleasure, "I didn't know I had so much in me." Babbling more freely and enjoyably contains much of what I call freer associating.[14]

Experiencing pulsating dynamisms opened the possibility for suggesting the valve analogy in connection with his labile hypertension. About the third month he began experiencing a sudden relaxing which he called a "kind of letting go," followed by the jitters minutes to hours later. After several such happenings, I introduced the image of "baling wires snapping," picked up from his association. I described how during his life he had added layer on layer, thereby burying his feelings and thus losing contact with them. As a result, he became so numbed he did not sense his fatigue and need for sleep, while concomitantly his blood pressure and general tension level kept rising. I explained that as an upper layer gave way, he had the jitters during the phase of reorganization, until the next lower layer took over. In the fifth month, following a tense weekend, he woke at 4:00 A. M. with the jitters. "After about fifteen minutes, I felt a sudden letting go all through my whole insides with a new kind of relaxation and pleasant fatigue, and I fell off to sleep." In the eighth month, letting go, without subsequent jitters and lasting two days, occurred for the first time.

After a year, with relief and great satisfaction, he found himself understanding some events, situations, and dreams which had been upsetting. When he couldn't, he remained tenacious until anxious drivenness took over, at times taking considerable help from me to free him. This pattern revealed how powerful were the needs to know and to control through knowing. Not knowing and being in doubt were torturing to him. At the same time, the torturing unexplained became a concretion out there around which he unified himself. Tied to a dream, his world remained constricted, painful yet relatively safer. If he moved from or let go of this constricted world, it began to disintegrate. He became mounting uncertainties and panic, a world without an object. He was anxiety (the catastrophic reaction--Goldstein),[15, 16] incapable of abstract thinking and limited concrete thinking.

ON BEING ABANDONED, DESERTED, AND REJECTED

Imminent experiencing of being abandoned, deserted, and rejected, announced in the first session through the memories from age three, was considerably amplified within the next few sessions.

14. Kelman, H. Freer associating: Its phenomenology and inherent paradoxes. Am. J. Psychoan., 1962, 22, 176-200.

15. Goldstein, K. The Organism. New York: The American Book Company, 1939.

16. Kelman, H. A unitary theory of anxiety. Am. J. Psychoan., 195 17, 127-160.

He could not recall his mother, father, or even kindly Katie Boyle ever holding him on their knees, or kissing him, tucking him in, sitting on or by his bed before sleep. At bedtime he was brought before his parents by his governess and stood there as they said goodnight, without touching him and requiring that there be no response. He was frequently criticized for being bad, but how was never explained to him. No one ever read to him. In spite of the supposed clan closeness, he had no playmates until he went to school.

From infancy his room was at the top of the five-story brownstone. It faced on the street, and in a long corridor going to the back of the house were the servants' rooms. Over the hallway was a roof trap door through which, in his frequent nightmares, he anticipated the descent of an "ominous something." He would pull the sheet over his head, lie still in paralyzed terror, literally holding his breath, uttering not a sound, not because he lost his voice but because there was no one to whom he felt he could appeal. Only as his anxieties abated could he finally go back to sleep. The terror on nocturnal awakening has diminished considerably. Merely in the last three months of our work could he get out of bed with or without turning on the lights.

AUTHORITY PROBLEMS AND THEIR RESOLUTION

Reinforcing each other since infancy were Mr. Stein's fears of abandonment and rejection as well as his obvious fears and buried hatreds of authorities, [17] female and male, which were clearly evident in the initial interview.

He opened the second session with comments about an attack of jitters and an argument with his wife, which I took as quite a declaration of trust in me. His fear of her, hostility toward her and himself for his dependency on her, were obvious and intense. From the fifth month on, his dreams revealed more of his hostility. In one, she somehow falls off a pleasure boat. He watches her "sink as the boat suddenly veers away." Discussion of his mother kept recurring and of a blood member of the clan, elderly, active, and a harridan of whom he was much afraid. At an important public affair eight months after our work began, to his surprise he found himself telling her off with controlled anger. He often referred to that occasion as a turning point. With increasing ease, pleasure, and openness at business meetings, family, and philanthropic occasions, he put her on the spot and needled her, enjoying her discomfiture and his relative strength.

---

17. Kelman, H. Rational and irrational authority. Am. J. Psychoan., 1952, 12, 50-61.

In our second year he became aware of how he had controlled and restricted his wife through his fears and that he did so to always keep her close to him, healthy and unharmed, to be available for him if he needed her. As he felt stronger, these fears gradually fell away. He found himself able to talk with her more freely, first about his jitters, then about what went on in the therapy, about things that worried him and ultimately about business matters. In the twenty-seventh month, he reported an extended discussion with his wife, containing sharp differences of opinion which had a quality of intimacy that was heartwarming.

Between the sixteenth and twentieth months he had a series of dreams, first of his wife, then of his wife and mother together, then of his mother without his wife but with a number of others from his early life, including his father. The potency of each figure decreased as the dreams evolved. By my questions I guided him toward experiencing his diminishing fear of and attachment to his mother, her increasing impotence through his telling her off, to his taking over with her sitting there and taking it. This last dream sequence surprised and pleased him, though he felt uneasy about it. Then followed a number about the old brownstone house. Several took place on the fifth floor, with one almost a replica of his childhood nightmare.

From our first session a possible call from Charles hung over him like an ominous shadow. Charles stood for his mother, as her favorite; for his father, because of his temper; and for himself, as a terrorizing bully. How my patient attempted to avoid his calls, responded when he couldn't and when Charles forced a meeting, were discussed, always implicitly indicating the changes taking place. After a year, with trepidation, he was able to tell him off. From then on, he gradually went over to the attack with increasing calmness and zest at dishing it back to him. He became more open in teasing, frustrating, and needling me. After a year, he expressed sympathy for his father because of what he suffered at his mother's hands. After twenty months, he dared to more carefully scrutinize the head of the bank, find him weak and himself the stronger and more competent, which was quite a turnabout. Shortly, he expressed a moderate rage at one of the partners whose competence and integrity he had taken for granted and now found sadly lacking. His poor relations with one son improved through realizing his early failures and through becoming more adult and fatherly with him.

DEPENDENCE AND INDEPENDENCE[18]

Through the neurotic solutions of love, mastery, and magic he attempted to ward off the terror of abandonment and rejection and

---

18. Horney, K. *Our Inner Conflicts*. New York: W. W. Norton & Co., 1945.

to deal with his fears and hatreds of authorities. In our second session he told me how relaxed he felt during both hospitalizations. "There was nothing I could do about it, so I stopped worrying." With his wife, on boat trips, in a train compartment, and in a plane, when they took longer trips he felt similarly. He insisted she was different on vacations, accounting for how well they got on. In the hospital, he had nurses and in his room, also for an extended period, his wife. He was living the unconscious fantasy, "I have mother all to myself in my little world. The real world is locked out, doesn't exist, and can't reach me." He needed to believe this was what obtained in the last years of his mother's life, when in fact, because of senility and desertion by her favorite Charles, she clung to Mr. Stein.

This fantasy, evident also in dreams and associations, experienced as though actualized, reveals how such a person experiences life. The notions of a return to the womb or the Oedipus complex are useful but inadequate formulations. The hunger for the biological communion of mother and infant is a better guide, the basis of my notions on "Communing and Relating."[19] Only as he experiences me as mother, mothering and feminine, as father, fathering and masculine, and all that these symbols subsume can he be the child he never was, learn the difference between being childish and childlike, have this second opportunity to experience childhood, maturing, being adult, a husband, father, and grandfather. And this is what has happened as the analysis proceeded.

In the sixth week of our work Mr. Stein phoned late one evening asking if he could talk to me immediately, saying, "My wife suggested I call you," and apologizing for having bothered me. Following my "Of course," he described his severe attack of jitters, said he had already called his internist who suggested an additional sedative which had not helped. He did not want to call him again. I gathered that only after he repetitively had asked his wife what he should do and after she as often suggested calling me did he do so with great trepidation. With little help, he kept detailing his jitters

---

19. Kelman, H. Communing and relating: Part I, Past and current perspectives. Am. J. Psychoan., 1958, 18, 77-98; Part II, The mind structure of East and West, Am. J. Psychoan., 1958, 18, 158--170; Part III, Examples: General and clinical, Part IV, Communing as therapy, Am. J. Psychoan., 1959, 19, 73-105; Part V, Separateness and togetherness, 1959, 19, 188-215; Communing and relating, Am. J. Psychotherapy, 1960, 20, 70-96; "Communing as Witness Consciousness (Communion et la conscience-temoin)." In Roger Godel: De l'humanisme a l'humain. Paris VI, Les Belles Lettres -- 95 Raspail, 1963.

until he said, "I'm feeling better. I'm sorry I bothered you, " and with effusive thanks hung up after I mentioned he could call me again at any time during the night.

Three weeks later he again called, early in the evening, soon after the jitters began. I suggested he call after 7:30 when I would be free, which he did on the dot. This time he hadn't called his internist; "I felt if I could talk it over with you it would help, and I know Dr. T would suggest I take another sedative, or he would come over and give me one, and I didn't want that. " I gathered his wife hadn't suggested he call me but that he might have asked her several times, for re-assurance, if he should. Again, after about ten minutes of talking with me, he felt quieter. I suggested he could call back if he wanted to or I would see him up to midnight if he felt the need. He did not call back, and there have been no more such calls since.

I felt I could do what I did because it wou d be helpful and because his tendency would be to ask for less help rather than for more. In fact, before the end of the year the whole theme of self-sufficiency, of trying to be a machine that never tired, began to come out, and all the feelings of shame at having to ask for help and at being and feeling helpless. His shame at the awareness of feeling dependent on me, experienced prior to my first summer holidays, exposed his need for self-sufficiency even more sharply.

NEED TO KNOW, CONTROL, AND BE PERFECT

Within the first months his need to know, to control, to fore-stall doubt, and to be perfect became obvious, all in the service of warding off fears and hates. He had to have a theater aisle-seat for immediate flight in case of an attack of jitters or a fire. It was six months before he could sit in a barber chair without feeling trapped. Being caught in traffic panicked him. Once, after seven months of therapy, he was stuck in a tunnel under the river. This really shook him. His terror of the seizures now became understandable. They were unpredictable and uncontrollable. An alien something in his own body with which he would be trapped and against which he would be powerless was liable to leap out and attack him. The seizures were a replica of his childhood nightmare. Also they might, as might the hypertension, damage his brain, which is crucial to his neurotic need to know. Within six months he stopped making emergency calls to his internist and within a year became less rigid about his monthly physical checkups. His hypochondriasis diminished considerably. Joy from his body and organ functions is just beginning to emerge. Through an occasional attack of diarrhea in the past two years, he has learned of their relation to his buried anxieties.

Because of his perfectionism, each obvious constructive change became a test situation. The first time he did not have the jitters for two days, he expected he should extend the two to three days.

Actually, nothing short of perfect relaxation all the time was the impossible goal he had set for himself. Understandably, he was most upset by his next attack. Gradually, I exposed more aspects of his perfectionism, but changes are slow because it is a most tenacious deeply imbedded problem.

COMPULSIVENESS

The compulsiveness inherent in his neurotic protective structure, of which his idealized image is an expression, manifested itself in obvious and destructive ways. He arrived at the fourth session ten minutes late, breathless, anxious and apologetic. "I ran the last ten blocks; I couldn't find a cab." Neurotic demands had again overriden medical contraindications. He had mentioned that for years his norm was five to six hours' sleep on business trips while working at a fever pitch. "During the years of my wife's illness, I slept with one eye open. I never felt tired, and I never felt sleepy," indicated his enormous pride in having turned his body into a machine and how alienated he had become. A year later he smiled less when he recalled how friends used to say, "How do you do it? You look so calm and so rested." He better understood the cost to his body, the original terror of further vascular occlusions and seizures, and how the perfect machine had broken down.

Running to his appointment opened the topic of compulsive punctuality. He was always early, even to an all-day open-house party. He was the first one at the office in the morning, was packed for a trip days in advance, even for a weekend, and felt unbearably anxious if bills were not paid promptly. This discussion brought out extensive rituals and much magical thinking. The intense anxiety when compulsive patterns were threatened and the fright at their exposure abated at varying rates depending upon their determinants. Being "at the office early" hadn't budged in twenty-seven months, though he became increasingly uneasy at its obvious irrationality.

HOLIDAYS: FEELING ABANDONED AND REJECTED

In the last session before my first winter holiday, Mr. Stein brought in a dream about an old friend in the travel business whose old offices were seriously fire damaged. He was worrying whether he could get them fixed up in time for the Christmas rush. Factually, this man had moved to new offices several months before when Mr. Stein had last seen him and been told business was very good. I waited until he ran down and began to look anxious before I asked if he could say something more about the dream. He added more about his friend and noted that he was more open and intimate with strangers than relatives and members of the family.

For the next year this theme kept emerging, quite intensively in the final two months. He noted, with increasing sharpness, feeling strange, feelings of not being there, of being far away, of distance, and of remoteness from people. At times it seemed they were so far away he couldn't hear them, or as though something was between him and people. What helped make possible experiencing alienation from himself and others was the resolution of his fears about his wife. He was aware that he had restricted her by them and felt guilty about his possible responsibility for her problems. He now understood an upsurge of his old hypochondriasis. "I transferred my worries to her, and now that I'm less worried about her, my old worries about myself are back. "

After another pause, I asked about the jitters with which he had opened the session. He was upset about the death, since the last session, of two acquaintances, immediately thinking that "things happen in threes" and fearing he was next. This led to a discussion of his thinking and feeling about catastrophe and his conviction that good things can't last.

I then asked whether there was anything further he wanted to tal about that had happened since our last session. He was surprised as more and more came out, but when asked about our last session, he could recall very little of it. Even after twenty-seven months, if very anxious at the beginning of the session, he remains glued to what he regards as the anxiety-precipitating topic. As he relaxes, what happened since the last session slowly comes back, less about the last session itself, and only rarely can he recall a dream he had related. For a long time this failure of recall terrified him, since he was convinced of brain damage from the illness of July, 1961, in spite of repetitive evidence to the contrary.

Mr. Stein's dream, coming before my holidays and after the death of the two acquaintances, was quite informative. He experienced my leaving as an abandonment, desertion, and rejection which evoked quite some anxiety and hostility. The hostility and death wishes he felt toward me had to be turned against himself and people to whom he feels close. The travel and Christmas holiday business connected the dream with me. His friend is a stranger, as I am, with whom he can be more intimate than with his family. He releases his hostility against me via him, but only in a limited way and against the old office. His friend had moved into the new one about the time Mr. Stein first came to see me. Through the dream and his associations he expressed a deep hopelessness and despair, and the conviction that it is dangerous to tell anyone that you feel good, are doing well, or making progress because something bad will happen. There was evidence of a fear of thinking of death wishes and associations and suggestions of the notion of the evil eye.

Having somewhat worked through being left at Christmas, his response to my Easter absence was more open. I told him of my extended summer holiday in early June, he having surmised it long before. In a chronological year, I see each patient for about thirty-six weeks for a total of about one hundred and five hours on a three-times-a-week program. As my summer holiday approached he became aware of mounting terror and shame at his helplessness and dependency. I now frequently chanced the limits of his tolerance for experiencing being abandoned. In our last week I indirectly suggested he could contact a colleague in my absence. He picked up the suggestion reluctantly. Aware of the potency of his having my whereabouts, he almost snatched my summer address from my hand as if it were a magic talisman. He contacted neither me nor my colleague.

He was less upset by my second Christmas absence. In the February following, he mentioned that he would miss two sessions during a short holiday, to which I responded with a silent acceptance. I had wanted him to have the experience of abandoning and rejecting me. He had one very upsetting night, almost called me, and returned two days ahead of time. He assumed I would again give him my summer address. His anxiety abruptly mounted when it dawned on him that I wasn't going to do so. He had been daring to be hostile and aggressive, first subtly through teasing and frustrating, then more obviously, discovering that much of it really was being assertive. In our last week, driven to get my address, he became openly hostile, using cunning and shrewd maneuvers to trip me, at times badgering me, even to the point of ridicule. He was both pleased and frightened at his audacity. When we resumed work in September, he informed me that he had the "best summer in my life," and his hypochondriasis about himself and his wife had almost disappeared.

ANALYSIS IN DEPTH

As we proceeded, he detailed the patternings of his jitters, relaxing, and visceral sensations. Symbolically, in my meaning, he was going into the heart and guts of many issues long held down by "valves" and "baling wire." In the first session burst forth the two painful memories at three in Berlin and Rome. A month later he recalled a third terrifying experience from that summer, when their car broke down at dusk. It was two more years before the name of the couple accompanying his parents emerged. Although he felt kind Katie Boyle was with him on the occasion of those painful experiences, to date he has no recollection of her being there. However, after a year, he had his first pleasant memory from that summer, and a second four months later, but it was a year more before he clearly remembered Katie was with him on both occasions.

It was in the second year that more occasions of fun, enjoyment, and laughter began to emerge as he realized how few such instances had been in his life, particularly up to the time of his marriage, and how alien such feelings were to him. The fact of a trip in Europe, at seventeen, with a friend, came up in the second month; in the ninth, the recollection that it was pleasant; in the twenty-sixth, his friend's name. These and other memories, the nature of their emergence, the feelings associated with them, and the influence of these events on his life, plus other data, as well as the evolution of the therapy could be seen as a validation of many Freudian hypotheses. Such thinking would be a manifestation of the delusion of explanation, of post hoc reasoning, of facts being made to fit a theory, since the therapy is premised and conducted on the basis of models of more and different dimensions.

In late Setpember, his son Arthur went through a crisis in his personal analysis. His father was firm and even callous, while his mother was supportive and helpful. Mr. Stein was enraged at his son and at himself, feeling humiliated and guilty, holding himself largely responsible for his son's condition. When he was seven, he was seriously ill, after which he became extremely fat and awkward, almost a replica of his father during the same age period. This shamed, humiliated, and frightened his father, evoking feelings of unbearable helplessness. He covered them by aloofness, callousness, and harshness which he realizes must have had a destructive impact on the boy.

Concomitantly, Mr. Stein began going into his own eight-to-fifteen period, which had been a blank up to then. At first it was like coming up against a stone wall, he insisted, because it was so unpleasant, but bit by bit it began to open up. As it did, which was within two to three weeks, he talked less about his son, whose crisis passed and who has shown steady improvement since.

From other sources I knew of the accuracy of what he reported about his son. He confirmed to me the facts of what had happened to him during that period. Facts also have meaning and can be used for defense. He responded with rage against his son and himself at the enforced self-confrontation with that painful period on which he was blocking. The rage also covered panic at not being able to keep it buried, at the fear he might not be able to deal with it if it came out, and at what else it might bring up. He did take back his externalizations and explore that period. Concomitantly, his relations with his son became better than they ever had been since he was seven. I feel this, previous, and subsequent sequences of happening expose the limitations of the notion of re-experiencing the past, of the repetition compulsion, and of the greater adequacy of the concepts that were used.

PERIOD EIGHT TO FIFTEEN

From ages eight to fifteen, he was ridiculed, felt shy and rejected. He did not withdraw but clung to the periphery. Slowly, by putting colossal demands on himself no matter how excruciatingly painful, he found ways of moving into his peer group. He was aware of what he was doing, having had long practice at it. As we discussed the pain and the cost of such demands, he said, "And the last time I

cried was when I was three. " The futility of doing so had been beaten
into him. But the price of not crying and of getting into the group he
did not realize. It was self-benumbing and severe alienation. As the
eight-to-fifteen period opened more, he was finding himself telling me
of enjoyable times with peers, and their names, which previously had
never come through.

About the third week of our eight-to-fifteen discussion he
opened the session by saying he had experienced the most horrible
dream in a year and the worst jitters in eight months. Several days
before, he heard news that a big business deal might fall through. He
had grave doubts about it, which he wouldn't let himself fully experience or express. He feared he might turn out to be wrong and open
to criticism. His own, of course, would be the worst. Only on asking
him to repeat the dream a second time did I get a fuller picture of the
dream and what was occurring within him. It was morning, and as
usual when he wakens, he goes to the window to close it. As he looked
out, he saw the wreck of two cars. There were no people. He turned
away to call to his wife who was asleep. He believes he woke her.
When he turned back and looked the second time, he saw that it was
only a pile of dirt in the middle of the street. He recalled a feeling
of embarrassment and woke in a panic.

As an expression of his anxiety, he kept talking about the deal
that might fall through and that this was another one of those explosion
dreams. After the dream of his friend's place burning down, he had a
number of dreams of explosions, of cars going out of control, and of
auto accidents. By my questions I pressed him to look at the actual
details of the dream and their relation to what was coming up about the
ages eight to fifteen. I reminded him that initially he adamantly insisted
that this period was one solely of humiliation, pain, and drabness.
I also pointed out, in the face of considerable resistance, how intense
was his need to be right, to be certain, to know, and to control.

To his embarrassment, the dream clearly said that what was
right in front of his nose, in front of his home, he could not see for
what it was, because he insisted that it could only be bad, catastrophic,
and painful and that for the first time he had the courage to take a
second look and see how wrong he had been. Such an admission was
enough to waken him in panic. The dream was connected with the
certainty of his negative perception of the eight-to-fifteen period and
his discovery, in the many second-looks in our sessions, of how
wrong he had been about what was right in front of his nose, in his
past, inside his home, inside himself, in his past and his present.
The dream also says that to justify calling his wife for help, he must
feel helpless, and this comes through the effects of his negative perceptions of harmless or even joyous events.

Finally, the possible falling through of the deal confronted
him with a panic-laden dilemma. When it did fall through , he had

abdominal cramps during the final discussions, woke at night with anxiety and diarrhea, and had it for the next twenty-four hours. "I must have known I didn't want it, but I couldn't let myself know what I knew I wanted and also because of the fear I could be wrong. Once we decided, I let go of some baling wires."

HIS MOTHER, HIS WIFE, AND SEX

Shortly after we resumed work in September, while being critical of his mother, he was aware enough of his slip, "my Mother, my wife," to have an anxious tight smile. A week later he had a dream in which he shouted at his wife for being extravagant, which she is not. From associations and previous material, he could clearly see it was his mother, not his wife, whose behavior forced him to build his extravagant defense system to conceal from her his deepest feelings and to hide behind a front of misery and non-communicativeness. "When I went to a party and I came home, my mother never asked me did I enjoy myself, did I have a good time, but always who was there and how did she look?"

In talking about the eight-to-fifteen period, the subject of sex was opened for the first time by me. His shyness was painful, the events associated with it frought with fright, the few wet dreams, the short period of self-discovered masturbation, and the first visits with friends to bordellos in Europe. Before going abroad with relatives at sixteen, he recalls his mother in bed one evening closing her talk on "the facts of life" with, "Sex isn't all it's cracked up to be." This was the total of his sex education; nothing from his father. He had heard very little about it from his playmates. In his late teens, over a period of months, he and a friend visited two "nice out-of-town girls" in their apartment. He had occasional sex with one, which was quite secondary to the feeling of ease, camaraderie, and acceptance by women.

Although from the sixth month of our work there were increasing occasions when I could have opened a discussion of sex, I did not, realizing what an anguish-laden subject it was. For similar reasons I have not pressed a discussion of the subject of money, which as a topic has come up innumerable times and to a slight extent has been worked through implicitly. Over the years I have learned to give weight to my intuitive feelings that discussion of certain subjects would be premature, harmful, or diversionary, and will not open or follow up a discussion even if pressed for by a patient. Conversely, when I feel a particular area must be gone into at times I will maintain quite some pressure in the face of considerable opposition.

In the fourth week of our discussion of ages eight to fifteen, he dreamt he was on a wicker stool, leaning against a bar of the early twenties vintage, with a Coke in his left hand. To his right, his mother appeared dressed and looking exactly as she did twenty years ago. His response was a shocked, "But she is dead," followed by, "but she is very much alive right there in front of me. She had a smile on her face, and I woke with a start." The following night he dreamed he was in Jersey City on his way to his appointment with me. First, he got trapped in traffic and became anxious about being late. Finally, after many obstructions and delays, he got to a phone station to call me and found all the phone booths in use, one becoming free after a long wait. "The telephone book was a mess, the pages torn, and spread over the pages was a mess, some stones, bits of bread, peanuts, and shrimps."

Opening up the subject of sex shortly before, with the implied criticism of his mother, truly awakened her from the dead. I had frequently suggested that his mother was still very much alive in him. But this was too frightening for him to admit, as was the notion of the unconscious. That it was only a Coke showed how frightened he still was of her. He wouldn't dare, even in a dream, face her with hard liquor in his hand. Once she had viciously criticized his wife for drinking too much when she had had nothing. The second dream became obvious as we examined the mess. The stones were from the Connecticut beach where he spent his summers from earliest childhood. His father was constantly munching on peanuts. For years the bank had heavy investments in flour mills; the bread had to do with the flour. The shrimps referred to his mother who was extremely fond of them. He kept blocking on the fact that he was not late for the appointment but had missed it. Only one hour after it was over did he get a booth, and the dream ended without his ever speaking with me. Obviously, he was putting off facing the mess and all it clearly implied.

YEARS THREE TO FIFTEEN

While he kept talking about eight to fifteen, I kept repeating three to eighteen. After four weeks he began talking about three to fifteen, with the recollection that it had been Katie Boyle that summer at three. Reluctantly, he admitted how resentful he was toward his mother for not having been loving -- the first time he used the word -- the way Katie had been. He reported a relaxing evening of doing nothing, followed by a restless night, but awakening refreshed, and enjoying -- which he called being selfish -- having the run of the bank without the annoying presence of the other senior officers who were away on business or holiday. Incidentally, he mentioned no bowel trouble, for the first time since our work began. He now reported being given enemas and cathartics from earliest infancy, and often giving himself enemas for constipation. I helped him connect babbling, being a child, and open bowels with loosening and relaxing, clamps and baling wires, the embarrassment about enjoying and the incident at three on the "potty". The way it all became connected "was amazing" and pleasing to him.

In connection with an unpleasant recollection at eight, he said, "I don't know who was with me, but I know that Charles was alive." Keeping him associating to this comment, finally he cautiously said, "At first maybe I wished he hadn't been born," and later he came out with, "Maybe for a long time I have wanted to kill him." Several days later, commenting on a trip with his mother and a chum in his teens, he said, "Charles and Evelyn were alive then," Evelyn the sister he loved. By my persistence he became aware of his need for exclusive love and devotion from his mother or any equivalent surrogate, no matter what the price.

MALES: COMPETITION AND COOPERATION

In early October he dreamed of seeing blood on the sidewalk, immediately assuming it was his. He looked for a bathroom, to which he was led by an older man, where he "let his pants down in a toilet without a door and examined himself." Finding nothing, he leisurely urinated and walked out. He was embarrassed by being confronted with more of his catastrophic thinking, but pleased at his openness about body function. These attitudes, plus his depiction of the older man, supported my opening the subject of sex. Shortly therafter, he discovered he had leisurely and continuously walked four miles, having originally anticipated visits along the way and taking a taxi. His doctor had said he would never again be able to walk over a mile.

In early November he dreamed he was driving down Fifth Avenue when a young chap with brown hair and a round face cut in front of him. Mr. Stein raced ahead and cut him off. The young fellow got away. Again Mr. Stein raced him and cut him off so he couldn't get away. He got out of his car, and bawled the young chap out, the latter now looking sheepish. Then they both drove off, parallel, down Fifth Avenue, amicably chatting to each other. This is the first time he tenaciously stayed with a friction situation in a dream, expressed his anger, came out triumphant, and amicably resolved the struggle.

Up to my departure before Christmas he reported definitively and quietly telling Charles off, firmly and supportively giving his son Arthur a talking to, and a number of conversations with the head of the bank, whom he respects less and less. In these conversations he went over to the attack, and with shrewd deftness made the man back down. Mr. Stein finally quietly and confidently came out with the feeling he is the most competent one and should be running the bank, something with which I agree.

BEFORE THREE AND THREE AND ONE-HALF TO SIX

He arrived at his session (November 22, 1963) several hours after President Kennedy was assassinated, eyes brimming with tears, holding back a flood with iron control. "All the girls at the bank were sitting around the radios, breaking down and crying. I felt I should not break down in front of them. " This again brought up "I haven't cried since I was three. " I indicated that maybe there was some hidden corner inside of him where he dared to cry. During the next week, bit by bit, he let on how much he had cried over the weekend; he cried only when his wife couldn't see him, and several times he "had to go out and get some fresh air" and cried on the street while walking.

The following week he spontaneously asked, "Who took care of me from three and one-half, when Katie Boyle left, to six, when Mrs. Walters came?" With more bulldog than anxious tenacity, he kept staring at "that blank period" which had not opened up when I left before[20] Christmas. By that time, in 224 sessions in the vis-à-vis position over twenty-seven months,· he had begun to feel and express variations of wanting, asking and answering, giving and receiving, being angry, anxious, fearful, sad and joyous, and feeling all of it was all right. His confidence in himself and trust in others had increased considerably and his relations with himself and others were much improved. His hypochondriacal symptoms were practically gone. Except in periods of crucial self-confrontation, his blood pressure was normal and no longer so labile. He felt fitter than in years. He was looking forward to years of continued business activity and with zest to further analysis and greater self-understanding to make that possible. *

THEORY AND THERAPY OF ESSENTIAL HYPERTENSION

"Any hypothesis concerned with psychosomatic functions or disturbances should deal with the intermediate process of development between the undifferentiated whole functional pattern and the integrated

---

20. Kelman, H. The use of the analytic couch. Am. J. Psychoan., 1954, 14, 65-82.

* At Christmas, through an expansion and reorganization of the bank, Mr. Stein was propelled into the leadership position, in fact though as yet not in title. As his reluctance to accept his role and the moderate exacerbation of symptoms abated, he cautiously became more assertive with increasing enthusiasm for taking over the directorial status. Because of personnel changes, a number of peers, superiors, and subordinates left the bank. Mr. Stein's initial response was of being abandoned and rejected by them, with increased insomnia which now is seldom present. He has been accepting and fulfilling the outstanding and standing-out position, an inner and outer world-structure not only opposite to but ontologically different from his previous lifelong patterns of being-in-the-world. (April, 1964)

matured process." However, most of that "vast area of the 'in-between' . . . unobserved and unmeasured" remains "completely mysterious" (Grinker). "The search for typical conflicts, defenses, fixations and meaning of symptoms for each neurosis . . . specific formulas for organ neuroses . . . has come to grief." The need for a "wider vista" was realized in "the concept of the field." It "implies multiple causality and necessitates multiple observers organized in a multidisciplinary group."[21] It has become evident that "effective therapeutic work with patients does not depend upon knowledge of how emotional conflicts are translated into physiologic malfunction or upon resolution of problems concerning specificity."[22]

Mr. Stein's history and therapy affirm this critique of psychosomatics and confirm the necessity for openness, tentativeness, and rigor in our methodologies and techniques. These attitudes should also restrain us from discarding what might be valuable in the sequence of hypotheses concerning psychosomatic phenomena and the rich observations on which they were based. Clinically they can suggest where and what to look for and how to organize our findings. Alexander's psychosomatic formulations[23] are in this category, as are the conjectures which came from my effectively working with two other people with essential hypertension and two more with a more malignant variety of it.

Among the unfavorable prognostic features were Mr. Stein's heredity, chronically rising blood pressure with vascular changes, and his severe emotional problems. Some of the factors which gave the therapy a constructive momentum were the fear and threat of death, of a recurrence of seizures and vascular occlusions in his extremities, the support of his internist, wife, and friend (including their responses to therapy), a high degree of psychic and physical vitality, as well as a tenacity for life in the face of great odds, the availability of time and money, and my positive response to him and his problems. Openness and tentativeness cautioned against an initial poor prognosis. Rigorous evaluation of the constructive factors made understandable the mitigation of the effects of the observable liabilities and the positive direction which the therapy took. Even the most comprehensive

21. Wittkower, E. D. & J. Aufreiter, "Education in Psychosomatic Concepts." In Science and Psychoanalysis. Vol. V. Psychoanalytic Education. Masserman, J. H. (Ed.) New York: Grune & Stratt 1962, pp. 118-128.

22. Lidz, T. "General Concepts of Psychosomatic Medicine." In American Handbook of Psychiatry. Vol. I. Arieti, S. (Ed.) New Yo Basic Books, 1959, p. 654.

23. Alexander, F. "The Psychosomatic Approach in Medical Therapy." In The Scope of Psychoanalysis. Selected Papers of Franz Alexander. New York: Basic Books, Inc., 1961, pp. 345-358.

description of identifiable assets and liabilities would leave many factors still unknown and unformulated as far as their import for diagnosis, prognosis, and therapy is concerned.

"The general principles which guide psychotherapeutic efforts with patients suffering from psychosomatic disorders are similar to those used in other psychiatric conditions."[24]   Though the therapy of persons with essential hypertension does not require a "knowledge of how emotional conflicts are translated into physiologic malfunctioning," an understanding of pathophysiology can give a therapist a feel of the processes obtaining, a more organic experiencing of his patient, and make possible the emergence of symbols, analogies, and metaphors having greater immediacy and effectiveness for communicating and communing. Also, though "the general principles . . . are similar," their application is not identical, owing to the experience gained from treating patients with essential hypertension, and because of a therapist's utilization of more and different models of human motivation, personality, and being in a tentative, open-ended, and rigorous manner.

This presentation and these closing comments are an affirmation of the need for continued scientific investigations while maintaining our respect for clinical research and therapeutic experience in the field of psychotherapy, in which the person of the therapist is still his most significant instrument.

---

24. Kelman, H. Diagnosis and prognosing. Am. J. Psychoanal., 1955, 15, 49-70.

ADDENDUM

Q. Did you formulate a specific diagnosis before you began psychotherapy, or was it made after psychotherapy was in progress?
Do such pre-therapeutic diagnoses inhibit or facilitate taking a
patient into treatment? Are your diagnoses subject to revision
as psychotherapy proceeds, and do they vary depending on the
way the patient responds to the treatment? Do you distinguish
between diagnosis as such and simple spontaneous diagnostic
reflections?

A. Diagnosing, a continuing process from the moment of first contact, includes the diagnosing by the therapist of himself, the
guiding values of standard nosologies gained through clinical
experience, and simple spontaneous diagnositc reflections. The
latter means my immediate and continuing intuitive responses,
which take the form of feelings, sensations, metaphors, analogies,
and images carry great weight with me. At times, I have an immedi
ate feeling of clarity regarding their meaning; at others, only after
an extended period will I feel I have arrived at a satisfactory understanding. Such holistic diagnosing determines if and how I begin
and continue therapy. Diagnosing means openness to revision on
the basis of emerging information and responses to therapy.

Assuming time and financial arragements are satisfactory, what
may decide me against working with a patient is insufficient seriousness about the work, inadequate availability for it, or hospitalization being preferable at the time. I would not take a patient
if some measure of the following were not present: liking, interest,
and challenge. If a patient required intensive extended therapy,
I would not start close to a break in my work schedule, particularly
if I felt it unwise to do so. Also, I would not take on a patient whose
problems demanded considerable time and energy if I were already
working with, at most, two such patients at that time, preferably
only one.

Q. Did you approach your patient with a consistent and verbalizable
theory or set of hypotheses on personality structure and/or the
genesis of psychic illness? Was such theory used directly (or
indirectly) in selecting the patient for treatment? How was it
applied in the treatment and how effective was your theory in
reaching the goals of treatment? What do you see as the function
of such hypotheses or theories?

A. I approach my patients with a set of hypotheses on personality
structure and the genesis of psychic illness, being guided in the
main by Horney's formulations, with which I have the greatest
familiarity and working experience. In addition, I make use of
hypotheses from Freud, Adler, Jung, Reik, Sullivan, and others,
from phenomenology and existentialism, and from my experience
with and understanding of Eastern philosophies. This spectrum

of concepts, plus some I have evolved, constitutes an open-ended changing matrix of guides for selecting patients and for the conduct of therapy. I have attempted to indicate in this presentation how I have applied these various theoretical constructs and how they were effective in reaching the goals of treatment. I see the function of hypotheses as provisional conveniences for ordering data; for throwing into the foreground facts which cannot be understood in terms of them; and for those facts stimulating revision of existing hypotheses and evolving new formulations which could more effectively take those facts into account.

This attitude presupposes the learning of and experience with available theories and techniques, so that they become an embedded aspect of one's being, immediately available on reflection and for use with inventiveness and orginality appropriate to the unique situations in each therapy. Theories as provisional conveniences and as the loosest, though clearly stated kinds of guides for application with tentativeness and clarity can only be possible on the background of rigor, discipline, and practice.

Q. What did you think of the prognosis of your case before you accepted the patient for treatment? What did you think during the first several interviews; and during the latter stages of treatment? Do you feel prognostic judgments about ultimate health or ultimate illness are useful? Can we dispense with a prognosis as a formal event in clinical treatment?

A. Prognosing, not prognosis, is the diagnosing of future growth possibilities and impediments to it. I felt the prognosis was good, not only for the alleviation of symptomatology of a physical and psychic nature, e. g., the consistent lowering of the patient's labile blood pressure and the resolution of neurotic character attitudes but also for an increasing capacity for happiness and enjoyment and a more effective utilization of his capacities. For me the initial interview is crucial and includes concern for how a patient comes to me and with what attitudes. How an initial interview is conducted, and how the patient responds to it, can significantly determine the future of that therapy for a long time to come, and even to its completion.

I feel prognostic judgments about the ultimate health or illness of a patient are very important. Mr. Stein's physical history and life expectancy would be crucial factors. My unverbalized feelings about both, and his responses to me, could have had a weighting effect on the movement in the therapy.

Q. What particular therapeutic techniques did you apply in this case? Which of them were most effective and which ineffective, and for what reasons? Did you attempt any technical innovations on an empirical basis? When did you feel that a "peak" experience or turning point occurred?

A. I have used free association, dream interpretation, interpretation-at-all-levels, communing, and relating. To date, we have worked in the vis-à-vis position, and I am anticipating using the couch. A few major and many minor peak experiences occurred throughout the therapy. Among them were: finding himself telling off his harridan of a relative; the first time he realized he made sense to himself in discussing an attack of jitters; the time he woke in the night and experienced a sudden letting-go with deep sleep and two days of no jitters; when he realized he had talked for forty minutes; and when he walked four miles. The meaning and use of all techniques is embedded in the moving matrix of hypotheses which are my guide. Most crucial are communing and relating toward more here-now experiencing in my meaning of symbolizing.

Q. Did you feel that Freud's formulation of transference and counter-transference were sufficient to account for the therapeutic encounter with your patient? How would you describe your encounter?

A. I feel that Freud's formulation of transference and countertrans-ference, even in its most elaborated form to date, are not adequate to account for what happens in a therapeutic encounter. I have elaborated my notions of communing and relating which include and transcend the concepts: the doctor-patient relationship, the transactional approach, and the existential encounter.

Q. It has been said that psychotherapy is a white, middle-class, urban phenomenon which does not necessarily apply to other social stratifications or cultures. In what way did your patient's cultural background influence his illness and treatment? In what way did your own cultural background assist or deter the treatment?

A. Psychotherapy is at present a white, middle-class, urban phenomenon, but it need not be. How this has evolved and currently obtains has been amply documented. I have observed psychoanalysts in training, in personal analysis with me, in supervision and in classes, unwittingly and in a measure consciously operating according to three different value systems regarding the depth of psychotherapy, depending upon whether the patients described were in private therapy, in therapy at the Karen Horney Psychoanalytic Clinic where their work was closely supervised, or in a community or private clinic where it was not. I feel the spread of welfare state programs will force present psychotherapists out of this attitude and that future therapists, brought up and trained in and by a welfare state, will find it natural to use psychotherapy with all groups and at all class levels, as has been my therapeutic experience.

This viewpoint is substantiated by repeated contacts with psychotherapists in European countries with different histories of welfare

programs, [25] working privately and in partially or totally fee-
supported programs. In the United States we are having accumu-
lating experience with partial payment of analysis through insur-
ance programs. Visits throughout Asia and continuing contacts
with psychotherapists trained in Asia and abroad reveal that not
only can its principles be applied and translated into the patient's
idiom, but that psychotherapy can be effective even with the most
illiterate. [26, 27] One of the most misguided notions becoming
rampant is that the practice of psychotherapy is easier, requires
less training, and does not go to the depths that analysis does.
I feel just the opposite. Good psychotherapy requires more
training and experience because it is much more demanding and
requires immediate intense involvement and greater resourcefulness deriving from only the most solid and extensive kind of
grounding in theory and practice.

How my patient's background influenced his illness and treatment
I have indicated. Its significance was evident to me, having been
born and raised in a multilingual, high economic and cultural
milieu, and having been influenced by unusual history teachers.
This broadly based orientation is rare, as I have learned from
years of teaching younger colleagues and in discussion with older
ones.

Q. There is an increasing tendency for neo-analytic thinking to
ascribe the genesis and treatment of psychic illness to the social
psychology of the family. How did this apply in your case?

A. Neo-analytic thinking gives more and proportionate weight to the
social psychology of the family than it can to the individual factors
determining the genesis of psychic illness and its therapy. In
Life History as Therapy and other publications, I have attempted
to show how Horney's concepts and methodology make possible
an even more comprehensive use of the genetic approach, long-
itudinally, vertically, and horizontally as history, ontology, and
in terms of gestalt, process and field theory. Although the social
psychology of Mr. Stein's family contributed significantly, of
greater consequence was the unique family constellation, particularly the influence of his mother's, but also his father's, special
emotional problems.

25. Kelman, H. Psychotherapy in Scandinavia-- An American viewpoint. Int. J. of Social Psychiatry, 1964, 1, 64-72.

26. Kelman, H. "Psychotherapy in the Far East." In Progress in
Psychotherapy. Masserman, J.H. and Moreno, J.H. (Eds.) New Yor
Grune & Stratton, 1959.

27. Hoch, E. A pattern of neurosis in India. Am. J. Psychoan.,
1960, 20, 8-25.

Q. If your treatment was concluded what criteria did you use for terminating it? If it is still in process, what guide points would you use to determine when your patient is sufficiently improved to discontinue treatment? Do you feel that a patient should be seen as long as he feels he needs it and is willing to pay the fees?

A. The treatment is still in process. The notion of termination is not in keeping with either my open-ended viewpoints in therapy or Horney's, namely, that we can go on growing as long as we are alive. Also, the structure of my working year gives my patients shorter and longer periods of working through on their own previously discussed issues and new ones that may come up. I would consider diminishing stepwise the number of sessions to once a week, possibly on the occasion of one of my holidays, after discussion and mutual agreement, and suggesting a definite or indefinite period of interruption of regular sessions, with an occasional sequence of sessions should the patient wish them. With these available alternatives, in practice patients rarely contact me before one or several years, usually after attempting to work through their problems on their own, when they feel they want help with some old or new problems, or when confronted with an acute external or internal situation.

On the patient's side, what would determine it would be his predominatly healthy wish for an interruption, with an openness for possibly contacting me later. Should I feel a desire to interrupt as an expression of a block in therapy, I would attempt to analyze it. Failing to do this, I would clearly indicate to the patient what I believed was happening. Important for my agreeing to an interruption would be a patient's ability to work on his own, increased self-confidence, effectiveness, and enjoyment in living, with which would have gone a significant diminution of physical and psychic symptomatology. The patient's wish to continue in therapy on the basis of need and willingness to pay fees would have to coincide with my evaluation of the situation. The matter of fees from his or my side would not be a significant factor.

Q. Did you make any mistakes in this case -- in the sense of "if you had to do it over"?

A. I do not feel I would have conducted this therapy significatly differently on hindsight, though I would have with some others. Quite favorable for a constructive beginning was the constellation of circumstances under which Mr. Stein came into therapy. Staying well within his tolerance-limits from the outset has been of paramount importance. As a result, there was a steady accrual of comfort and confidence, with greater self-understanding and falling away of symptoms, an increasing ability to communicate and be open about himself with another, which had to be learned as a human experience in the therapeutic situation.

Q. In treating your case did you perhaps feel that the classical distinctions between psychoses and neuroses were breaking down? (This question may apply even if your case represents neither a psychotic or neurotic.)

A. I feel the classical distinctions between psychosis and neurosis are breaking down. However, as additional guides they are of crucial import. In fact, I regard the lack of training in and feeling for nosological entities among many American psychiatrists reflects a serious inadequacy. This is particularly evident in comparing the training psychiatrists receive in European countries, where the genetic and constitutional factors are more thoroughly studied, as well as the natural history of the various mental illness categories. A resurgence of interest in the United States in using the phenomenologic approach for detailed description of clinical entities reflects a healthy development. Such experience, integrated with process perspectives in a holistic approach to health and illness, gives us a more comprehensive diagnostic and therapeutic vision and effectiveness. This orientation, I feel, has been responsible for opening a spectrum of investigations regarding schizophrenia. From a holistic viewpoint, I have attempted to define the process of becoming more rational, i.e., in ratio with reality and irrational, i.e., out of ratio with reality. I see the neurotic, psychopathic, and psychotic processes as aspects of the process of becoming more irrational, each blending into the other but each having a defined external form and internal structure. Such a viewpoint makes understandable the shifts in foreground symptom pictures which should not be the sole basis for diagnosing. They may or may not indicate a movement toward greater rationality or irrationality, seen holistically. A person is then seen at any moment not as rational or irrational but as predominantly one or the other while moving toward greater health or greater illness.

HOMOSEXUAL REACTIONS

Chapter XII

THE ANALYSIS OF A FEMALE HOMOSEXUAL

By Cornelia B. Wilbur

INTRODUCTION

The case of female homosexuality described here was treated according to basic psychoanalytic principles, including the concepts of repression and transference. It is extremely difficult to describe in a few pages what actually goes on in 234 hours of psychoanalysis. Severe condensation of material is necessary, and yet this may markedly affect the concept the reader obtains of the interchange between the patient and therapist. Although little is said about the actual interpretations, I have tried to convey the feeling tone of this particular analytic situation.

INITIAL INTERVIEW

A. was first seen in September a number of years ago. A month before she came she had been in another state and, under stress, had taken an overdose of phenobarbital. She called her father, who went to her. After she had recovered from the effects of the phenobarbital (which did not require hospitalization), her father asked her to return to the family home.

He consulted a psychiatrist on his return who suggested that he send his daughter to me, and he arranged the first appointment for her. She made no contact with me before the initial interview.

She was a fine-looking young woman, tall, graceful, dressed in excellent taste. This facade covered quietness and shyness. I thought it might be best to start with factual material.

She was soon to have her twenty-fourth birthday. She had been born, raised, and continued to live in the same section of the city. Her mother was thirty-three, and her father was thirty-seven when she was born.

She started school at the age of five, went to public school, took academic work in high school in addition to special art work, graduated from high school when she was sixteen, and started college. She received a Bachelor of Arts degree in three years and did graduate work.

She stated that her mother was a native-born American and said, "She is good, I guess. She lives for her children." She also said that her mother did not finish high school, but went to business school and worked for a short time. She was religious, kept a religious home, and did some work in charitable organizations.

Her father worked hard, she said, for he operated two offices and also had a faculty position.

She had a sister ten years older than she, who was married and had three children. She said, "She is very good to me and always has been."

She had a brother four years older who was married. He and his wife were about to have a child. Her brother graduated from professional school. Of him she said, "He is very bright. He was Phi Beta Kappa in college, is very intelligent, very nice, good to me, and he is understanding."

A. offered a great deal more information than the questions required. When asked what had brought her to me, she related the following:

"When I went to California I had a very upsetting time. I was so upset that I ended up running to my father. I left for California in June. I was on a vacation. Actually, my father confronted me before I left, as a matter of fact the day I left, with the word 'homosexual.' I got upset out there. I called him, and he flew out. I had always thought he knew, that is, about the homosexuality, but he was surprised; he hadn't known. He ordered me to come back with him, and I wouldn't do it. I said I would come back, but I'd drive. He flew back, and I came back about ten days later. After I got back, I went away again with my friend. We stayed in a hotel, and then we looked for an apartment. I was living at home before I went to California. I have been with the same girl for four months and one week, and now I'm living with her."

She was asked to tell about her earliest memories. She remembered moving out of the apartment that the family lived in when she was two and one-half, and she recalled that the memory is fixed because she was given Charlie Chaplin cut-outs to play with. She also remembered her brother's taking her to the movies when she was seven or eight, that he played basketball, and she remembered watching him. She remembered when she was five and her sister was fifteen. Her sister would take care of her, and her sister always had friends in because she had "lots of friends" in the neighborhood.

This reminded A. that she had friends in the neighborhood also. They played many of the games, potsy, jump rope, roller skating, biking, and she and her friends played with dolls. In the summer the family would go to the beach or the country. When she was eight she went to day camp.

Talking freely and quietly, she hesitated and was asked what she could say about the experiences that she felt led to her present problem.

She put it this way:

First, I was playing with a girl; she was my closest friend at that time. I was in grade school, and she went to a private high school. It was in my brother's room. Mother came in and got very angry at me for being on a bed with a girl. We were doing nothing. Mother said I shouldn't lie on top of a girl.

In junior high school I liked being with boys. I was about twelve; I kissed boys. I dated in high school and petted slightly.

In college I went steady, and I was pinned. I went to bed with him; I didn't enjoy it. It was sneaky and terrible. We busted up. Actually, he went into the Army and went overseas. We wrote to each other. He said he was coming back. I went to meet him. I had some moles removed, and my sister said I looked terrible. He told his cousin to call me and tell me he changed his mind. Six or seven months later, he wanted to come back. I was already involved with girls then; that was two and a half years ago.

In my freshman or sophomore year I went downtown after a high school prom to a gay nightclub and I was absolutely fascinated. In college I went back to the same club. I met a woman there; she was a waitress. When I went in, I chose her table so that she would wait on me. I found out who she was, called her, and went to see her. I had an affair with her that lasted for three weeks.

I didn't find any physical satisfaction with girls until last summer; I was then with another girl, not the one I'm going with now. I find physical satisfaction with the girl I'm with now. For eight months during the past two and a half years I tried to stay away from girls. In April I went downtown with the girl that I am with now. I talked with her. The following Friday I saw her again. What I did was go out with a guy, then I went home early and left him so I could go downtown to see Lilly, and I've been seeing her ever since. I have dated only once since then.

It was arranged that she come for treatment twice a week. Her schedule did not permit more intensive therapy than three times a week, and she was encouraged to come three times a week whenever she could arrange it. She came three times a week the first three weeks, the fifth week, and then not again until the following May. Otherwise, she came twice a week for about two years. After two years of treatment she came once a week for a year, then once every two weeks, and once a month for the final nine months. She had 234 hours of treatment.

A. had been so cooperative in relating historical material that I felt there must be more to her coming than the fact that she had been ordered to do so by her father. I thought that this would be a worthwhile matter to discuss with her. At the next hour she was asked about her attitudes toward treatment. I said I was aware that she had been referred to me by Dr. L. Had she seen Dr. L? Had she herself any genuine interest in change?

She said she had not seen Dr. L. She did want to change. She did not know whether psychiatric treatment would help homosexuality. She was not happy that she was compelled to function as she did. She did get physical gratification from the homosexual act, but she would change if she could. She asked me what I felt the prospects were. I told her that it was a very difficult thing to know how far one could go in the resolution of these problems. [1] I had had some experience and some results. I was perfectly willing to try, and I was pleased that she wished treatment and that she was also willing to try.

I said that she could expect to be in treatment for a considerable time. She expected this. She would be willing to work as long as I felt that it was valuable. I pointed out to her promptly that any decision in relation to treatment should be made by both of us and not by either of us alone. She thought about this, then agreed.

THE FATHER

She felt that she was more closely tied to her father than she had realized since she had been earning her own living and going her own way, although staying in her parents' apartment in a room of her own. When she went to California, she went without her parents' approval on a vacation that was strictly hers. As soon as she got into difficulty in California she telephoned her father. She said it was so spontaneous she did not think about what she was doing until after she had done it.

She said that her father wanted to see me. I told her that if she wished me to, I would see him. She wanted me to see him if I did not believe it would interfere with treatment. I said I did not believe that there would be any interference with treatment, since I was seeing her father at her and his request. I would discuss nothing with him which she did not want me to discuss. I told her the value in seeing her father might lie in obtaining information about her which she could not give and in evaluating his attitudes toward her.

---

1. I would say now that homosexuality can be treated.

She asked me what I would tell him in regard to her future. I told her I would tell him precisely what I had told her. She said since her father was a physician, he understood the treatment of some illnesses took time. He came to see me during the third week of her treatment.

I asked him to tell me as much as he could about his daughter, what she was like when she was small, how she seemed to develop and mature, and if he had any feelings at any time that she had difficulty. He gave the following information:

She was always so sweet. She was the sweetest and quietest one of the children. It seems to me that she always smiled in the morning. I tried very hard to get her into our top private grade school at six, and I did not succeed. I was disappointed. I watched over them all; I always pushed them to eat. When she was in the third grade she took an examination for another fine private school, and she didn't pass. My wife didn't want any more children after she had A. She pushed the children in another way; she made them all take piano. A. was always amiable to everything. When the children took piano lessons I used to call for them, and I called for her. She was a willing student, both in school and in piano. She never made you feel she was difficult. When she was in public school she was in plays, and she was very cooperative in school too. Somehow, in her mother's mind there was always the feeling that children may do wrong, and she always dogged A. not to sit in the park with boys, not to do this, and not to do that. This may have something to do with her problem. When she was in her early teens her mother saw her in the park across from the house. She was sitting on a bench with a boy and necking with him. Her mother was very upset, called her in, and scolded her severely.

I like children. I've always considered it a great responsibility to have children, and I spent a great deal of time with them. I fed them sometimes. She wasn't as sickly as the others. I was strict with them with their schoolwork, and I often helped them, but this is the only way that I was strict. My wife had a very bad habit of "comparing," and the children resented this. I cared about all of the children, but I never fondled them. I'm not demonstrative. We always kept the door open to our bedroom. We used to argue sometimes at night, and we always bickered in one way or another. My wife thought that my method of punishment was not right, and I thought that hers was not right. My wife had a nagging way with the children. She'd get angry and wouldn't talk to me, and I, being sensitive, would get annoyed. She

never wanted anyone to be close to me, not even the
children. I would say that the whole family is not really
intimate. My wife threatens everybody; she even
threatens me.

Two years ago A. wanted to leave home. Her
mother was very upset with her. I said to A., "The way
you're carrying on, one would think you're a homosexual."
I didn't really know that she was. At that time she was
terribly antagonistic, and I couldn't talk to her. Her
brother said she should go to a psychiatrist. She was
very angry when he said this. I must say that her brother,
my son, gave me a hard time when he was in professional
school. He kept getting tied up with older women -- women
who were much older than he was. I sent him to Mexico to
get rid of one woman and brought him home to get rid of
another one. I suppose you could say that he had his
difficulties too, but he seemed to get over it, and he's
all right now. Maybe he could have used psychiatric
treatment at that time. Our oldest daughter is supposed
to be her mother's favorite. When everything was upset
two years ago, her brother talked to A. and things quieted
down. Her mother never let her have any privacy; she
always went through her drawers and read her letters.
She found a letter last June, and that was how we really
found out she was a homosexual. I don't think at first
that we realized what that letter meant. Now her mother
knows her problem, and she is hysterical all the time.
She can't sleep, and she is very upset. Whenever they
come together, her mother is always punishing her. I
guess I have to say that my wife has been the dominant
one in the household. I could never handle her. She is
very rigid and hard to move. I have never been able to
discuss sex with my daughter. My wife and I have never
been able to discuss sex with each other, and A. has
been given the impression by her mother that sex is bad.
Her mother always had that attitude.

It was obvious that the mother and father did not get along.
Mother was the dominant individual in the family. She was anti-
sexual and anti-heterosexual (note the fact that she punished A. when
she saw her necking with the boy on the park bench). The mother
and father bickered often about many things. From the father's
attitude in talking about his daughter, it was evident she was his
favorite child and the least favored child of the mother. The father
was relegated to a lesser role in the household. He was inclined to
give up or give in to his wife, but would go to the defense of A. if
there was difficulty. They were thus allied against the mother. One
other item of interest emerged. The patient's room in the apartment
was adjacent to the parents' bedroom, and the headboards of the beds

in the two rooms were against the same wall. A's father learned that A. used to listen at night to the bickering between his wife and himself, and possibly to their sexual activities.

THE MOTHER

About five months after A. started treatment, her mother asked to see the therapist. She came with the understanding that she wanted some explanation of A's difficulty. This had been discussed with A. When the mother arrived, she offered the following information:

"I gave her a lot of attention; she was a wonderful baby." Then she said, "Tell me about my daughter." An attempt was made to explain to A.'s mother what the difficulties were. I gained the impression that she was not really grasping what was being said or that she had withdrawn her attention. When I hesitated, she looked up inquiringly, and the explanations were continued. After about twenty minutes the feeling that A.'s mother was not listening was so strong that I stopped and said to her, "You do not seem to be listening or understanding what I am saying; what did you really come here for?" At which point A.'s mother said, "I came to ask you to tell my daughter to come home!" I replied that A. was coming to me for treatment of her problems and that I did not tell her what to do, but tried to help her to make her own decisions. A.'s mother erupted. She was incoherent, crying, shaking, and hysterical. She screamed at me that someone needed to tell her daughter what to do, that she was irresponsible, that she was in a horrible situation, and that I lacked a sense of responsibility. It took another twenty to twenty-five minutes to quiet her enough so that she could leave the office. She never returned nor asked to see me again. This domineering woman had wanted to use the therapist and the therapeutic situation as an extension of her own domination, and had been unable to cope with my refusal.

A. talked at length about her mother. She stated that she had been given a girl's version of a boy's name by her mother, that her mother had told her that she had expected her to be a boy, and that she was very disappointed when she was not a boy. She also told A. that she did not like girls at all, but that she preferred A.'s older sister to A., and that A. was a disappointment to her in every sense. She felt the greatest hostility toward her mother. Two weeks after the mother's visit to the office, A. brought me a letter that her mother had written to her. Two quotes from the letter are significant: "... besides the stole, the pin, and so forth, I gave to you as part of a dowry, the car as a means toward making your livelihood, not for any other purpose ...."

"If you come home and you want me to see a doctor, I will. I wouldn't last long this way. After all, I did do things for you. Don't disappoint Daddy and me. If we mean anything to you, if in the past I've brought you any happiness, please come home. From morning 'til

night you're on my mind. Please come home." Both A. and I felt
that the letter was a result of my refusal to insist that A. go home
to live. She was still involved with her homosexual partner, but
quarrels were becoming more intense and frequent. She was
considering going home to live for some of the practical conveniences
involved, but the letter blocked her so that she was unable to do so
until several months after she received this letter from her mother.

THE HOMOSEXUAL RELATIONSHIP

The patient was able to talk freely about her homosexual
behavior, although she stated that the behavior was "perverse and
depraved." She said that although she worked and earned a good
living, her partner insisted on carrying the larger part of the
financial burden. Her partner made more money as a call girl than
A. made as a teacher. She would never permit A. any contact with
any aspect of her call girl life. A. associated with a group of girls,
many of whom were beautiful, and almost all were call girls and
homosexuals. She and one other girl earned their living as teachers
and were looked up to because they were not whores.

She said that her homosexual partner was extremely proud
of her. She, the partner, would frequently brag about A. and her
work. A. described the social life of this group of women. They
spent a good deal of time in a nightclub which catered to homosexual
women, drinking, smoking "pot," and dancing. The club had been
raided and closed at least once, and they expected that it would be
raided and closed again. A. said that if this occurred, their
activities would be transferred to another nightclub catering to
homosexual women. A. described the numerous fights, arguments,
jealousies, and flirtations of the women in the homosexual group.
She said that there was always some kind of trouble brewing or
taking place. She was asked if she felt the homosexual relationship
was doomed to failure, and she said that it was. She had seen many,
many changes of relationships between a variety of homosexual
partners. Her current partner was her fifth. She said that she had
not been homosexually promiscuous, but that she had been involved
with an older woman who was a waitress in a nightclub, then with a
younger girl for a few weeks, then with an older partner with whom
she had remained for almost a year.

She stayed away from homosexuality for eight months, then
had become involved with a younger girl whom she described as being
extremely sexual, very pretty, and very seductive. It was with this
girl that she had her first physical gratification. She then became
involved with her current partner, who was older than she. She and
her partner quarreled frequently, and it was a quarrel in California
that had precipitated her taking the overdose of phenobarbital. She
had no confidence that the relationship could persist without quarreling and believed that it would eventually break up. She said that

although she knew this, she could not leave her partner; she could neither desist from the involvement nor from the quarrels. She recognized that there was a large element of hostility in the relationship with her partner, and she felt that this was true in all homosexual relationships.

SEXUAL ATTITUDES

When asked about autoeroticism, she expressed excessive feelings of shame, embarrassment, and guilt. She had tried masturbation and was so guilt-ridden about it that she was unable to continue. When asked if she had had other heterosexual experiences besides that which she had reported in her history, with obvious embarrassment and shame she said, "I slept with four different men." Under patient questioning, she said she had gone through a period of promiscuity (apparently in a flight from homosexuality). The shame and guilt associated with this had been so severe that when Suzie (the fourth partner) came along and seduced her, she was back in the homosexual fold. She said that she had precipitated the sexual relationship with the young man to whom she was engaged and that she had expected to enjoy this. She said that her fling with the several men brought no satisfaction, only deep feelings of shame and distress.

Evaluating her feeling about the three types of sexual activity, she stated that she was least embarrassed by homosexuality. She said she felt more shame and guilt talking about her heterosexual affairs, and the most shame and guilt about masturbation. She had no fantasies with masturbation. She felt that the incident of being severely scolded for sitting on a park bench and necking with a boy had driven her away from ordinary heterosocial and heterosexual activity because she was so guilt-ridden. She also believed that her mother had the attitude that sex was bad. She admitted that she listened to her parents through the bedroom wall, and when it was suggested that her bed be moved, she objected because she felt drawn to listening. She was aware that she was listening for sexual activity, and she felt repelled.

She said her mother had taught her very little about clothes. Her partner had extremely good taste in clothes and gave her an education in materials, colors, and styles. The dress of these women in their in-group were tailored tight slacks, tailored shirts, and sweaters of considerable bulk. Because of her height, everything she bought had to be altered, and her partner altered her clothes so that they fit her perfectly. A. said that her mother did not teach her anything about housekeeping, cooking, or sewing. Her partner helped her to learn these things, but she found she had relatively little interest in cooking, and there were constant quarrels about who was to do the housework. It was pointed out to A. that her homosexual partner was acting in a maternal role. It gradually emerged that A.'s homosexual partner played the role of a hostile mother figure. A. also said that she had a great deal of interest and curiosity about the activity of the call girls who were in the group, and she constantly inquired from both her partner and the other girls about what they did. This fit in with her sexual curiosity about her parents, and the connection was pointed out to her.

SIBLINGS

A.'s relationship with her sister was good. Apparently, early in life, she had appreciated and enjoyed her sister's friendship and her sister's friends. Her sister never criticized her, even after she found out that A. had a homosexual problem. The spring of the first year of A.'s treatment, her sister's husband, also a physician, came into the city and spent part of a weekend interviewing A. about her problem. She was under the impression that he was involving himself more out of curiosity and a kind of prurient sexual interest than out of a genuine effort to help her. She became very antagonistic and decided not to see any more of her brother-in-law than necessary.

As she had already indicated, she had something of a problem with her brother, who insisted that she "pull herself up by her bootstraps" and function normally. Because of these various difficulties she was cut off from her entire family, and this threw her back into the homosexual situation. It was not until she had shown considerable change that she was able to re-establish relationships with all members of her family, and it was only after she began dating the man she eventually married that she was able to spend any time with her brother, sister-in-law, or brother-in-law, although her relationship to her sister remained good.

Following A.'s experience with her brother-in-law she made a move in the analysis. This began with the discussion of her brother-in-law and his failure to really understand the compelling nature of her difficulties and the fact that she had improved. She went from this to a discussion of her problems with her father. She evaluated all of the positive things that he had done for her and expressed her appreciation for them. It was pointed out to her that some of the things that he did for her should have been done by her mother. This led to her evaluation of the sins of omission on her father's part, the fact that he never stood between her and her mother, that he never did anything about her mother's attempts to dominate her, that he did nothing to help her with her problems of sexual adjustment, and that he complicated the situation by being thoughtful, warm, and considerate. This made it difficult for her to criticize him for what he did not do. She was clearly aware of the fact that she was her father's favorite child, and she felt that her difficulties in heterosexual adjustment might very well have been complicated by his warmth toward her, intensifying her Oedipal wishes toward him. She was able to free herself from her father when she began to talk about his office adjustment. He had had the same secretary in his office for twenty-eight years, and A. recognized that when things were too difficult at home her father would go to the office to work, since in the office he had sympathetic companionship. A. was quite sure that there was never anything other than a doctor-secretary relationship between her father and his office girl on the surface; but she did comment that his secretary did everything for him and made life very easy whereas his wife did not make things easy and constantly bickered. She clearly understood that there were nuances in the working relationship which were compensatory for her father.

BEGINNINGS OF CHANGE

In spite of the fact that A. and I had agreed that all homosexual relationships, filled with ambivalence and hostility, do not persist, we agreed that the beginnings of change in A.'s case came with increasing quarrels between A. and her homosexual partner. These quarrels increased in frequency and violence until toward the end there were physical battles. In the early summer of the first year of treatment her partner went to a hotel and A. went home to live.

Leaving the apartment was precipitated by the fact that their quarrels had become so noisy that their landlady asked them to leave. A. was intensely embarrassed about this and avoided the landlady during the short period of time that they remained in the apartment.

Interpretations of the hostile elements conflicting with the longing and need for love in the transferential situation between A. and her homosexual partner were made over and over during the months that A. lived with her partner.

As A. began to be able to pull away from her partner, she needed a bulwark against her mother. Since she was going home to live, she developed a strong positive transference in the analytical situation. She was given a maximum amount of support so that she could live at home without being thrown back into the homosexual situation.

I made it quite clear to A. that I recognized she had no one to turn to at this particular time except me, and until she could work out her own feelings enough to develop other relationships, I would understand this fact and help her accordingly. At the same time, however, the transferential elements of the analytic situation were interpreted. A. herself said that given a choice of three people as maternal figures, her mother, her homosexual partner, or myself, it was obvious which choice did not involve the severe hostility that she had in dealing with both her mother and her homosexual partner. She wanted to keep clearly in mind that I should not remain a substitute mother, since she should grow up and not require mothering.

An element occurred providentially that helped in her move from her homosexual partner to her home. Her mother and father decided to take a vacation and stay out of the city, and A. could have the parental apartment to herself for a minimum of a month. She moved home about two weeks before her parents went away.

Later in the summer A. decided that she wanted to go to Europe, and she did. She had not become entirely free of her homosexual partner, since the partner had called her and she informed the partner that she was going to Europe. When she returned from Europe, she informed me that her partner had met her in Europe, and they had planned to spend the whole time together. They had not done so, since they were still quarreling and extremely hostile toward each other. A.'s attitude when she told me this was one of sheepishness, since she had not informed me that she was going to meet Lilly in Europe even though she knew that she was. Since their meeting in Europe turned out so badly, A. felt that this was the end of the situation between herself and her partner. As a matter of fact, she had one subsequent meeting with her, in the late fall, when she spent one night in a motel with her partner, and this turned out to be very upsetting. A. did not see her again after this.

At the beginning of the second year of treatment A. began to experiment with social situations. She tried two things: to make friends with heterosexual women and to have dates. She developed a relationship with one of the women teachers. She met a professional man about ten years older than she, attractive, wealthy, and a bachelor. She liked him because of his attention to her and because he drove a fast and expensive sports car. She never had any genuine personal feelings toward him.

A. also experimented with a relationship with a man who was her intellectual, social, and financial inferior, and whom she believed to be bisexual. She found that she could talk to this man because he understood something about her problems. Other than this, the relationship had little value to her and persisted only a short time.

A. recognized that these relationships with men were fairly superficial.

Her mother was not understanding about A.'s social activity. As soon as it seemed reasonable, she began to pressure A. to marry the wealthy professional man. A. told her mother that this man had not asked her to marry him, that he was closely tied to his own mother, that he was well up in his thirties, was a bachelor, and that possibly he was not a good marriage candidate. Her mother insisted that A. was being silly and was carrying out some kind of continuing perversity by not promptly becoming engaged to him. Because A. was not yet free of her mother's influence, her mother's attitude infuriated her and increased her antipathy to the man, since he was the object of a struggle between herself and her mother.

The continuing struggle with her mother was analyzed during the fall of the second year. Every time A.'s mother put pressure on A. to involve herself in a situation, it was reviewed carefully in the analysis, and the mother's necessity to push A. out of the home into a socially acceptable marriage was underlined by me. Gradually A. was able to stop reacting to the pressures of her mother, and toward spring she dealt with her mother by listening graciously and then doing what she felt was best.

By late spring of the second year of analysis, a great deal of work had been done in relation to all of the important elements: the relationship between the parents, the relationship of each parent to the patient, the complicated Oedipal situation, the sexual attitudes of the parents, the sexual attitudes of the patient, the relationship of the patient to the partner, and the transferential aspects of this relationship. The patient had moved from the homosexual relationship into a hetersocial series of relationships.

When the teaching year was over, the parents went to a large summer hotel, and A. went with them. The third week there, she met a young man. They started dating and dated all summer. When A. returned to work in the fall she continued to see the young man approximately once a week. Her mother continued to pressure her to date the wealthy professional man, and she saw him on two occasions, once for a yachting party and once for a weekend. These episodes occurred about two months apart. She decided that the relationship was not worth while and discontinued it.

In the first few months of dating the young man she had met during the summer, they went about almost entirely on their own, while he saw his friends at other times during the week. At about Christmas time a new phase of A.'s adjustment developed. The young man whom she had been dating began to include her in his relationships with his friends, and A. began to form friendships among the wives and girl friends with whom she came in contact. During this period she suffered from a great deal of anxiety and guilt. On one occasion she saw a man who had associated with the homosexual girls at the nightclub. She felt sure that he recognized her, but he passed her by without saying anything. She had some anxiety when she was on the street with her friend for fear she would run into some of her old crowd. There were a great many discussions as to what she would do if she were ever challenged. Gradually she began to gain confidence, her anxiety diminished, and I asked her, since she knew a number of homosexual women who had married, whether anyone had ever carried out any destructive, revealing behavior toward any of the girls. She said that they had not, and was reassured.

She began to go to many social functions, took her boy friend to visit her sister and brother-in-law, took him to family dinners, and found that he got along extremely well with her family. She commented that actually he got along better with her mother than she did, because he could joke with her mother and she could not. As their social relationship developed, they began to have sexual relations. A. enjoyed these, but without orgastic response. She discussed this on several occasions. It was pointed out to her that there might be residual fears in the heterosexual situation. She stated that there were some things that her boy friend did that were not particularly pleasant. On occasion, he was rough physically, being a powerful man. It was suggested that when she felt able to, she discuss this with him. She made another significant move when she was able to talk sexually with him. She became orgastically responsive. One other complication existed. He was divorced and had a child. He took her to visit the child, and they got along so well that he was momentarily jealous. He also took her to meet his mother, with whom A. got along well. He took her to see his grandparents whom he adored and with whom he had lived. She also got along well with them. A. was distressed because his father was a ne'er-do-well who had wasted a modest fortune and who lived a dissolute life. Her friend did not care for his father, and on one occasion they met him with his current female. A. did not care for him. She felt insecure because her friend had been divorced and because the father had not made a good adjustment to marriage. After discussion in the analytic situation she was able to discuss this with her friend. The following summer they joined a club and spent a great deal of time together. They had talked of marriage on occasion. A. was now eager to get married, and her friend was cautious. A. was somewhat distressed but decided not to press the situation.

With fall and the onset of a working schedule, they began to discuss marriage seriously. It was agreed that they would become engaged at Christmas time and married the following June.

When A. became engaged, things were going well. She was free of anxieties and the terrors of discovery; she had resolved her problems and was functioning heterosexually and heterosocially. She had made friends with women in her peer group. She was getting along well with both of her parents. At this point she was asked if she wanted to continue her analysis. She surprised me by saying, "Of course I do. There will be problems that will continue to come up, and I feel I need your help and advice." It was obvious that A. was using me as the substitute good mother. Although this had been interpreted to her many times before, it was pointed out to her again, and she agreed that this was perfectly true. Since she and her mother differed considerably in their tastes, she wanted to have the opinion of another woman. Her mother never knew this, as A. treated her with much consideration. The analysis was terminated early in June. At the last appointment I asked A. what had happened to the homoerotic object. I said that I would like to know what happened when she saw a girl who was beautiful, seductive, and whom she knew was homosexual. She said, "I recognize that she is beautiful because there are both beautiful homosexual women and beautiful heterosexual women, but I have no response. The sexual response to these people is gone."

DISCUSSION

Important elements in the analysis were the relationship between the parents, the relationship of each parent to the patient -- including the Oedipal situation -- the sexual attitudes of the parents, and the sexual attitudes of the patient. Also important in the analysis was the relationship of the patient to the partner and the transferential aspects of this relationship. As these elements emerged and enough information was obtained to convince the therapist that particular things had taken place which had influenced the patient, these convictions were presented to the patient as tentative interpretations. Where these interpretations were really meaningful to the patient they were taken up, and additional material either emerged or the patient correlated material which was already known, and the analysis progressed satisfactorily.

The family constellation in this case is one that has been seen before and since, and appears to be fairly common when the patient is a female homosexual. The mother is dominating, hostile, and anti-heterosexual. The father seems weak, unassertive, but "nice." The deprivation of feminine love in these cases appears to be a female homosexual dynamic. The hostility of the mother and the nurturing qualities of the unassertive father tend to severely intensify the Oedipal problems of the female homosexual. In this case the father expressed special interest in his daughter, which further intensified the Oedipal problems. The homosexuality then is a defense against the incestuous wishes for the father and against arousing maternal hostility.

This patient's relationship with her various homosexual partners was characterized by great ambivalence, with an intense longing for love and equally intense hostility which were acted out. The patient had no real confidence in the homosexual relationship, as far as the gratification of the need for love was concerned, and this tended to make her relationships perhaps less stable and more transient.

One of the most important factors in the entire case was the fact that this patient, although sent to the psychiatrist, herself wished for change and was most cooperative in the analytical situation. In view of what is known about homosexuality and its treatment by psychoanalytic techniques, when such a patient comes for treatment, the therapist can help by adopting an attitude of optimism in relation to the outcome of such treatment and by conveying this to the patient.

ADDENDUM

Q. Did you formulate a specific diagnosis before you began psychotherapy, or was it made after psychotherapy was in progress?
Do such pre-therapeutic diagnoses inhibit or facilitate taking a
patient into treatment? Are your diagnoses subject to revision
as psychotherapy proceeds, and do they vary depending on the
way the patient responds to the treatment? Do you distinguish
between diagnosis as such and simple spontaneous diagnostic
reflections?

A. A specific diagnosis of homosexuality was made before psychotherapy was begun, but no decision in regard to the general
diagnosis was made. The general diagnosis of character
disorder emerged as the total history was obtained over several
interviews. The pre-therapeutic diagnosis facilitated taking
this patient into treatment because of my interest in this
particular disturbance. I seldom revise my diagnoses, and
they do not vary depending on the way the patient responds to
treatment. I distinguish between diagnosis versus diagnostic
reflections. For example, I may make a diagnosis of character
disorder which is then not changed. Diagnostic reflections occur
during treatment, in that I may observe that a particular bit of
business on the part of the patient is an "hysterical mechanism."

Q. Did you approach your patient with a consistent and verbalizable
theory or set of hypotheses on personality structure and/or the
genesis of psychic illness? Was such theory used directly
(or indirectly) in selecting the patient for treatment? How was
it applied in the treatment and how effective was your theory in
reaching the goals of treatment? What do you see as the function
of such hypotheses or theories?

A. The patient was approached with a consistent and verbalizable
theory of the structure of the homosexual problem. Such theory
was used directly in selecting this patient for treatment, and the
basic theory that homosexuality is a result of life experiences
and is modifiable through psychotherapy was applied in the
treatment. The goal was achieved. Such hypotheses or theories
form a frame of reference for the patient and the therapist and
help to set the goal of treatment as well as assisting in maintaining treatment in the face of setbacks.

Q. What did you think of the prognosis of your case before you
accepted the patient for treatment? What did you think during
the first several interviews; and during the latter stages of
treatment? Do you feel prognostic judgments about ultimate
health or ultimate illness are useful? Can we dispense with a
prognosis as a formal event in clinical treatment?

A.   I did not know the prognosis of this case before the patient was accepted for treatment. In view of the fact that I had had some success in treating homosexuality, I had some hope that the outcome might be favorable. When I discovered that the patient was interested in change and was coming voluntarily, I felt much more sure that the outcome would be satisfactory. During the later stages of treatment it became obvious that the patient was on the way to an exclusive heterosexual goal. Prognostic judgments about ultimate health are useful in terms of establishing an attitude for the therapist and the patient. If the prognostic judgment is on the positive side, the patient might be taken on for treatment. If the judgment of ultimate illness is made, it is possible that the therapist should transfer the patient to another therapist for treatment and/or evaluation. In view of the influence of prognostic judgments and the fact that we do make them, they cannot be dispensed with as a formal event in clinical treatment.

Q.   What particular therapeutic techniques did you apply in this case? Which of them were most effective and which ineffective, and for what reason? Did you attempt any technical innovations on an empirical basis? When did you feel that a "peak" experience or turning point occurred?

A.   "Active" psychoanalytic psychotherapy was the therapeutic technique that was applied in this case. This indicates that there were not long periods of silence on the part of the therapist, but that verbal and nonverbal communications were used to amplify material the patient was discussing. The patient did not lie down on the couch. The fact that the patient sat up and could look at the therapist at will was by a preference of both the patient and myself. Because the patient was shy and tended to be quiet, I wanted to keep her in an active relationship. She wanted to "face her problems" and acted this out in facing me. An innovation in this case was the interview of both parents and the evaluation of these interviews with the patient. These two experiences were "peak" experiences with the patient.

Q.   Did you feel that Freud's formulation of transference and counter-transference were sufficient to account for the therapeutic encounter with your patient? How would you describe your encounter?

A.   Freud's formulation of transference and countertransference were certainly part of the therapeutic encounter. I would add the reality factor of understanding, respect, and the free opportunity for re-evaluation and re-education. The encounter was an opportunity for the patient and myself to revise destructive and handicapping convictions and defenses for the patient.

Q. It has been said that psychotherapy is a white, middle-class, urban phenomenon which does not necessarily apply to other social stratifications or cultures. In what way did your patient's cultural background influence her illness and treatment? In what way did your own cultural background assist or deter the treatment?

A. The patient was raised in an upper-middle-class, Eastern urban background. I was raised on a western ranch and in the Middle West. I have treated patients psychotherapeutically from intellectually and socially deprived backgrounds and from other cultures. I do not think this patient's treatment was successful because of her background. I do think my early earthy background was helpful. I also think psychotherapy is applicable to all backgrounds and cultures.

Q. There is an increasing tendency for neo-analytic thinking to ascribe the genesis and treatment of psychic illness to the social psychology of the family. How did this apply in your case?

A. This patient's difficulties stemmed from the interrelationships between her and her parents. Her much-older sister did not seem to influence the genesis of the psychopathology. The brother had psychological problems that were of no interest to the patient and did not seem to influence her pathology. Rather than calling this illness one owing to social pathology I would say it was owing to psychopathological interrelationships between the parents and between each parent and the patient.

Q. If your treatment was concluded what criteria did you use for terminating it? If it is still in process, what guide points would you use to determine when your patient is sufficiently improved to discontinue treatment? Do you feel that a patient should be seen as long as he feels he needs it and is willing to pay the fees?

A. Treatment was concluded by first, a careful evaluation of the relationship of the patient to her prospective husband, and second, by an analysis of the transference residuals. The transferential aspects of the treatment were kept clearly before both of us during treatment, so that the final analysis of the residuals took only a few weeks. I think there is a risk in seeing a patient as long as he feels he needs it and is willing to pay the fee; both physicians and patients can get into an interminable dependency problem. The physician can unwittingly come to exploit the patient by not referring the patient for a period of time to another therapist to see if the problem can be improved or resolved by another approach. It is true that some patients can only function with continuing support, but all avenues should be explored to see if a way can be found to free the patient from such a necessity.

Q. Did you make any mistakes in this case -- in the sense of "if you had to do it over"?

A. I would not do this one over differently. There was some surprise in the intensity of the patient's involvement in the entire therapeutic situation. For many months she was active and cooperative but appeared emotionally cool; then, when it was suggested that an hour be cut, she expressed her intense involvement and her sense of ongoing relief from internal stress directly, and suggested that her treatment continue as before until she was more sure of resolution.

Q. In treating your case did you perhaps feel that the classical distinctions between psychoses and neuroses were breaking down? (This question may apply even if your case represents neither a psychotic or neurotic.)

A. In the treatment of this case there was no suggestion that the classical distinctions between psychoses and neuroses were breaking down. During the most stressful time in treatment and in her relationship with her homosexual lover there were no diagnostic signs of psychosis.

EXISTENCE REACTIONS

CHAPTER XIII

FRAGMENTS FROM THE LOGOTHERAPEUTIC TREATMENT

OF FOUR CASES

by Viktor E. Frankl

(With an Introduction and Epilogue by G. Kaczanowski)

INTRODUCTION

Viktor Frankl of Vienna is an outstanding representative of the existentialist movement which has swept over Western Europe and is seeping into the American continent. [1] This movement was inspired by the teachings of such philosophers as Martin Heidegger and Karl Jaspers, and by the writings of Jean-Paul Sartre, Albert Camus, Franz Kafka, and others. The basic core of existentialialism is the presumption that man is not only an object open to deterministic influences, but that man is also a "subject," and as a "subject," he creates his world and determines who he is. Existentialists believe that man's self-determination, as a typical human characteristic, is not sufficiently recognized in a mechanistic and dynamic approach to the nature of man. The contemporary overobjectification of the human being may thus be an impediment in the search for valid conclusions concerning man. As an object, man may be studied just as all things are. Existentialism is certainly not opposed to any organic, biochemical, reflexological, or psychodynamic method of investigation of man's thinking, feeling, drives, and behavior. However, it claims that each approach, isolated from all the others, merely gives a partial insight into the most complicated creature we call man. It emphasizes the need of the search for a truly holistic concept of man. It contributes to this concept a dimension which is not new but which for unknown reasons was forgotten. The neglect of this dimension, which may well be the height of the image of man, is in a way understandable. It cannot be investigated by the usual methods of science; that is, its phenomena cannot be measured, abstracted, and predicted with statistical proba-bility. Does this mean, however, that what cannot be examined by the historical or contemporary tools of science does not exist? Or does

---

1.   Birnbaum, F. Frankl's Existential Psychology from the view-point of Individual Psychology. J. Indiv. Psychol., 1961, 17, 162-166; Polak, P. Frankl's Existential Analysis. Am. J. Psy-chother., 1963, 17, 554-568; Weiss, M.D. Frankl's approach to the mentally ill. Assoc. Ment. Hosp. Chaplain's Newsletter, 1962, 39-42.

it mean, perhaps, that new and different ways of exploration have to be found, and when they succeed in giving us new insights, they will be included in our scientific armamentarium? It would be serious mental rigidity to exclude this possibility.

A temporary difficulty is apparent in formulating the proper nomenclature which may be used in describing that aspect of man which is the "subject." The term "existential" is probably the best. If we knew the parameters, we could use the concept "spiritual" dimension. As psychiatrists, we are inclined, of course, to shrink away from whatever is called spiritual because this word had non-biological connotations. This may be an emotional reflex, since we feel more secure on the biological ground. At the same time, most of us feel that a person is something more than an organism.

In logotherapeutic terminology the word "spiritual" has no association with any religious or supernatural sense. Doing this would be a semantic misunderstanding caused by the difficulty in the precise translation of existential terms. In German the two similar words, geistig and geistlich, have different meanings: in English both words are translated as "spiritual." To avoid this confusion Frankl has formed a neologism: he likes to speak of noëtic phenomena and noödynamics (noös - the spirit). [2]

The basic existentialist concepts, such as freedom and responsibility or Frankl's "will to meaning,"[3] are based on phenomenological observations. They are not metaphysical speculations. These concepts are reflections of human reality -- at least, as much as the human mind is able to grasp reality.

Frankl teaches that, in addition to Freud's "will to pleasure" and Adler's "will to power," the human being is motivated by a search for the meaning of his existence, for a sense of his personal life. Contemporary man in Western society is preoccupied with functioning at his optimal level of efficiency and with reaping the fruits of his labors, but he neglects to ask himself the most important question: What is the use of it? What am I living for? Sooner or later this question hits everyone who wants to live and not just to vegetate. It is usually

---

2. Frankl, V. E. On logotherapy and existential analysis. Am. J. Psychoan., 1958, 18, 28-37; Existential dynamics and neurotic escapism. J. Exist. Psychiat., 1963, 4, 27-42.

3. Moholick, L. T. and J. C. Crumbaugh. The case for Frankl's "Will to Meaning." J. Exist. Psychiat., 1963, 4, 43-48.

a crisis in a person's life which makes him reflective. There is a risk that life may seem useless, empty, and unfulfilled, but this "existential frustration or vacuum" is not a pathological condition. It may be a stimulus to start looking around and into oneself. If the search for the meaning of one's existence does not give a proper reply, anguish and guilt may arise. Anguish, or dread, is more than anxiety. As an existential state, it is the reaction to the threat of non-being, of death. Existential guilt has to be distinguished from neurotic guilt feelings. It is caused by neglecting, or refusing, to use all available human potentialities. The states of anguish and guilt may be far away from the center of consciousness, and they may be the roots of emotional disturbances. Frankl gives them the name of noögenic neurosis. They can be found in a certain percentage of patients seeking psychiatric help.

In order to deal with these disturbances, Frankl has formed a specific treatment which he calls logotherapy (logos = meaning).[4] Although Frankl modestly prescribes his logotherapeutic method as the treatment of choice in noögenic neurosis, it can be applied in other emotional and mental disorders as a supplement to conventional methods. To help the patient discover his unique sense of life, to become aware of his freedom and his dignity, to accept his responsibilities, to help him to find and to actualize his creative, experiential, and attitudinal values -- this is the aim of logotherapy, and this is what almost every patient needs. Not only in therapy but also in mental hygiene, the logotherapeutic approach may lead us out of stagnation and open new horizons.

The practical application of logotherapy does not differ much from other forms of psychotherapy. The patient's deterministic and conformistic attitudes are questioned until he finds the core of his personal freedom. He is encouraged to take the risks which life offers and which are inextricably connected with making decisions. The therapist shows genuine respect for the patient as a human being, whoever he is. The therapist tries not only to know but to understand the patient. This involves not only the intellect but feelings, as well as psychic capacities and the whole of human nature. It is an "encounter" which results from complete openness toward the patient. It allows the patient to open up, too, and to experience the impact of meeting a significant other. There is in logotherapy, perhaps, more explanation and interpretation than in other forms of psychotherapy; but the respect for the patient does not allow the therapist to impose upon the patient any of his own values -- at least, not intentionally. The patient must feel free to accept, or to reject, or to argue, any point

---

4. Frankl, V. E. Man's Search for Meaning: An Introduction to Logotherapy. Boston: Beacon Press, 1963.

made by the therapist. In the therapeutic sessions the patient begins learning to make his own free choices and to take the responsibility for whatever he chooses. He begins to appreciate what it means to be human.

With some patients the logotherapeutic process is accelerated and facilitated by the use of two techniques which Frankl has developed. They are "paradoxical intention"[5] and "de-reflection." Paradoxical intention is used with patients suffering from phobias and obsessive-compulsive neurosis. It aims to counteract the anticipatory anxiety which aggravates and perpetuates the pathological condition, and contributes to the formation of a vicious circle of behavior. The more the patient fears an event or his reaction to such an event, the more the fear provokes its occurrence. The technique of paradoxical intention attempts to cut through this vicious circle by changing the patient's attitude toward his symptom. The patient is encouraged to stop fighting against it and, instead, to evoke in his mind a strong wish and intention to do, or to experience, just what is most terrifying and embarrassing to him. When the patient hears his therapist giving him such emphatic advice, he is shocked, and a kind of crisis occurs. If he trusts and understands his therapist, he may be able to attempt it. The first, and often slightest success will convince the patient that he has found a way of counteracting his compulsion. He feels enormous relief and begins seeing his situation in a different, and often humorous light. This helps him create a distance between himself and his neurotic behavior. The therapist's support gives him the courage to throw off a merciless master who manipulated him with irresistible force.

De-reflection, the second technique developed by Frankl, is applied when we want to help the patient to turn his anxious preoccupation away from his troublesome condition and direct his attention and interest toward healthy and positive goals. This technique is less specific and more difficult than paradoxical intention. It requires letting the patient become aware of his capabilities and potentialities which were never used before, or were overshadowed by his troubles and forgotten. It is a kind of appeal to the patient's deeply buried values. Once they are uncovered, they assert themselves and give the patient a feeling of uniqueness, of usefulness, and of a sense of life. De-reflection produces results in varying emotional disorders such as

---

5. Gerz, H.O. The treatment of the phobic and obsessive-compulsive patient using paradoxical intentions. J. Neuropsychiat., 1962, 3, 375-387; Miller-Hegemann, D. Methodological approaches in psychotherapy. Am. J. Psychother., 1963, 17, 554-568; Weisskopf-Joelson, E. Logotherapy and existential analysis, Acta Psychotherapeutica, 1958, 6, 193-204; Frankl, V.E. Paradoxical intention: A logotherapeutic technique. Am. J. Psychother., 1960, 14, 520-535.

somatic preoccupations, neurotic sleep disturbances, and in such sexual disorders as impotence and frigidity.

Both techniques are not just a superficial removal of troublesome symptoms, but they seem to act on a deeper or, perhaps, higher level. They can be tools of an existential reorientation.

EXCERPTS FROM RECORDED INTERVIEWS WITH VIKTOR FRANKL

LAST AID IN A CASE OF CANCER

The patient was eighty years of age and suffering from a cancer which had eventuated in metastases so that she could not be helped by way of surgery. Because of this fact, which was well known to her, she had become increasingly depressed. I demonstrated the case to the students who attended my clinical lecture on logotherapy, and the following is an excerpt from the tape-recorded interview which developed. Needless to say, everything was sheer improvisation on my part.

Professor Frankl: What do you think of when you look back on your life? Has life been worth living?

Patient: Well, Doctor, I must say that I had a good life. Life was nice indeed. And I must thank the Lord for what it held to me: I went to theaters, I attended concerts, and so forth. You see, Doctor, I went there with the family in whose house I have served for many decades as a maid, in Prague at first, and afterwards in Vienna. And for the grace of all of these wonderful experiences I am grateful to the Lord.

I nevertheless felt that she was doubtful insofar as the ultimate meaning of her life as a whole was concerned. And this was the reason why I wanted to steer and pilot her through her doubts. In the first place, however, I still had to provoke them and then to wrestle with them -- wrestle with them as Jacob did with the angel until he blessed him. That is how I wanted to wrestle with my patient's repressed and unconscious existential despair until the moment when she, too, finally could "bless" her life, say "yes" to her life in spite of everything! So my task consisted in having her question the meaning of her life on the conscious level rather that repressing her doubts.

F: You are speaking of some wonderful experiences; but all this will have an end now, won't it?

P: (thoughtfully) In fact, now everything ends . . .

F: Well, do you think now that all of the wonderful things of your life might be annihilated and invalidated when your end approaches? (And she knew that it did!)

P: (still more thoughtfully) All those wonderful things . . .

F: But tell me: do you think that anyone can make undone the happiness, for example, that you have experienced -- can anyone blot it out?

P: (now facing me) You are right, Doctor: Nobody can blot it out!

F: Or can anyone blot out the goodness you have met in your life?

P: (becoming increasingly emotionally involved) Nobody can blot it out!

F: What you have achieved and accomplished --

P: Nobody can blot it out!

F: Or what you have bravely and honestly suffered: Can anyone remove it from the world -- remove it from the past wherein you have stored it, as it were?

P: (now moved to tears) No one can remove it! (After a while): It is true, I had so much to suffer; but I also tried to be courageous and steadfast in taking life's blows. You see, Doctor, I regarded my suffering as a punishment. I believe in God.

Per se, logotherapy is a secular approach to clinical problems. However, when a patient stands on the firm ground of religious belief, there can be no objection to making use of the therapeutic effect of his religious convictions, thereby drawing upon his spiritual resources. In order to do so, the logotherapist may put himself in the place of the patient. That is exactly what I now tried to do.

F: But cannot suffering sometimes also be a challenge? Is it not conceivable that God wanted to see how Anastasia will bear it? And perhaps He had to admit, "Yes, she did so very bravely." And now tell me: Can anyone remove such an achievement and accomplishment from the world, Frau Anastasia?

P: Certainly no one can do it!

F: This remains, doesn't it?

P: It does!

F: By the way, you had no children, had you?

P: I had none.

F: Well, do you think that life is meaningful only when one
    has children?

P: If they are good children, why shouldn't it be a blessing?

F: Right. But you should not forget that, for instance, the
    greatest philosopher of all times, Immanuel Kant, had
    no children; but would anyone venture to doubt the extra-
    ordinary meaningfulness of his life? I rather think if
    children were the only meaning of life -- life would be-
    come meaningless because to procreate something
    which in itself is meaningless, certainly would be the
    most meaningless thing. What counts and matters in
    life is rather to achieve and accomplish something. And
    this is precisely what you have done. You have made the
    best of your suffering. You have become an example
    for our patients by the way and manner in which you take
    your suffering upon yourself. I congratulate you on
    behalf of this achievement and accomplishment, and I also
    congratulate your roommates who have the opportunity to
    watch and witness such an example. (Addressing myself
    now to my students): Ecce homo! (My audience now
    bursts into a spontaneous applause.) This applause con-
    cerns you, Frau Anastasia. (She is weeping now.) It
    concerns your life, which has been a great achievement
    and accomplishment. You may be proud of it. And how
    few people may be proud of their lives . . . I should say,
    your life is a monument. And no one can remove it
    from the world.

P: (regaining her self-control): What you have said, Pro-
    fessor Frankl, is a consolation. It comforts me. In-
    deed, I never had an opportunity to hear anything like
    this . . . (Slowly and quietly she leaves the lecture hall.)

Apparently, she now was reassured. A week later, she
died -- like Job, one could say, "saturated of years." During the
last week of her life, however, she was no longer depressed, but on
the contrary, full of faith and pride! Obviously, the interview which
we had had together had made her aware that her life was meaningful,
that even her suffering had not been in vain. Prior to this she had
admitted to Dr. Gerda Becker, who was in charge of her on the ward,
that she felt agonized, and, more specifically, ridden by the anxiety that
she was useless. The last words, however, which she uttered immediately
before her death were the following ones: "My life is a monument. So
Professor Frankl said it to the whole audience, to all the students in
the lecture hall. My life was not in vain . . ." Thus the report of
Dr. Becker reads. And we may be justified in assuming that, also
like Job, Frau Anastasia "went to her grave as the harvest was brought
to the granary."

A SCHIZOPHRENIC ART STUDENT

The main objective of the logotherapeutic approach to schizo-phrenic cases can be delineated by what I call de-reflection, i. e., de-focusing the patient from his illness and reorienting him toward the meaning of his life. Needless to say, this is no cure of schizo-phrenia itself; it is rather an attempt to draw upon the patient's exist-ential resources which, according to a logotherapeutic tenet, are available even in psychosis.

The following excerpts are taken from a tape-recorded inter-view with a nineteen-year-old schizophrenic girl who was a student at the Vienna Academy of Arts. She had been admitted to my depart-ment at the Poliklinik Hospital because she had displayed severe symptoms of incipient schizophrenia, such as auditory hallucinations. She also exhibited the corrugator phenomenon which I had described as early as 1935. (It is characterized by fibrillar twitches of the corrugator muscles and is a typical sign of imminent schizophrenia.)

At the outset the patient complains of apathy, then she refers to her "being confused" and asks me for help. So I start de-reflecting her:

F: You are in a crisis. You should not concern yourself with any specific diagnosis; let me just say that it is a crisis. Strange thoughts and feelings beset you, I know; but we have made an attempt to tranquilize the rough sea of emotion. Through the quieting effects of modern drug treatment we have tried to have you slowly regain your emotional balance. Now you are in a stage where recon-struction of your life is the task awaiting you! But one cannot reconstruct one's life without a life goal, without anything challenging him.

P: I understand what you mean, Doctor; but what intrigues me is the question: What is going on within me?

F: Don't brood over yourself. Don't inquire into the source of your trouble. Leave this to us doctors. We will steer and pilot you through the crisis. Well, isn't there a goal beckoning you -- say, an artistic assignment? Are there not many things fermenting in you -- say, un-formed artistic works, undrawn drawings which wait for their creation, as it were, waiting to be produced by you? Think about these things.

P: But this inner turmoil . . .

F: Don't watch your inner turmoil, but turn your gaze to what is waiting for you. What counts is not what lurks in the depths, but what waits in the future, waits to be actualized by you. I know, there is some nervous crisis which troubles you; but let us pour oil on the troubled waters. That is our job as doctors. Leave the problem to the psychiatrists. Anyway, don't watch yourself; don't ask what is going on within yourself, but rather ask what is waiting to be achieved by you. So let's not argue about what we have to deal with in your case: an anxiety neurosis or neurotic obsessions; whatever it may be, let's think of the fact that you are Anna, for whom something is in wait. Don't think of yourself, but give yourself to that unborn work which you have to create. And only after you have created it will you come to know what you are like. Anna will be identified as the artist who had accomplished this work. Identity doesn't result from centering on oneself, but rather from dedication and devotion to some cause, from finding one's self through the fulfillment of one's specific assignment. If I am not mistaken, it was Hölderlin who once wrote: "What we are is nothing; what matters is where we are going. " We could say as well: "Meaning is more than being. "

P: But what is the origin of my trouble?

F: Don't focus on questions like this. Whatever the pathological process underlying your psychological affliction may be, we will cure you. Therefore, don't be concerned with the strange feelings haunting you. Ignore them until we make you get rid of them. Don't watch them. Don't fight them.
(Rather than reinforcing the patient's schizophrenic tendency to autism through plunging into psychodynamic interpretations I try to elicit her will to meaning, as it is called in logotherapy.)

F: Imagine, there are about a dozen great things, works which wait to be created by Anna, and there is no one who could achieve and accomplish it but Anna. No one can replace her in this assignment. They will be your creations, and if you don't create them, they will remain uncreated forever. If you create them, however, even the devil will be powerless to annihilate them. Then you have rescued them by bringing them to reality. And even if your works were smashed to pieces, in the museum of the past, as I should like to call it, they will remain forever. From this museum, nothing can be stolen since nothing we have done in the past can be undone.

P: Doctor, I believe in what you say. It is a message which makes me happy. (And with a bright expression on her face, she gets up from the couch and leaves my office.)

Within a few weeks the patient was free from schizophrenic symptomatology to the extent that she could resume her work and study.

A SCHIZOPHRENIC TALMUD STUDENT

The patient was a seventeen-year-old Jewish youth. His foster father had applied for a single consultation. The young man had been rescued by him during World War II when a group of Jewish people were executed by the Nazis. Later, however, the patient had to be institutionalized in Israel for two and a half years because of severe schizophrenic symptomatology. Now he discusses his problems with me, among others the problem of his detachment from the Jewish theological background, the world in which he was brought up.

F: When did your doubts develop?

P: I started doubting when I was in confinement -- during my stay at the hospital in Israel. See, Doctor, the police had caught me and brought me to an institution. And I blamed God for having me made me different from normal people.

F: Is it not conceivable, however, that even this was purposeful, in one sense or another? What about Jonah, e.g., the prophet who was swallowed by the whale: Wasn't he also "confined"? And why was he?

P: Because God had arranged it, of course.

F: Well, it was certainly no pleasure for Jonah to find himself caught in the bowels of a whale, but only then was it possible for him to recognize his life task which he had previously rejected. Today, I think it is hardly possible to institutionalize people in a whale, is it? Anyway, you didn't have to stay in a whale but rather in an institution. However it might be, is it inconceivable that through the two and one-half years of confinement God wanted to confront you, too, with a task? Perhaps your confinement was your assignment for a specific period of your life? And didn't you eventually face and tackle it in the proper way?

P: (now becoming more emotionally involved, for the first time) You see, Doctor, that is why I still believe in God.

F: Say more.

P: Possibly God wanted all of that; possibly He wanted that
I recover . . .

F: Not just recover, I would say: To recover is no achievement and accomplishment. What is demanded of you is
more than recovery: Your spiritual level should be
higher than before your illness. Haven't you been in
the bowels of a whale for two and one-half years, a
little Jonah, as it were? Now you have been freed from
what you had to undergo there. Jonah, before his confinement, declined to go to Ninevah to proclaim God;
afterward he did so. As to you, it may well be that from
now on you will penetrate deeper into the wisdom of
the Talmud. I don't wish to say that you should study
more than you hitherto did, but your study will be more
fruitful and meaningful. For now you have been purified
like gold and silver, as it is said in the Psalms (or
somewhere else), is purified in the furnace.

P: Oh, Doctor, I understand what you mean.

F: Didn't you sometimes weep during your stay in the hospital?

P: Oh, how much I did!

F: Well, through the tears which you wept out of yourself,
the clinkers might have been removed from yourself . . .

The impact of the single interview resulted in a remarkable
decrease of the patient's aggressiveness toward his foster father and an
increase of his interest in the study of the Talmud. For a period of
time the patient got a perscription for phenothiazines; later on, he
no longer needed further treatment except for small doses of them.
He became quite sociable and could resume his handicraft work.
Apart from a diminution of initiative, his behavior and conduct are
normal. As for the single interview, however, which has been
outlined above, I had succeeded in having the patient re-evaluate his
plight in the light of meaning and purpose accessible to him, not only
despite but because of psychosis. And who would doubt that it was
legitimate to draw from the definitely religious resources available
in the case? Anyway, I deliberately refrained from analyzing the
walls, as it were, which separated the patient from the world. For
that matter, I did not care about their origin, but I did try to challenge
the patient out of these walls. In other words, I tried to give him a
ground to stand upon.

YOUNG MAN BETWEEN ABYSS AND "PEAK" EXPERIENCES

The patient is twenty-five years of age. For several years he has been suffering from states of anxiety. Throughout the last three years he has been under psychoanalytic treatment. Now he is seeking help at the Outpatient Ward of the Neurological Department of the Poliklinik Hospital, and after one of the doctors on its staff had presented him to me, the following dialogue took place:

F: What is your trouble?

P: Often life seems to lack any meaning, but mostly I suffer from this experience of life's total meaninglessness during sleep!

F: You mean: while dreaming?

P: That's right. Sometimes it even happens that I am dreaming all night of the apparent meaninglessness of my life; then I find myself in my dreams among people whom I urgently ask for a solution of my problem, for liberation from this situation -- "Help me! Show me a meaning," I beg them with passion; "Free me from the anxiety that my life is in vain and that there is no task awaiting me!" But they just continue enjoying their lives, enjoying their meals, enjoying sunshine, or whatever life has to offer them . . .

F: That is to say, in a wholly unreflective manner?

P: Right! While I am caught and crippled by my doubts as to the meaning of my life.

F: And what did you try to do against this experience?

P: See, Doctor, sometimes it brings relief to me to hear and play music. After all, Bach, Mozart, and Haydn have been deeply religious personalities, and when enjoying music, I enjoy the fact that at least its creators have been granted the good fortune to arrive at a full conviction that there is a deeper or even ultimate meaning to human existence.

F: So, even if you do not believe in such a meaning yourself, you believe at least in the great believers, one could say, couldn't one?

P: You are right, Doctor.

F: Well, isn't it the mission of the great leaders in religion

and ethics to mediate between values and meanings on
the one hand, and man on the other? Man is thus given
a chance to receive out of the hands of a genius of humanness, be it Moses or Jesus, Mohammed or Buddha --
he is given the chance to receive from them what he is
not is not in each instance apt and able to obtain by himself. You see, in the field of science our intelligence
might do; with respect to our beliefs, however, we must
sometimes rely on and trust in other people greater than
ourselves, and adopt their visions. In his search for an
ultimate meaning of being, man is basically dependent
on emotional rather than merely intellectual resources,
as we know; in other words, he must trust in an ultimate
meaning of being. What is more, however, this trust in
something must be mediated by his trust in someone, as
we now see. But now let me ask you a question: What
if music touches you down to the depth of your being and
moves you to tears, as it is certainly the case at some
moments, isn't it? -- do you then, too, doubt the meaning of your life, or do you not even question it at these
moments?

P: This problem then does not come to my mind at all.

F: Right. But isn't it conceivable that precisely at such
moments, when you get in immediate touch with ultimate
beauty, you have found the meaning of life, found it on
emotional grounds without having sought for it on intellectual ones? At such moments we do not ask ourselves
whether life has a meaning or not; but if we did, we
could not but shout out of the depth of our existence a
triumphant "yes" to being. Life, we would feel, would
be worth while even if only lived for the sake of this
unique experience.

P: I understand and agree; there are certainly moments in
my life at which I do not reflect at all, and just then,
meaning simply is there. I even experience a kind of
union with being, and one could say as well that this is
akin to the experience of being close to God as it has
been reported by the great mystics.

F: Anyway, one could say that you then feel close to truth,
and we are certainly justified in assuming that truth is
an aspect of Deity also. Just look above my head: on the
wall behind my seat you will see the shield of Harvard
University, and inscribed thereon you will read veritas,
which means truth; but as you also notice, this word is
divided into three syllables which are distributed over
three books, and we may well interpret this by saying

that the total truth is no more a universal truth, for it is no longer accessible to every one. Man has rather to be satisfied with getting hold of one single aspect of the whole truth. So much more is this true of God, of whom truth is in turn no more than merely an aspect.

P: What intrigues me, however, is the question of what I should do when I feel haunted by the experience of emptiness, void of any values and meanings, and even alienated from both artistic beauty and scientific truth.

F: Well, I would say that you then should not cling only to those great spirits who have found meaning but also turn to those who have sought for it in vain. What I mean is that you should also study the writings of those philosophers who, like the French existentialists Jean-Paul Sartre and the late Albert Camus, have seemingly suffered from the same doubts that you do but have made them into a philosophy, albeit a nihilistic one. However it may be, you will put your problems on an academic level, as it were. In this way you will put a distance between your problems and yourself. What has beset you is now seen in the light of one or another paragraph on a certain page in a given volume of one or the other author. You will recognize that to suffer from these problems is something human, even honest, an achievement and accomplishment rather than a neurotic symptom. Anyway, you will find that there is nothing to be ashamed of, but rather something to be proud of, namely, intellectual honesty. Rather than interpreting your problems in terms of a symptom, you will learn to understand it as an essential aspect of la condition humaine to which you then confess. You will regard yourself a member of an invisible community, the community of suffering humans, suffering from that abysmal experience of a basic meaninglessness of human existence, and at the same time struggling for a solution to the age-old problems of mankind. The same suffering and the same struggling unites you, in fact, with the best exemplars of humanity. So try to be courageous and patient: courageous in leaving the problems unresolved for the time being, and patient in not giving up the struggle for their final solution.

P: So you don't think, Doctor, that my condition is just a neurosis to overcome?

T: If a neurosis at all, I would say it is simply the collective neurosis of our day, and consequently could also be cured only on a collective level. Viewed in this manner, your suffering stands for that suffering which afflicts mankind as a whole, at least in the most sensitive and open-minded representatives; it is their suffering which you are shouldering!

P: And I don't mind suffering, but it should have a meaning.

F: Neither your quest for meaning nor questioning the meaning of your life is pathological. It is rather a prerogative of youth. A truly young man never takes the meaning of his life for granted but dares to challenge it. What I want to say is that you need not despair because of your despair. You should rather take this despair as evidence of the existence of what I am used to calling "the will to meaning." And in a sense, the very fact of your will to meaning justifies your faith in meaning. Or, as the famous Austrian novelist Franz Werfel once said, "Thirst is the surest proof for the existence of water." He meant, how could a man experience thirst unless water were in the world. And do not forget the words of Blaise Pascal which read: "Le coeur a ses raisons que la raison ne connaît pas." (The heart has reasons which are unknown to reason.) I should say your heart has believed in an ultimate raison d'être all along. Sometimes the wisdom of our hearts proves to be deeper than the insight of our brains. And sometimes the most reasonable thing is not to try to be too reasonable.

P: This is precisely what I have found by myself: that in order to get relief, I just need to turn to the immediate tasks confronting me.

A COMMENTARY TO FRANKL'S EXCERPTS

by C. Kaczanowski

When one reads Frankl's tape-recorded fragments of interviews for the first time, one feels surprised and puzzled. They appear so very different from what most readers are used to finding in recorded psychotherapeutic interviews. A simple instruction is offered: After having read the excerpts with the normal speed of four hundred to five hundred words a minute, it is good to read them again slowly and reflectively. Then one may feel that there is something which is not expressed in the dry letters of the words. Whoever has had the opportunity to be present when Professor Frankl interviews a patient can see the difference between what was really going on between Frankl and the patient and what was recorded on tape. If, furthermore, the interview is translated into another language, the reproduction of the therapeutic situation is still further distorted.

What cannot be reproduced in words is the contact between the patient and his therapist: the encounter of two persons. This is something which cannot be abstracted and presented properly in verbal form; it has to be experienced and lived. Any witness to Frankl's interview feels the impact of Frankl's personality, his genuine sincerity, his complete openness toward the patient, and his high respect for the other human being. These are factors which help the patient to discover in himself an echo resounding from what he hears from the therapist. The actual words used in the interview thus seem to be the less important component of the therapeutic situation. It is unfortunate that only the words can be transmitted to the reader.

1. Last Aid in a Case of Cancer

In this interview Frankl demonstrates the possibility of using logotherapy against the despair of unavoidable suffering and death. Under the therapist's questioning, the patient gains insight into the meaning of her suffering. She takes a stand toward her illness, and she develops an "attitudinal value."[6] It is her last chance to make a free choice. She may submit to her fate in despair, as a helpless victim, or she may find strength and pride in her ability to understand that her life was not useless, that she had fulfilled her task in life, and that even her approaching death was not devoid of meaning.

2. A Schizophrenic Art Student

Here Frankl uses the technique of "de-reflection."[7] The patient's concern with her morbid experiences is disregarded. Her attention and interest are turned to her artistic, creative, values, which have to be, and can be, actualized by the patient alone.

3. A Schizophrenic Talmud Student

This short excerpt shows that Frankl does not hesitate to use any available means in order to restore a patient's faith in a meaning or purpose of life. Frankl teaches that every person has a unique task to perform in life and that no other person can do it for him. This is true if we assume that every human being is unique and cannot be replaced by any other. The awareness of this truism, and of a persona

---

6. Frankl, V. E. The Doctor and the Soul. New York: Knopf, 1963.

7. Tweedie, D. F. Logotherapy and the Christian Faith. An Evaluation of Frankl's Existential Approach to Psychotherapy. Grand Rapids: Baker Book House, 1961.

life task, gives a feeling of dignity and security, and it counteracts existential emptiness.

4. Young Man between Abyss and "Peak" Experiences

The patient described in this interview was already investigated and was presented to Professor Frankl by one of his assistants. He was diagnosed as suffering from "noogenic neurosis." [8] Frankl starts with asking questions, and the patient's answers disclose his existential emptiness and his struggle for finding a meaning of his life. Frankl gives the patient explanations which sound simple but which are rich in meaning and understandable. The patient starts seeing his existence in a never-before-perceived light.

8. Frankl, V. E. Man's Search for Meaning: An Introduction to Logotherapy. Boston: Beacon Press, 1963.

A PARTIAL READING BIBLIOGRAPHY OF VIKTOR E. FRANKL

(1) Birnbaum, F. Frankl's Existential Psychology from the view-point of Individual Psychology. J. Indiv. Psychol., 1961, 17, 162-166.

(2) Frankl, V. E. Man's Search for Meaning: An Introduction to Logotherapy. Boston: Beacon Press, 1963.

(3) Frankl, V. E. Existential dynamics and neurotic escapism. J. Exist. Psychiat., 1963, 4, 27-42.

(4) Frankl, V. E. Basic concepts of logotherapy. J. Exist. Psychiat., 1962, 3, 111-118.

(5) Frankl, V. E. Psychiatry and man's quest for meaning. J. Relig. and Ment. Heal., 1962, 1, 93-103.

(6) Frankl, V. E. The Doctor and the Soul. New York: Knopf, 1963.

(7) Frankl, V. E. Logotherapy and the challenge of suffering. Rev. Exist. Psychol. and Psychiat., 1961, 1, 307.

(8) Frankl, V. E. Dynamics, existence and values. J. Exist. Psychiat., 1961, 2, 5-16.

(9) Frankl, V. E. Paradoxical intention: A logotherapeutic technique. Am. J. of Psychother., 1960, 14, 520-535.

(10) Frankl, V. E. Beyond self-actualization and self-expression. J. Exist. Psychiat., 1960, 1, 5-20.

(11) Frankl, V. E. The spiritual dimension in Existential Analysis and Logotherapy. J. Indiv. Psychol., 1959, 15, 157-165.

(12) Frankl, V. E. On logotherapy and existential analysis. Am. J. Psychoanal., 1958, 18, 28-37.

(13) Gerz, H. O. The treatment of the phobic and the obsessive-com-pulsive patient using paradoxical intention. J. Neuropsychiat., 1962, 3, 375-387.

(14) Maholick, L. T. and J. C. Crumbaugh. The case for Frankl's "Will to Meaning." J. Exist. Psychiat., 1963, 4, 43-48.

(15) Muller-Hegemann, D. Methodological approaches in psychotherapy. Am. J. Psychother., 1963, 17, 554-568.

(16) Polak, P. Frankl's Existential Analysis. Am. J. Psychother., 1949, 3, 617-622.

(17) Tweedie, D. F. Logotherapy and the Christian Faith: An Evaluation of Frankl's Existential Approach to Psychotherapy. Grand Rapids: Baker Book House, 1961.

(18) Weiss, M. D. Frankl's approach to the mentally ill. Assoc. Ment. Hosp. Chaplan's Newsltr., 1962, 39-42.

(19) Weisskopf-Joelson, E. Logotherapy and Existential Analysis. Acta Psychotherapeutica, 1958, 6, 193-204.

(20) Crumbaugh, J. C. and L. T. Moholick. An experimental study in Existentialism: The psychometric approach to Frankl's concept of noögenic neurosis. J. Clin. Psychol., 1964, 20, 200-207.

Chapter XIV

THE PSYCHOTHERAPY OF A NON-DISEASED PERSON

by Arthur Burton

INTRODUCTION

The question of treatment for a normal or non-diseased person cannot by definition arise in medicine. Medicine is that aspect of science which mitigates disorder or dysfunction, and to treat, let us say, a normal liver would be a violation of all those canons by which medicine itself became an accepted scientific discipline.

In psychiatry, the aspect of medicine given over to the treatment of mental disorders, the above situation still holds, but a qualification creeps in. Thus, while psychiatry attempts to establish the "sick" entity in traditional medical ways, it is not always precisely certain that such a model fits. Psychiatry quite often deals with social illness which masquerades as mental illness, and a whole host of sociologists, [1] anthropologists, and even psychiatrists[2] are challenging the traditional conception.

In psychiatric treatment which is family oriented, for example, the "identified" (or "committed") patient does not always turn out to be the "real" patient -- and shifts in patient status quite commonly occur during family therapy. Patients committed to public mental hospitals sometimes attain such status because they represent the fulcrum of familial or societal forces rather than being sick as such. On the level of personality organization and disorganization, the medical model loses its diagnostic sharpness, possibly because the most useful tools in physical medicine -- the X-ray, the analysis of secretions and tissues, encephalography, and such -- are only of minor and ancillary value. There are few personality handbooks comparable to the legion of medical ones which give tables of normative limits for various organic functions. In the absence of personality or behavioral norms of this kind, each psychiatric investigator-therapist more or less becomes his own handbook, and he may not always be aware that he personally comes to represent the norm. Yet he makes constant judgments regarding the pathology of the personality, or of cure, without a handbook and, if challenged, will

---

1. Goffman, E. Asylums. Essays on the Social Situation of Mental Patients and Other Inmates. Chicago: Aldine Publ. Co., 1962.

2. Szasz, T. The Myth of Mental Illness. New York: Harper and Row, 1961.

talk about intuition, his "feelings" about the patient, or point to certain behavioral acts of the patient which, if the truth be known, may have no precise meaning without their proper context.

The recognition of this state of affairs in psychiatry has led to increasing attempts to study psychically normal or non-diseased groups of people as a baseline not only for diagnosis but for treatment. [3,4] The inherent scientific error in generalizing from pathological cases without any form of normative control is now so well known as to not warrant repetition here. What is, however, not so numinous is the fact that pathology (diagnostically) seeks out pathologies that the aspect of science which has pathology as its function tends to find it wherever it looks! It is also bound to it in tight sociological ways not readily discernible or definable. Pathological sciences cannot seriously countenance the average or non-diseased within their phenomenological scope even though their function is "normalizing" the patient; as hard as they may try, they are simply not organized to proceed from this stance. There is in psychiatry an inadequate image, not only of the personality properties of the normal or non-diseased person, but of the ideal person; that is, the becoming possibilities of the human being in his more glorified and non-diseased moments.

Most people dislike accounting for their lives as average -- even though most people are average -- and when they are ready to die, they may evaluate their contribution to themselves and humanity by a rare and occasional supra-average experience which may have occurred to them. It is thus not enough at this time to have an intact liver or even an intact ego! The human cortex -- unlike lower orders -- makes "meaning" possible in existence, and every organ of man may therefore be healthy and the patient still sick if such "meaning" is absent. Where microscopes and X-rays are determinatively impossible, disease and non-disease may become a matter of forensics, as it so often does in the case of "not guilty by reason of insanity." Such differences of scientific opinion occur precisely because X-ray or microscopic analysis of the ego is impossible.

When we come to the form of healing known as psychotherapy, we are in deeper trouble still. Not only have we failed to define adequately the parameters of psychotherapy -- its necessary dimensions -- but we are not quite certain of the persons best treated by it. Each

3.   Maslow, A. H.   Toward a Psychology of Being.   New Jersey: D. Van Nostrand Company, 1962.

4.   Rogers, C. R.   "The Actualizing Tendency in Relation to 'Motives' and Consciousness," in Nebraska Symposium on Motivation, 1963; The process equation of psychotherapy. Am. J. Psychother., 1961, 15, 27-45. Also, personal discussion.

psychotherapeutic patient has more or less to be empirically subjected to its procedures, and only then can we tell for certain whether or not the process will succeed. Add to this the facts of the relative rarity of psychotherapeutic practitioners and the exceedingly high cost of treatment, and you have an ambiguous situation which seems to betray its scientific paternity. The most that can be said with certainty about psychotherapy is that certain select people in our culture have nonphysical (or physically non-locatable) complaints, i. e., anxiety, guilt, fear, unhappiness, loss of meaning, and so on, for which they seek interaction with a certain kind of (medical) person, and for which they pay by time and energy represented in a money form. We know something of their make-up and composition from sociological and psychiatric studies; but we do not know why they and not their neighbors, who may have similar difficulties, appear in the consulting room, and we do not know precisely what troubles them in their deepest recesses. Our hypotheses about such matters are as yet inadequate for conclusive melioration.

Psychotherapists will informally acknowledge that they treat many people whom they do not consider diseased in a medical way. [5] Their discomfort is no less or no greater than thousands of their peers; but they seek either a complete freedom from the pain and symptoms of existence, or a transcending ecstasy such as comes temporarily from alcohol, drugs, or sexual orgasm. They are often lonely, alienated, bored, frightened, or pained, but not to the level of social inhibition of the classical neurotic or the psychotic. But they can also at times be genuine neurotic personalities and even ambulatory psychotics. They often represent the most gifted sections of the population, and they are invariably dissatisfied with the way their gifts are being used. Are they sick? Should they be given psychotherapy? This depends upon a complex of factors and one's vantage point; but I would say that they are existentially sick, and psychotherapy can help them. But if the psychotherapist treats non-diseased people, then he is departing from the medical model of which he is an integral part, and severe tensions are thereby induced in him by this split. His ethical responsibility is to cure. But what if there is nothing to cure? There is simply an existence no longer satisfying or tolerable for a number of reasons. How does one cure a fear of death, or a feeling of being a "hole, " or of a loss of meaning in life -- particularly when religion, the usual reply to such queries, has more or less failed in this area? This is not a frivolous statement, for underneath the anxious or psychosomatic barrage the patient brings to us just such questions are posed.

To better understand these matters I instituted a project involving doing psychotherapy with non-diseased subjects; the case

---

5. One psychiatrist of repute told me recently that half of his practice consists of non-diseased people. His referrals come from regular medical sources.

reported here represents one such person treated. [6A] The criterion of non-disease for this study was that the subject had never before been treated by a psychiatrist, psychologist, or social worker in his lifetime, that he was functioning satisfactorily in personal, social, and occupational realms (by self-report and by investigation), and that he came to psychotherapy at my request rather than through a felt need. [6B]

Now on what theoretical or practical basis is such a project justified? Here are a number of people going about their daily lives with more or less satisfaction. They then are offered the opportunity of spending twenty-five individual hours, for which they can see no good earthly reason, as a patient with a psychotherapist. [7] They are oriented toward cooperation in scientific research, but to become a patient side by side with my other patients is difficult for them to understand. After some of their questions were satisfied, I simply said, "If you have the time, why don't we just spend the twenty-five hours together and see what we discover about each other -- what the fundamental ground of human relationships is -- what our creative resources are." This and similar variations sufficed, albeit with a context of some wit and anxiety.

In presenting this case history of Eric Swenson, the possibly novel thesis will be offered that the psychically diseased and the non-diseased are not such polar opposites as we had formerly believed --

---

6A. Thus far only two cases of non-diseased people selected as such have been treated to completion. The observations in this paper, however, are dependent not only on these two but on a large number who came through the disease channel. Further treatment of non-diseased cases is in process.

6B. This procedure does not, of course, give us a "normal" or even non-diseased sample. What it does do is provide subjects who have never used -- and who have no immediate intention of using -- psychotherapy as a means of problem-solving. They are non-diseased in the sense that they feel no need of such form of amelioration, take no steps to obtain it, and would not under any circumstances pay for it. They function without it. Possibly I would be on safer ground here if I talked about "psychotherapeutically-involved and non-psychotherapeutically-involved" groups.

7. A limit of twenty-five hours was set for each person in the experiment. This was arbitrary, but was all the time I had to give. In retrospection, this quantum served its function adequately.

that the existence of the diseased and non-diseased is fundamentally the same and differs only in the mode of being-in-the-world, i. e., in the expression of their humanness. Both have similar problems of being man, feel despair in the same way, and both are thrown into the world without choice and leave it in the same way. The diseased and the non-diseased both seek an interpersonal integration based on love, and both employ the same coping mechanisms. Possibly only the crucial intensity of existence in each differs from time to time, and the historical and contemporaneous way in which the human condition is met. [8]

A psychiatrist with a highly conventional orientation to the psyche and its melioration will at this point consider my thesis quite preposterous. He will be able to cite convincing proof that Eric, the non-diseased patient reported on here, is indeed autistic, mildly paranoid, and possibly has a thinking disorder. But Pearce and Newton [9] see a paranoid integration as merely one of several developmental phases in _all_ growth; some of society's most productive artists and others are autistic without being mentally ill as such; [10] and thinking disorders turn out to be no such thing once the inner world of the schizophrenic is penetrated and his message decoded. The point here is that autism, paranoid trends, and departures from logical thinking are socially pathological only when they are set within a framework of society's discontent with such departures in mentation. If they serve integration and creation, they cannot be judged socially pathological on any meaningful scale. And, of course, I have taken here the most extreme example of mental illness when, indeed, the most prevalent problems are the more subtle and innocuous-appearing ones.

People I call psychically non-diseased are more and more coming to psychoanalysis and psychoanalytic psychotherapy, not necessarily for the removal of their symptoms, but for the rediscovery

---

8. I may be accused here by some people of either overlooking clinical facts or of imposing a metapsychological structure of some artificiality on such things as pain, suffering, and despair. To this one must say that it is demonstrated over and over again in treatment that pain, suffering, and despair are reduced or disappear once the patient finds a creative or meaningful mode of existence. Clinical psychiatry suffers today from a concentration on the peripheral symptom rather than on the "heart" of the matter.

9. Pearce, J. and S. Newton. The Conditions of Human Growth. New York: Citadel Press, 1963.

10. Barron, F. Creativity and Psychological Health. New Jersey: D. Van Nostrand Company, 1962.

of a lost creativity which gives a meaning and purpose to their existance. They have id problems as in the past, but it is not the id which is disturbing to the ego. It is the ego's relationship to the world -- to people in it -- and being-in-it as such, which is the major coeval problem. Psychotherapy deals with the subjective life and the impulses and behaviors which come from it. But so much of psychotherapy -- designed to reduce repression -- is itself repressive in format. Psychotherapists fear their patients' impulses and acting out, even their creativity, without understanding that inner and outer -- subject and predicate -- are an indissoluble unity. [11] Deep impulses and acting out are to be feared only when they occur without a broader framework of existential meaning, that is, within a setting of nihilism. Control is not a problem if an impulse serves a higher creative aim -- pleasure qua pleasure is emptiness; but pleasure in the form of an over-all and tight grand design is transcending. Thus psychotherapy by definition becomes the unfolding of the creative potential in the individual in the widest sense possible.

It seems probable that the psychoanalysis and psychoanalytic psychotherapy of the future will be reserved for already sufficiently creative people who want to reach even greater creative levels, or who want to recover a temporarily lost creativity. That is to say, that already expressive people will through psychotherapy maximize their expressiveness, or extract the last iota from life itself. As it is, the majority of elective patients are intelligent, verbal, creative, and with strong achievement needs. They have a sense of guilt regarding a failure of self-actualization, and the Judaic and Protestant ethic drives them to produce as a source of self-worth. They everlastingly feel that they are missing the creative boat even if in reality they are not. This urge-to-creation and self-fulfillment in Western man is to be contrasted with the Oriental and African who has considerably less of such drives. Just so long as such ethic operates in Western man, work and creation will be the basic source of his well-being, and psychotherapy will need to stress this rather than "adjustment." Of course, creation here must not be interpreted as the production of a socially useful product but rather as the actualization of potential that gives a sense of meaning and transcendence of being and unites one with his culture. It is the need to be-in-the-world as a unique part of the totality of humanness and to contribute to it. It may perhaps be that the treatment for psychic illness will develop on several levels -- this may already be the case today -- and that the supreme level will be the kind described here, whereas lower levels will involve instrumental therapies of a quick nature and not called psychotherapy at all.

Clients who come to psychotherapy are a selected group, and culture provides a pool of available people from which we make

---

11. Burton, A. The transference and countertransference of acting-out behavior. American J. of Psychoanalysis (in print).

our choice. [12] But the nature of the pool is determined by social forces not yet delineated in any precise way. In every culture the healer has filled a specific role; his limits are set by such role and are not easily modifiable. Today the hallmark of psychic healing is the "verbal symbol" and the process, the vicissitudes of the symbol. We psychotherapists have become adept at the manipulation of such symbols, and we cater to culture's need for these liberating and transcending symbols. Symbolization and abstraction are thus both the curse and the salvation of Western man.

Whatever theoretical system is employed, the healing operations themselves seem to come to the same thing. [13] We can only speculate as to the reasons for this, and the available speculation has not yet delineated the basic parameters. Some psychotherapists, for example, Carl Rogers[14] and Marguerite Sechehaye, [15] place the emphasis on the "regard" of the psychotherapist for his patient. Others consider the patient's "regard" for the therapist as critical. Still others stress the learning opportunities in treatment, or the emotional response to the special interaction of the two people. Any one of these views may be correct, or they all may be correct; I would modify the emphasis slightly by a simple generic addition to all of them. What determines the effectiveness of any psychotherapy is the depth of the encounter the therapy affords, its symbolic and existential significance, and the opportunities it provides for Eros once again to function. [16]

People who come to psychotherapy see themselves as dead symbolically and seek re-creation. Many of them tell you that they "feel dead in life," by which they mean that they have lost Eros to Thanatos and want to regain the former. The id and the superego then have to be seen within this larger framework, and the pleasure

---

12. We lack an exact definition of the psychotherapeutic patient. While we feel that we select the patients we treat, in fact they may be selecting us.

13. Ellis, A. Thoughts on theory versus outcome in psychotherapy. Psychotherapy, 1964, 1, 83-87.

14. Rogers, C. R. The interpersonal relationship: The core of guidance. Harv. Educ. Rev., 1962, 32, 416-429.

15. Sechehaye, M. A New Psychotherapy in Schizophrenia. New York: Grune & Stratton, 1956. Symbolic Realization. New York: International Univ. Press, 1951.

16. Eros has in modern times become corrupted to mean principally sexuality, which is itself a sign of the dehumanization of our times. I am here returning it to its original Greek and broad usage.

principle becomes over-limiting as an explanatory principle, particularly for the mature individual. Psychotherapy is the joint discovery of re-creativity -- that it is still present under the facade of symptoms -- that it transcends the symptoms -- that it provides a motive force in life -- that it offers interpersonal communion of a high order. Unfortunately, psychotherapy today in its quest to be a scientific discipline limits its goals at the same time it artistically approaches its subject. It then perforce must deny a part of the data which the encounter produces since its artistic uniqueness does not permit quantification or replication.

PROLOGOMENON TO PSYCHOTHERAPY

Eric Swenson is a twenty-year-old senior psychology major at a large and important western university. He is blond, on the tall side, wears a crew-cut, and is not remarkably different from the average fraternity member in this university. His speech is crisp but clear, and he avoids intellectualisms or affectations. He is almost the all-American prototype of the middle-class Aryan stereotype.

Eric has a slight sense of unease about him. He seems to be searching, but this is not an overt anxiety. It is rather like finding one's place under changing circumstances. He was selected for treatment from seven other candidates because he not only met the criterion of psychic non-disease given above, but because his disinterest and even hostility toward psychotherapy challenged me. He agreed to come regularly for the twenty-five hours, but he did not necessarily agree to participate in the relationship. Obviously, as is also true in the patients I accept for a fee, he attracted me by his obvious intelligence, his upper-middle-class social background, his verbal facility and desire to learn, and by the fact that he represented modern-day college youth. (He attended the same university from which I had received my degree some twenty years earlier!) Eric denied having any problems or ever having sought counseling or psychotherapeutic help. He said he was happy at home, was making good grades, was a senior leader in his fraternity, and pointed to a host of other achievements. Of course, while all of this was true, it later turned out that he had dissatisfactions in several areas. Probably the tone of his mode-of-being at the time is best given by the following dream which came later and which will be left largely uninterpreted in the traditional sense.

I was tied upside down from the ceiling of a hall, helpless. Someone pushing me, making me swing, then laughing about the control which he was exercising over me. It seemed that it was not he who tied me, but some large organization. The next thing I knew, this man was also tied, but not upside down.

I found that I could wriggle free from my bonds,
and was soon free. My first response was to somehow tease the man (who was still tied), or otherwise
show him that now I had the upper hand. Instead, I
untied him. I was glad, because now we were both
together in our illegal attempt at escape from the
"organization." As we hopefully crouched on the
floor, about to plan our escape, I saw two large
shadows on the floor in front of us. My heart sank.
I turned around to see two men in uniforms, smiling.
They had known all the time that I never had a chance.

Eric in his dream presents the existential problem of unfreedom
-- of constriction -- of communality and divorcement -- of despair
and suspiciousness -- of the odds against him in an organized world.
He also reveals the "becoming possibilities" inherent in his "lack of
freedom," and the fact that he seeks desperately to actualize his
being.

The Swenson family is a large one. In addition to Eric there
are five siblings, ages nineteen, sixteen, eleven, eight and six years
of age. Four are boys and two are girls. Eric, of course, is the
oldest. A good family life is an important ideal to the Swensons, and
nothing is permitted to stand in the way of it. There is a family discipline which reminds one of the Puritans who settled this country,
or the Quakers or Amish. Personal feeling is probably sacrificed for
the group good, and arbitrary individual action of a hysterical kind
would be severely frowned upon. While Eric has most in common with
Frank, his brother next in age, there is no deep sharing of experience
or feeling as can occur between brothers.

Now, because Eric represents a non-diseased person, and
because it may be difficult to grasp why he should even stay in therapy
for twenty-five hours, the following excerpt from a tape recording
which came at about the twelfth hour gives us something about the way
he conceives of himself and his situation:

Dr. B.: Eric, would you say that your problem is one of a
gap between practice and an ideal rather than a
neurotic situation? If you were willing to settle
for less then there would be no problem?

Eric: Right.

Dr. B.: Well, what do you think about this business?

Eric: Well, really, you see, I don't know that much about
what constitutes a neurotic -- I haven't ever thought
of myself that way.

Dr. B.: You haven't.

Eric: Well, this has always been what I thought has been my problem - that I do have an ideal - that I do look at my capabilities and say "Well, I can do this," and yet I don't do it. And I do see, you know, I would like to - even with girls - I figure, well, heck, you know they're really going to like me because of the kind of guy I am, and yet I'm still kind of afraid with them. Sure, I'd like to be a great lover. You know, I was thinking of something else today that, well, I don't really want to be a conformist. The fact that I used to smoke Pall Malls - and everybody smokes Pall Malls, so I changed to Philip Morris. Then I tried these Old Golds which I don't like, just so I could be smoking something different from somebody else. I like the idea that I'm smarter than other people, that I can think things out for myself where they can't, that I can come to a better decision than they can, and yet, I don't allow myself to use this ability in a self-situation. I'll just retreat or give a kind of all-knowing glance, you know, like "Well, I know what's going on here," but I'm not going to fight it - there's nothing I can do about it but go ahead and act stupid.

Dr. B.: H'mm.

Eric: I was wholly avoiding your question. But I'm not in a constant state of - how I conceive of a neurotic is in a constant state of agitation about everything - because when I do think things out of a hole, that's the kind of hole it is - where I realize that I'm different from these guys. I have different ideas, and yet, I'll let them go on as they are. Even though I don't feel this is right, that's what I do because I don't want to get hurt. So, I just let it go and I don't feel terribly bad about it all the time, but there are times when I do. And I can go along for months just perfectly happy in my little cubbyhole, but the more I'm in this the more I realize that it is a cubbyhole. I'm kind of, as you can see, wrapped up in this cyclical kind of thinking. Do you have any thoughts from an outsider that might lend something to the situation? Do you think I'm neurotic?

Dr. B.: I'm indifferent to that question. I do think you have a discrepancy between your functioning and your ideals -- that some people ignore it, or can ignore it, and others can't or don't want to.

Eric: I've always had hope for myself. I've always considered that I'll do well. I always when I go into a test I figure that I'll get an A on it. I consider that I will do well in my life work – I figure that I will get a girl that is right for me – that has all the qualities that I like. I see these things in the future, and yet I'm getting more and more disgusted with evidence coming through that I'm not doing anything now to help myself toward that.

Dr. B.: Do you sometimes feel like it is no problem at all?

Eric: Not if I think about it. A lot of times I don't think about it. If I think about it, I'll realize that there is a problem.

Dr. B.: Well, why don't you make the decision, then, to live a more authentic life?

Eric: Because I have things – some of them which have been brought out here – they are my needs, they are irrational, they are the cause of fears but they are still there, and maybe if I could bring them out I could see them, maybe I can do something about them. Maybe I can't. Maybe they will just prey on my mind all the more. Or maybe I'll give in to them more and more when I realize what they are.

Dr. B.: You feel that it isn't in your power to be more authentic because of these irrationalities?

Eric: Well I certainly have – somewhere there is a desire to be more authentic. I don't know if it is in my power or not, and I don't even know what authentic is, yet. And I don't completely give in. I'll often retreat instead of fighting a battle that I don't feel is good, that would do any good. I couldn't convince those guys to be any different during Hell Week. I've worked on them a little bit – guys that I feel could understand. I kind of slip my views in, you know. But I'm not going to face up to them – I'm not going to make them my enemies. And sometimes – you're right – sometimes I don't give a damn! Just too much effort – is what I feel most of the time. But then when I come to the point – sometimes I come to the point and it just depresses me when I see the way that things are, and I feel that I should exert the effort but I don't. Whether it is in my power or not, I don't know. Whether it would be advantageous or not – I don't know. Whether I would lead a richer life. You see, I'm still looking for the things like sex and drinking and being one of the boys, that I didn't really have until I got in college, that I missed, you know, and I wanted to try it. And now that I'm starting to, you know, try these things. You know, I read a little more and get a little more sophisticated and they become less important to me and I have to start looking further ahead, which doesn't answer the question in your mind. I'll have to start answering pretty soon as far as my profession goes, I suppose.

As the therapeutic hours proceeded Eric became more and more like my paying patients, so that I tended to forget that he was not present for help. He developed a classical transference, and I a classical countertransference. I had difficulty recalling that he was merely part of an experiment and that I was to remain empirically dispassionate and objective. Interestingly enough, the necessary tension and substrate anxiety which motors all psychotherapy was present in sufficient quantity even though no disabling neurotic symptoms as such were present in sufficient quantity as the focus of the encounter.[17] The encounter progression was basically carried, not only by what I came to be represented for him by the past -- transference -- but a contemporaneous meeting in the present with all of its being-with possibilities. There was a subtle therapeutic reinforcement in each other of the creative properties of discovery, integration, and application, as occurs in any act of original creation. This was both binding and liberating for us, and no formal analysis of the transference was ever required to attain the therapeutic outcomes reported later.

If Eric had a problem in the psychotherapeutic sense, it was that he sought greater self-actualization and authenticity as a person. He had a number of personality defenses which permitted him to take a lofty view of himself and his world, and such a view deprived him of fruition. But he had not consciously realized this when he came to the experiment, and one wonders if, and when, he might have without my intervention. Eric could have established a fully average, defensible adult life as he was going, and have taken in stride incompleteness, ennui, indifference, moderate attainment, pleasure, and a mar-

---

17. Based upon my experience with Eric and others like him, I now feel that the requirement of a neurotic symptom for progression in psychotherapy is partly mythical.

riage based on convention, etc. But both Eric and society would have been shortchanged by such a life if contemporary values are used as a guide.

PROBLEM THEMAS

Put more formally, the existential problem themas of Eric's being were as follows:

1. BEING-WITH. Most relevant to Eric's existence were his interpersonal difficulties. I had the opportunity of observing him in social situations -- the hospital where he trained for a summer -- and would rate him above average in interpersonal relationships for his peer group; but his feelings were that he could never penetrate to the heart of his respondent. He felt that he invariably missed the target by an infinitesimal amount; but miss it he did. This subtle difficulty seemed real as I perceived it. Missing the mark then led to a whole host of fine concealing mechanisms designed to protect him from the realization of his basic alienation. (Such alienation in Eric cannot be called schizoid in any sense of the word, either in terms of the Rorschach Test or the Minnesota Multiphasic Personality Inventory which a colleague gave him, or by clinical observations made of him.) These mechanisms ranged from an overweening interest in poker -- to the disadvantage of academic matters -- to Don Juanism, or to a self-righteousness which directly countered his weakness. But there were also more subjective and subtle mechanisms involving self-worth. He wanted to be fair, honest, and open -- but so fair, honest, and open that it was itself the reflection of a closed system.

It was only with his mother that he lost this sense of unease; but this was counterpoised by a displaced alienation from his father who, in a sense, paid for the mother-son relationship. As he grew older, even mother failed as the source of deepest comfort, possibly because of a growing self-consciousness on the part of each of the sexual implications of their relationship.

His father was an avid churchgoer, a fundamentalist from the Midwest, who by perseverance and grit had reached the level of principal of a large high school. He was respected in every way by both his students and his faculty. At the time of writing this report, he had attained some notice by sending a girl student home because he considered her coiffure outlandish for high school, and even though her mother threatened to sue the board of education, he did not back off. He tended to run his home in the same way he did his school, and Eric often had difficulty seeing the man behind the principal. In hour after hour he reiterated how "fair" his father was. Only in the arena of money could Eric feel that his father was not always the Mosaic figure he appeared to him.

I interviewed Mr. Swenson (with Eric) toward the end of the treatment and found him a well-meaning person, but so insensitive to his son's needs that he was genuinely astonished at the visible tension between them. He couldn't at all understand that his son might be alienated from him. He gropingly tried to cope with this revelation in a highly intellectual fashion, but not necessarily with a hostile defensiveness of any sort. It was rather that he expected a father-son relationship to fall into the ancient and honorable pattern established by his forebears, in which the roles were more or less fixed and emotion played little part. He did not behave as though his son was his rival, and he would have laughed at the idea that there was competition for his wife in the Oedipal sense.

2. BEING-IN-THE-HOLE. Eric attracts many girls, but he classifies them along two parameters: "pigs" and "good" girls. The former are simply to sleep with on a one- or two-shot deal; the latter cannot be touched in any way. Even so, denigrating the first group -- all of whom are also "good" girls by conventional standards -- does not leave him comfortable, for being-in-the-hole with a "good" girl makes him guilty if he does not supply what he thinks is the proper affection or "giving" to go with it. And this he cannot often do. He also tends to see sexuality as aggressing-against and the recipient as a helpless victim. He ardently woos the good girls but drops them when being-in-the-hole is expected of him. He unconsciously develops disaffections with the girl which eventually terminate the relationship. But he is not satisfied to go on without sexuality, which many of them would be willing to do. Eric feels that to do so would deny both partners a mature growth, and an improper marriage might result.

Conventionally, it would appear that Eric has a castration complex, and it would be possible to make formulations about his situation in this way. However, Eric is not actually castrated, and he does not behave like a castrate. He is potent, has no masturbation defenses, and rather seeks a total relationship with a woman which involves being-in-the-hole as well as feeling a transcending tenderness for her. He thus has his total growth with a woman in mind rather than merely a physiological experience. Castrates, symbolically or otherwise, do not behave in this exact way. [18]

---

18. The theoretical system one applies to describe a behavioral event is often a matter of economy and choice. In psychiatry and psychology, we cannot yet state affirmatively that one system is a "better fit" than another, and it often comes down to the preference of the observer. This may be overstating the case somewhat, but in this instance more of the phenomena of Eric is describable in "addition to" the Oedipal-castration formulation. This, then, is not to deny the validity of Freud's hypostatizations but to indicate their lack of total appositeness in this instance.

Eric knew that this kind of classificatory behavior of women was arbitrary and left him with considerable guilt after a relationship experience with both types of girls. He also felt guilty about his complicity in making them fall in love with him and then dropping them. Eric was attracted by beauty, and while he verbalized that it was skin-deep, he could not reduce its comparative pull among all of the virtues which were really more important to him.

3. BEING-IN-LOVE. Being-in-love is one form of being-with, and possibly its most intense manifestation. It deserves separate treatment here because all forms of being relate to this one.

Eric has trouble being-in-the-hole because he has trouble being-in-love. Since he cannot get to the heart of the girl he considers a marital candidate, he cannot bring the proper affection to being-in-the-hole. Now for most boys this would be of little consequence, but it looms large for Eric, for this is the way he is. While his fraternity pressures him to conform to manhood by getting notches "on his gun, " he holds out for a transcending love which he is certain exists but which he cannot yet define or find. So at times he bends with the pressure of the fraternity and at others stays aloof from it. But he wants very desperately to love and to be loved, and is now beginning to understand that love is an interpersonal attitude and experience which reaches into all relationships as the building blocks of existence. He feels guilty and ecstatic about the possibilities of love and understands that it is the leaven and the cement of all deep and fundamental human relationships. But the ego pulls back at surrender and is then urged forward by the id. Someone, he feels, gets cheated in marriage, and in this case he unconsciously believes it is the woman: his mother. But why is love reductive rather than ennobling? Could it be that in the Swenson family there was always the form but not the spirit of creative love -- that someone always felt emotionally cheated, not necessarily by deprivation but by the significant absence of integrated tenderness? It is normal under such circumstances for a boy to feel that the woman, the mother, gets the brunt of such deficiency which the father either withholds or offers. Can it be that Eric's guilt in regard to the emotional dryness of his family is the barrier to his complete participation with women, and also accounts for the angry feelings toward his father?

Interpersonal psychiatry tends to see the ability to love and be tender as the central problem of interpersonal relationships, and so it is. No true fulfillment is possible without deep and meaningful tenderness, for this provides the meaning-structure upon which other events are projected. In psychotherapy, the most flagrant and insidious of symptoms often drop away when love and tenderness become possible for the patient. But the important point is that tenderness and creativity are intimately related, and one grows out of the other. Eros is in this sense also the source of creativity, and this is what psychotherapy makes possible in a corrective way. Anxiety is the absence of love!

Eric's family anxiety is a part of his existential anxiety -- his place in the world -- and his guilt is the existential guilt of not living up to his ideals and expectations. Thus, to understand Eric and ameliorate his condition it does not necessarily help to invoke concepts of neurotic anxiety or neurotic guilt in the classical Freudian sense.

4. BEING-IN-TIME-AND-SPACE. Eric's being is compressed in space -- he feels the need and plans to travel soon for a year -- and temporality is his onus. He calculates time rather than lives it. Acts are valued against other acts in terms of the time they take. Time replaces money as the existential symbolic binder and, of course, behind it looms Thanatos. People who accept their finiteness, or who successfully masquerade an infiniteness, do not fall into Eric's state. Thus, the world shrinks and dilates as the psychological meaning of his time and space fluctuate -- and they tend to fluctuate with the state of his feelings of tenderness. The systems open and provide freedom to be and to progress when he feels tender. When he does not, space and time close in to narrow his world. When his world becomes extremely narrow, then the fear of death or mental illness supervenes.

THE COURSE OF PSYCHOTHERAPY

The foregoing observations were all derived from the on-goingness of the psychotherapy itself, and it only remains to describe something of its course and its outcomes. As previously stated, Eric was conceptualized and treated side by side with patients -- and as though he were a patient who had applied for help. I did not charge him a fee only because he had no funds of his own; otherwise the conditions of treatment were the same.

The initial stages of psychotherapy varied somewhat from the usual patient. The latter usually comes loaded with anxiety and a set of complaints, and one usually waits passively until such facade is drained. Eric came without this, so more of a dialogue was consequently indicated. He used the first hour gingerly to make clear that he had no problem and was not a patient. Indeed, I sympathized with him, for neither of us knew exactly how to proceed with each other. * I reinforced the nature of the experiment, and restated that two people with professional intent systematically together could discover a great deal about themselves in terms of their growth -- that he might be willing to try this. Since he was training to become a psychologist, he wanted a professional identification with me, but he did not permit this to interfere with the acceptance of a patient status. The end of the first hour left us both uncertain, but he agreed to return and actually kept every single one of his twenty-five appointments.

---

* He was the first non-diseased person I treated.

As a matter of fact, when it was necessary for me to cancel two appointments he eagerly asked for alternate times.

At the end of the third hour he had worked through the uniqueness of being a "patient without an illness" and could see that the relationship might help with certain existential and personality questions he had had and from time to time posed to himself in unguarded moments. All of the usual manifestations of the transference then slowly became evident. This appeared particularly when he began verbalizing about his father whom he likened to me in various respects. His position vis-à-vis his father was an ambiguous one: He both revered and hated him. He admired his scholarship, administrative ability, and his voluntary church work, but saw him deficient in warmth, insight, and comradeliness. It later turned out that some of these weaknesses he also attributed to me!

From his father, he could go on to talk about his mother and tell me of certain historical situations in his growth which he felt had dependent, pleasurable, or sexual overtones. I mentioned the word Oedipus to him, knowing full well that no clinical psychologist in training could escape this unfortunate Theban. He overreacted with much hostility to this, but it seemed more mother-directed than father-directed. He said that he could understand an attachment between a male child and a mother but severely rejected the Freudian formulation of this particular event (which may thereby in itself give it credence!).

In the middle third of treatment he was able to bring up the problems of being-with, being-in-love, and being-in-the-hole. He recognized his need, not necessarily to achieve, but to come to fulfillment -- to be authentic -- and verbalized that regardless of attainments, he would never reach his goals if his interpersonal relationships were not changed. For the first he could time see his defensive mode-of-being, and that, on one count or another, he had been fencing with people. He was particularly distressed at his dichotomization of women, and it genuinely hurt him to denigrate any woman. He intellectually knew that there are no good and bad women -- just women who become what they are because of their own existence. This sexual attitude mirrored a phobia toward life in its positiveness and had to be seen in this framework rather than as a simple competition device in his family. Nor did I see any basis for postulating anything homosexual which could help us.

In the final third of the hours he developed an intense hostility toward me which we only incompletely resolved by the end of the twenty-five hours. But I interpreted the total resistance of his being to the deeper insights and understanding of his life. I also conventionally interpreted the transference in terms of his historical father and mother, but this took a back seat to his total creative setting as a person. He then made attempts to bring his mode-of-being more in line with his new-found insights. He began to merge the bad and good girls -- and to see them more as people than as holes or as goddesses. He let them get closer and feel him. He stopped being shattered by occasional rejections of his invitations to them, and he began to enjoy being-with-them for its own sake. He now played poker in the fraternity for its social-gain quality rather than an all-consuming defense against studying and interacting with people. His grades improved and as a graduating senior he began thinking of delaying entrance into graduate school while he spent a year away from his parents in the world of work, possibly in Europe.

Because twenty-five hours of psychotherapy were arbitrarily set as the empirical quantum of treatment and did not necessarily fit the needs of any single patient, I asked him to write to me if he felt the need for it, and told him that I would arrange for infrequent interviews as a follow-up. In the five months since termination he has not used the written document form of communication, but he did call me for an interview. This interview took place about two months before this was written.

He has preserved and extended his gains in all areas. Eric is by self-report and observation much more of a person, happier, and much readier to help people as a future psychologist and man. Not that Eric has overcome all his felt deficiencies. He still has some trouble with girls. It is rather that he now understands that these are existential deficiencies and knows how to go about altering them. He has made the choice to be authentic, but it will require years of living before we really know how effective our work was.

CONCLUSION

This unconventional case history is offered here for heuristic purposes only to illustrate the unity of the personalities of the psychically diseased and non-diseased. Most of us secretly believe that the neurotic non-psychotic, and that different order from the non-neurotic and non-psychotic and that separate theoretical and meliorative systems of human change apply to the former and not to the latter. Working with Eric Swenson, and others, as though they were patients, has convinced me that what distinguishes the patient from the non-patient is something entirely different from what we had formerly supposed. Becoming-a-patient is sometimes a selective fact of culture, or of opportunity, or of social coercion.   It is not analagous to the person who has a fever and for whom a microbe or other infectious organ is demonstrable. Psychic illness, in many aspects, seems to be a disorder of the patterning or integration of existence and its meaning rather than a disease as such.   It is gauged by the state of Eros and Thanatos rather than by a thermometer -- the life and death forces which are at the basis of creativity. In this sense we are all diseased and all non-diseased! We suffer from humanity and the human condition.

Such thesis is more than mere philosophizing, for it has the greatest of implications for the treatment of man. If psychotherapy restores wholeness, purpose, and creativity to the patient, and if this should turn out to be its prime medium of interaction, should we not stop trying to find disease on the basis of the ancient medical analogue? Should we not give greater thought to the basic nature of creativity, and to the social possibilities of creativity and meaning for more people than even psychotherapy makes possible? Is it not, then, the particularly gifted who will receive the psychoanalysis and psychoanalytic therapy of the future, since in the face of the rising demand and fewer therapists our selection is becoming narrower and narrower? Most of us are already treating large numbers of non-diseased patients if we look carefully at our practice. Is it fantasy to believe this could eventually rise for some of us to close to 100%?

The case of Eric Swenson makes it possible for me to integrate to some extent the disintegrating theoretical findings of psychotherapy. It reveals that classification of disease and non-disease in personality are often arbitrary acts of the observer because we conceptualize them along this parameter to begin with. Beneath the divergencies of psychotherapeutic theory lies the core concept of existence as creation and re-creation in a complex and myriad of forms. When this dynamic re-creation ceases, death -- or its symbolic equivalent, psychic illness -- supervenes.

Other researchers seem to be coming independently to a similar point of view. Maslow [19] says in a recent paper, "My feeling is that the concept of creativeness and the concept of the healthy, self-actualizing, fully-human person seem to be coming closer and closer together, and may perhaps turn out to be the same thing." Carl Rogers in his recent formulations comes very close to saying the same thing and, I believe, eventually will do so.

---

19. Maslow A. H. The creative attitude. The Structurist, 1963, No. 3, pp. 4-10.